NFPA® 58

Liquefied Petroleum Gas Code

2020 Edition

This edition of NFPA 58, *Liquefied Petroleum Gas Code*, was prepared by the Technical Committee on Liquefied Petroleum Gases and acted on by NFPA at its Association Technical Meeting held June 17–20, 2019, in San Antonio, TX. It was issued by the Standards Council on August 5, 2019, with an effective date of August 25, 2019, and supersedes all previous editions.

This document has been amended by one or more Tentative Interim Amendments (TIAs) and/or Errata. See "Codes & Standards" at www.nfpa.org for more information.

This edition of NFPA 58 was approved as an American National Standard on August 25, 2019.

Origin and Development of NFPA 58

The first NFPA standard on LP-Gas was adopted in 1932. In 1940, several standards were combined and adopted as NFPA 58.

Revisions of NFPA 58 were adopted in 1934, 1937, 1939, 1940, 1943, 1946, 1948, 1950, 1951, 1952, 1953, 1954, 1955, 1956, 1957, 1958, 1959, 1960, 1961, 1965, 1967, 1969, 1972, 1974, 1976, 1979, 1983, 1986, 1989, 1992, 1995, 1998, 2001, 2004, 2008, 2011, 2014, 2017, and the latest one, in 2020.

The 2011 edition of NFPA 58 included several significant changes. The installation of underground LP-Gas storage containers required cathodic protection systems, and the systems were required to be monitored to verify that they were protected. The requirement that a pressure relief valve be piped vertically upward 7 ft (2.1 m) from the valve was deleted because the technical committee could find no technical reason to justify it. Former railroad tank cars were no longer allowed to be installed as permanent storage containers because they were not constructed to the ASME *Boiler and Pressure Vessel Code*, and additional recommendations for training were added to Annex A.

The 2014 edition harmonized container requirements for containers with equal to or less than 4000 gal water capacity (w.c.) (15.2 m³) and greater than 4000 gal w.c. (15.2 m³). Bulk plants and industrial plants are defined as facilities that store more than 4000 gal w.c. (15.2 m³), which is the reason for the demarcation point of 4000 gal w.c. (15.2 m³). A new definition was added for *vehicular barrier protection (VBP)*. There were many installations where the container and valves were required to be protected from vehicular impact, but no specific information was available as to what constituted such protection. In addition to the definition describing VBP, extensive annex material was incorporated. Prescriptive requirements also were added for VBP of LP-Gas dispensers.

Qualifications of personnel were expanded for clarification in Chapter 4 of the 2014 edition. The requirements, which originated as a Temporary Interim Amendment (TIA) to the 2011 edition, specified which personnel and in which topics they must be trained. New requirements included the covering of tank heaters, and requirements for vaporizers were updated.

The 2014 edition included new requirements to provide cathodic protection for underground metallic piping systems greater than 2 in. (5.08 cm) diameter. Previously, all underground metallic piping was only required to be coated or painted. The new requirements for piping systems were very similar to those for cathodic protection of underground containers.

In previous editions, hot air balloons were not covered under the scope of NFPA 58. The 2017 edition added requirements referencing the current state of federal law regarding their use and construction. The requirements for hot air balloons were included in the corresponding sections for scope, construction, and liquid transfer. The requirements for when a container or piping must be protected from snow loads were altered to allow for calculations and snowfall maps from ASCE/SEI 7, *Minimum Design Loads for Buildings and Other Structures*. The threshold for protecting containers and appurtenances from snow was raised to 100 lb/ft² (488 kgf/m²). Vehicle barrier protection

(VBP) for cylinders protected in a metal cabinet was removed. The VBP requirement for 12,000 lb (53,375 N) protection for vehicle fuel dispensers was also removed.

A new Chapter 12 in the 2017 edition updated the technology available for over-the-road vehicles utilizing LP-Gas. New definitions, construction, transportation, and location requirements were added for skid tanks and porta-pacs. Also, requirements were added in Chapter 6 for the placing of ASME tanks that have been disconnected from use.

Fire extinguisher requirements were centralized to Section 4.7 for basic requirements in the 2017 edition, with individual capacity requirements remaining in the specific application section. The appurtenance requirements in Table 5.9.4.1(B) were expanded to cover containers, except DOT Spec. 39, less than 2 lb (0.9 kg) propane capacity. Universal tanks were permitted to be filled in the horizontal or vertical orientation as long as the positioning slot was in the correct orientation.

In the 2020 edition, new requirements for fire resistance rating and noncombustible materials have been added to specify when materials are required to have a certain fire resistance rating or when they must be noncombustible. Schedule 10 steel piping has been allowed for use in aboveground vapor service only and austenitic stainless steel has been allowed as a piping material.

Fire extinguisher requirements have been revised to specify that fire extinguishers shall not be used for LP-Gas pressure fires unless the source of fuel can be shut off promptly, a revision that removes conflict between industry standards and this code when choosing a fire extinguisher for an application.

Requirements have been added to require inspection of the face seal on CGA 791 and CGA 793 connections prior to filling because defects in the connection face seal will degrade the effectiveness of the seal; if any defects are found on the face seal, the cylinder is not to be refilled and the valve is to be replaced.

Purging of piping within the scope of NFPA 58 has been revised in the 2020 edition to direct the user to the purging procedures of NFPA 54, regardless of the system's operating pressure. In previous editions, NFPA 56 had been referenced for purging procedures; however, LP-Gas systems under the scope of NFPA 58 are excluded from consideration in NFPA 56. While NFPA 54's scope only covers LP-gas systems up to 125 psig (0.86 MPag), the purging procedures in NFPA 54 are also appropriate for NFPA 58 applications.

Revisions were made to Chapter 15, Operations and Maintenance, to specifically reference operations and maintenance requirements and to remove a number of unrelated installation requirements. Additionally, the scope of Chapter 15 has been revised to exclude systems regulated by the U.S. Department of Transportation because its requirements for operations and maintenance are more stringent.

Technical Committee on Liquefied Petroleum Gases

Richard A. Hoffmann, *Chair*
Hoffmann & Feige, NY [SE]

Donald Barber, Enmat International (UK), United Kingdom [SE]

James C. Belke, U.S. Environmental Protection Agency, DC [E]

Joseph M. Bloom, Bloom Fire Investigation, OR [SE]

Kody N. Daniel, EMC Insurance Companies, IA [I]
Rep. Property Casualty Insurers Association of America

Kevin Joseph Dowling, The Public Utilities Regulatory Authority (PURA), CT [E]
Rep. National Association of Pipeline Safety Representatives (NAPSR)

Thomas B. Dunn, Iowa Propane Gas Association, IA [IM]

Mark Fasel, Viega LLC, IN [M]

Alberto Jose Fossa, NEWEN Creative Engineering, Brazil [SE]
Rep. NFPA Latin American Section

Richard G. Fredenburg, State of North Carolina, NC [E]

Cesar E. Garza-Obregon, Gas Campanita, TX [IM]
Rep. Asociación Mexicana de Distribuidores de Gas

Steven T. Gentry, Worthington Industries, OH [M]
Rep. Compressed Gas Association

Richard L. Gilbert, Texas Propane Gas Association, TX [IM]

James Kendzel, American Supply Association, IL [U]
Rep. American Supply Association

John W. King, Federated Mutual Insurance Company, MN [I]

Joseph Labonte, Navistar Corporation, OK [M]

Theodore C. Lemoff, Naples, FL [SE]

Jean L. McDowell, McDowell Owens Engineering Inc., TX [SE]

David W. Meyer, Gas Training & Development LLC, MN [SE]

Gerry E. Misel, Jr., Georgia Gas Distributors, Inc., GA [IM]
Rep. National Propane Gas Association

Sam Newman, Flame King, CA [M]

Stephen Pepper, Phillips 66, TX [U]
Rep. American Petroleum Institute

Phillip H. Ribbs, PHR Consultants, CA [L]
Rep. California State Pipe Trades Council

April Dawn Richardson, Railroad Commission of Texas, TX [E]

Eric C. Smith, State of Nevada, NV [E]

David J. Stainbrook, Engineered Controls International, LLC, NC [M]

Bruce J. Swiecicki, National Propane Gas Association, IL [IM]
Rep. National Propane Gas Association

Randy D. Warner, Ferrellgas LP, MO [IM]
Rep. National Propane Gas Association

Edgar Wolff-Klammer, Underwriters Laboratories LLC, IL [RT]

Leslie Woodward, Fairview Fittings & Manufacturing Inc., NY [IM]
Rep. Canadian Propane Association

William J. Young, Superior Energy Systems, Ltd., OH [M]

Steven E. Younis, Steven E. Younis PE, Inc., MA [SE]

Alternates

Joseph M. Bablo, UL LLC, IL [RT]
(Alt. to Edgar Wolff-Klammer)

Eric M. Benstock, McDowell Owens Engineering, Inc., TX [SE]
(Alt. to Jean L. McDowell)

Robert S. Blackwell, Action Gas Incorporated, CO [IM]
(Voting Alt.)

Christopher J. Bloom, CJB Fire Consultants, OR [SE]
(Alt. to Joseph M. Bloom)

Thomas R. Crane, Crane Engineering, MN [SE]
(Alt. to Theodore C. Lemoff)

James R. Freeman, III, Freeman Gas & Electric, Inc., SC [IM]
(Alt. to Gerry E. Misel, Jr.)

Swapan Kumar Hazra, GF Natural Gas LNG Ltd/CNG Technology Ltd., India [U]
(Voting Alt.)

Jerry Kowalski, Protech Resources, MN [IM]
(Alt. to Thomas B. Dunn)

Robert E. McKinney, AMC/Fairmont Insurance Company, TX [IM]
(Alt. to Richard L. Gilbert)

Jose Antonio Morales, Admiral LPG Services, Inc., FL [SE]
(Alt. to Donald Barber)

Frank J. Mortimer, EMC Insurance Company, IA [I]
(Alt. to Kody N. Daniel)

Carlton S. Revere, Revere Gas & Appliance, Inc., VA [IM]
(Alt. to Bruce J. Swiecicki)

Steven D. Ruffcorn, Standby Systems, Inc., MN [M]
(Alt. to William J. Young)

Kent Lowery Thompson, Railroad Commission Of Texas, TX [E]
(Alt. to April Dawn Richardson)

Erich Wolf, Cavagna North America, OH [M]
(Alt. to Steven T. Gentry)

Nonvoting

Bernardo Bohorquez, Saena de Colombia S.A., Colombia [IM]

William R. Hamilton, U.S. Department of Labor, DC [E]

Kenneth Lun, KL Consulting Engineers Ltd., China [SE]

Al Linder, Watsonville, CA [SE]
(Member Emeritus)

Lisa Hartman, NFPA Staff Liaison

This list represents the membership at the time the Committee was balloted on the final text of this edition. Since that time, changes in the membership may have occurred. A key to classifications is found at the back of the document.

NOTE: Membership on a committee shall not in and of itself constitute an endorsement of the Association or any document developed by the committee on which the member serves.

Committee Scope: This Committee shall have primary responsibility for documents on the design, construction, installation, and operation of fixed and portable liquefied petroleum gas systems in bulk plants and commercial, industrial (with specified exceptions), institutional, and similar properties; truck transportation of liquefied petroleum gas; engine fuel systems on motor vehicles and other mobile equipment; storage of containers awaiting use or resale; installation on commercial vehicles; and liquefied petroleum gas service stations.

Contents

NFPA 58

Liquefied Petroleum Gas Code

2020 Edition

IMPORTANT NOTE: This NFPA document is made available for use subject to important notices and legal disclaimers. These notices and disclaimers appear in all publications containing this document and may be found under the heading "Important Notices and Disclaimers Concerning NFPA Standards." They can also be viewed at www.nfpa.org/disclaimers or obtained on request from NFPA.

UPDATES, ALERTS, AND FUTURE EDITIONS: New editions of NFPA codes, standards, recommended practices, and guides (i.e., NFPA Standards) are released on scheduled revision cycles. This edition may be superseded by a later one, or it may be amended outside of its scheduled revision cycle through the issuance of Tentative Interim Amendments (TIAs). An official NFPA Standard at any point in time consists of the current edition of the document, together with all TIAs and Errata in effect. To verify that this document is the current edition or to determine if it has been amended by TIAs or Errata, please consult the National Fire Codes® Subscription Service or the "List of NFPA Codes & Standards" at www.nfpa.org/docinfo. In addition to TIAs and Errata, the document information pages also include the option to sign up for alerts for individual documents and to be involved in the development of the next edition.

NOTICE: An asterisk (*) following the number or letter designating a paragraph indicates that explanatory material on the paragraph can be found in Annex A.

A reference in brackets [ ] following a section or paragraph indicates material that has been extracted from another NFPA document. Extracted text may be edited for consistency and style and may include the revision of internal paragraph references and other references as appropriate. Requests for interpretations or revisions of extracted text shall be sent to the technical committee responsible for the source document.

Information on referenced and extracted publications can be found in Chapter 2 and Annex N.

Chapter 1 Administration

1.1* Scope. This code shall apply to the storage, handling, transportation, and use of liquefied petroleum gas (LP-Gas).

1.2 Purpose. (Reserved)

1.3 Application.

1.3.1 Application of Code. This code shall apply to the operation of all LP-Gas systems, including the following:

(1) Containers, piping, and associated equipment, when delivering LP-Gas to a building for use as a fuel gas.
(2) Highway transportation of LP-Gas.
(3) The design, construction, installation, and operation of marine terminals whose primary purpose is the receipt of LP-Gas for delivery to transporters, distributors, or users, except for marine terminals associated with refineries, petrochemicals, gas plants, and marine terminals whose purpose is the delivery of LP-Gas to marine vessels.
(4)* The design, construction, installation, and operation of pipeline terminals that receive LP-Gas from pipelines under the jurisdiction of the U.S. Department of Transportation (DOT) whose primary purpose is the receipt of LP-Gas for delivery to transporters, distributors, or users.

Coverage shall begin downstream of the last pipeline valve or tank manifold inlet.

△ 1.3.2 Nonapplication of Code. This code shall not apply to the following:

(1) Frozen ground containers and underground storage in caverns, including associated piping and appurtenances used for the storage of LP-Gas
(2) Natural gas processing plants, refineries, and petrochemical plants
(3) LP-Gas at utility gas plants (including refrigerated storage) *(see NFPA 59)*
(4)* Chemical plants where specific approval of construction and installation plans is obtained from the authority having jurisdiction
(5)* LP-Gas used with oxygen
(6)* The portions of LP-Gas systems covered by NFPA 54 where NFPA 54 is adopted, used, or enforced
(7) Transportation by air, rail, or water under the jurisdiction of the DOT
(8)* Marine fire protection
(9) Refrigeration cycle equipment and LP-Gas used as a refrigerant in a closed cycle
(10) The manufacturing requirements for recreational vehicle LP-Gas systems that are addressed by NFPA 1192
(11) Propane vehicle fuel dispensers located at multiple fuel refueling stations *(see NFPA 30A)*

1.4 Retroactivity. The provisions of this code reflect a consensus of what is necessary to provide an acceptable degree of protection from the hazards addressed in this code at the time it was issued.

1.4.1 Unless otherwise specified, the provisions of this code shall not apply to facilities, equipment, appliances, structures, or installations that existed or were approved for construction or installation prior to the effective date of the code. Equipment and appliances include stocks in manufacturers' storage, distribution warehouses, and dealers' storage and showrooms in compliance with the provisions of this code in effect at the time of manufacture. Where specified, the provisions of this code shall be retroactive.

1.4.2 In those cases where the authority having jurisdiction determines that the existing situation presents a distinct hazard to life and property, the authority having jurisdiction shall be permitted to apply any portions of this code retroactively.

1.4.3 Where the application of the retroactivity requirements of this code are determined to be impractical in the judgment of the authority having jurisdiction, alternate requirements that provide a reasonable degree of safety shall be provided by the authority having jurisdiction.

1.5 Equivalency. Nothing in this code is intended to prevent the use of systems, methods, or devices of equivalent or superior quality, strength, fire resistance, effectiveness, durability, and safety over those prescribed by this code.

1.5.1 Technical documentation shall be submitted to the authority having jurisdiction to demonstrate equivalency.

1.5.2 The system, method, or device shall be approved for the intended purpose by the authority having jurisdiction.

△ 1.6 Units and Formulas. The primary units of measure used in this code shall be U.S. customary units (inch-pound units).

N 1.6.1 International System (SI) units shall follow inch-pound units in parenthesis.

N 1.6.2 SI equivalents in this code are approximate and shall not be used to lessen any provision.

1.7 Enforcement. This code shall be administered and enforced by the authority having jurisdiction designated by the governing authority. *(See Annex J for sample wording for enabling legislation.)*

Chapter 2 Referenced Publications

2.1 General. The documents or portions thereof listed in this chapter are referenced within this code and shall be considered part of the requirements of this document.

Δ 2.2 NFPA Publications. National Fire Protection Association, 1 Batterymarch Park, Quincy, MA 02169-7471.

NFPA 10, *Standard for Portable Fire Extinguishers*, 2018 edition.
NFPA 13, *Standard for the Installation of Sprinkler Systems*, 2019 edition.
NFPA 15, *Standard for Water Spray Fixed Systems for Fire Protection*, 2017 edition.
NFPA 30, *Flammable and Combustible Liquids Code*, 2018 edition.
NFPA 30A, *Code for Motor Fuel Dispensing Facilities and Repair Garages*, 2018 edition.
NFPA 51B, *Standard for Fire Prevention During Welding, Cutting, and Other Hot Work*, 2019 edition.
NFPA 54, *National Fuel Gas Code*, 2018 edition.
NFPA 55, *Compressed Gases and Cryogenic Fluids Code*, 2020 edition.
NFPA 59, *Utility LP-Gas Plant Code*, 2018 edition.
NFPA 70®, *National Electrical Code*®, 2020 edition.
NFPA 99, *Health Care Facilities Code*, 2018 edition.
NFPA 101®, *Life Safety Code*®, 2018 edition.
NFPA 160, *Standard for the Use of Flame Effects Before an Audience*, 2016 edition.
NFPA 220, *Standard on Types of Building Construction*, 2018 edition.
NFPA 1192, *Standard on Recreational Vehicles*, 2018 edition.

2.3 Other Publications.

Δ 2.3.1 API Publications. American Petroleum Institute, 1220 L Street, NW, Washington, DC 20005-4070.

API-ASME *Code for Unfired Pressure Vessels for Petroleum Liquids and Gases*, Pre-July 1, 1961.

API 607, *Fire Test for Quarter-turn Valves and Valves Equipped with Nonmetallic Seats*, 2016.

API 620, *Design and Construction of Large, Welded, Low-pressure Storage Tanks*, 2008 with 2009, 2010, 2012, and 2013 Addenda.

2.3.2 ASCE Publications. American Society of Civil Engineers, 1801 Alexander Bell Drive, Reston, VA 20191-4400.

ASCE/SEI 7, *Minimum Design Loads for Buildings and Other Structures*, 2016.

2.3.3 ASME Publications. American Society of Mechanical Engineers, Two Park Avenue, New York, NY 10016-5990.

ASME B1.20.1, *Pipe Threads, General Purpose, Inch*, 2013.

ASME B16.40, *Manually Operated Thermoplastic Gas Shutoffs and Valves in Gas Distribution Systems*, 2013.

ASME B31.3, *Process Piping*, 2014.

ASME B36.10M, *Welded and Seamless Wrought Steel Pipe*, 2015.

Boiler and Pressure Vessel Code, 2013.

2.3.4 ASTM Publications. ASTM International, 100 Barr Harbor Drive, P.O. Box C700, West Conshohocken, PA 19428-2959.

ASTM A47/A47M, *Standard Specification for Ferritic Malleable Iron Castings*, 1999, reapproved 2014.

ASTM A48/A48M, *Standard Specification for Gray Iron Castings*, 2003, reapproved 2016.

ASTM A53/A53M, *Standard Specification for Pipe, Steel, Black and Hot-Dipped, Zinc-Coated, Welded and Seamless*, 2018.

ASTM A106/A106M, *Standard Specification for Seamless Carbon Steel Pipe for High-Temperature Service*, 2018.

ASTM A213/A213M, *Standard Specification for Seamless Ferritic and Austenitic Alloy-Steel Boiler, Superheater, and Heat-Exchanger Tubes*, 2018a.

ASTM A249/A249M, *Standard Specification for Welded Austenitic Steel Boiler, Superheater, Heat-Exchanger, and Condenser Tubes*, 2018.

ASTM A269/A269M, *Standard Specification for Seamless and Welded Austenitic Stainless Steel Tubing for General Service*, 2015a.

ASTM A312/A312M, *Standard Specification for Seamless, Welded, and Heavily Cold Worked Austenitic Stainless Steel Pipes*, 2018.

ASTM A395/A395M, *Standard Specification for Ferritic Ductile Iron Pressure-Retaining Castings for Use at Elevated Temperatures*, 1999, reapproved 2014.

ASTM A513/A513M, *Standard Specification for Electric-Resistance-Welded Carbon and Alloy Steel Mechanical Tubing*, 2018.

ASTM A536, *Standard Specification for Ductile Iron Castings*, 1984, reapproved 2014.

ASTM B42, *Standard Specification for Seamless Copper Pipe, Standard Sizes*, 2015a.

ASTM B43, *Standard Specification for Seamless Red Brass Pipe, Standard Sizes*, 2015.

ASTM B75/B75M, *Standard Specification for Seamless Copper Tube*, 2011.

ASTM B86, *Standard Specification for Zinc and Zinc-Aluminum (ZA) Alloy Foundry and Die Castings*, 2013.

ASTM B88, *Standard Specification for Seamless Copper Water Tube*, 2016.

ASTM B135/B135M, *Standard Specification for Seamless Brass Tube*, 2017.

ASTM B280, *Standard Specification for Seamless Copper Tube for Air Conditioning and Refrigeration Field Service*, 2018.

ASTM D2513, *Standard Specification for Polyethylene (PE) Gas Pressure Pipe, Tubing, and Fittings*, 2018a.

ASTM D2683, *Standard Specification for Socket-Type Polyethylene Fittings for Outside Diameter-Controlled Polyethylene Pipe and Tubing*, 2014.

ASTM D3261, *Standard Specification for Butt Heat Fusion Polyethylene (PE) Plastic Fittings for Polyethylene (PE) Plastic Pipe and Tubing*, 2016.

ASTM E84, *Standard Test Method for Surface Burning Characteristics of Building Materials*, 2018b.

ASTM E119, *Standard Test Methods for Fire Tests of Building Construction and Materials*, 2018b.

ASTM E136, *Standard Test Method for Behavior of Materials in a Vertical Tube Furnace at 750°C*, 2016a.

ASTM E2652, *Standard Test Method for Behavior of Materials in a Tube Furnace with a Cone-shaped Airflow Stabilizer, at 750°C*, 2016.

ASTM F1055, *Standard Specification for Electrofusion Type Polyethylene Fittings for Outside Diameter Controlled Polyethylene and Crosslinked Polyethylene (PEX) Pipe and Tubing*, 2016a.

ASTM F1733, *Standard Specification for Butt Heat Fusion Polyamide (PA) Plastic Fitting for Polyamide (PA) Plastic Pipe and Tubing*, 2013.

ASTM F1948, *Standard Specification for Metallic Mechanical Fittings for Use on Outside Diameter Controlled Thermoplastic Gas Distribution Pipe and Tubing*, 2015.

ASTM F2145, *Standard Specification for Polyamide 11 (PA11) and Polyamide 12 (PA12) Mechanical Fittings for Use on Outside Diameter Controlled Polyamide 11 and Polyamide 12 Pipe and Tubing*, 2013, reapproved 2018.

ASTM F2509, *Standard Specification for Field-assembled Anodeless Riser Kits for Use on Outside Diameter Controlled Polyethylene and Polyamide-11 (PA11) Gas Distribution Pipe and Tubing*, 2015.

ASTM F2945, *Standard Specification for Polyamide 11 Gas Pressure Pipe, Tubing, and Fittings*, 2015.

Δ **2.3.5 CGA Publications.** Compressed Gas Association, 14501 George Carter Way, Suite 103, Chantilly, VA 20151-1788.

CGA C-6, *Standard for Visual Inspection of Steel Compressed Gas Cylinders*, 2013.

CGA C-7, *Guide to Classification and Labeling of Compressed Gases*, 2014.

CGA S-1.1, *Pressure Relief Device Standards, Part 1— Cylinders for Compressed Gases*, 2011.

CGA S-1.3, *Pressure Relief Device Standards, Part 3 — Stationary Storage Containers for Compressed Gases*, 2008.

CGA V-1, *Standard for Compressed Gas Cylinder Valve Outlet and Inlet Connections*, 2013.

CSA CAN/CGA-8.1-M86, *Elastomeric Composite Hose and Hose Couplings for Conducting Propane and Natural Gas*, R2011.

Δ **2.3.6 CSA Group Publications.** CSA Group, 178 Rexdale Blvd., Toronto, ON M9W 1R3, Canada.

ANSI/CSA 6.26 (LC1), *Interior Fuel Gas Piping Systems Using Corrugated Stainless Steel Tubing*, 2016.

ANSI/CSA 6.32 (LC4a), *Press-Connect Metallic Fittings for Use in Fuel Gas Distribution Systems*, 2012 (R2016).

ANSI Z21.11.3, *Gas-Fired Room Heaters, Volume III, Propane-Fired Portable Emergency Use Heater Systems*, 2016.

ANSI Z21.18/CSA 6.3, *Standard for Gas Appliance Pressure Regulators*, 2012 (R2016).

ANSI Z21.80/CSA 6.22, *Standard for Line Pressure Regulators*, 2011 (R2016).

ANSI Z21.81/CSA 6.25, *Standard for Cylinder Connection Devices*, 2015.

CSA B149.5, *Installation Code for Propane Fuel Systems and Containers on Motor Vehicles*, 2015.

2.3.7 ISO Publications. International Organization for Standardization. ISO Central Secretariat, BIBC II, Chemin de Blandonnet 8, CP 401, 1214 Vernier, Geneva, Switzerland.

ISO/DIS 19825, *Road vehicles — Liquefied petroleum gas (LPG) refuelling connector*, 2017.

2.3.8 NBBPVI Publications. National Board of Boiler and Pressure Vessel Inspectors, 1055 Crupper Avenue, Columbus, OH 43229.

NBBI NB23, *National Board Inspection Code*, 2017.

N **2.3.9 SAE Publications.** SAE International, Society of Automotive Engineers, 400 Commonwealth Drive, Warrendale, PA 15096.

SAE J356, *Welded Flash-Controlled Low-Carbon Steel Tubing Normalized for Bending, Double Flaring, and Beading*, 2013.

SAE J1292, *Automobile and Motor Coach Wiring*, 2016.

SAE J2223-1, *Connections for On-Board Road Vehicle Electrical Wiring Harnesses — Part 1: Single-Pole Connectors — Flat Blade Terminals — Dimensional Characteristics and Specific Requirements*, 2011.

SAE J2223-3, *Connections for On-Board Road Vehicle Electrical Wiring Harnesses — Part 3: Multipole Connectors — Flat Blade Terminals — Dimensional Characteristics and Specific Requirements*, 2011.

2.3.10 UL Publications. Underwriters Laboratories, Inc., 333 Pfingsten Road, Northbrook, IL 60062-2096.

UL 21, *Standard for LP-Gas Hose*, 2015.

UL 125, *Standard for Flow Control Valves for Anhydrous Ammonia and LP-Gas (Other than Safety Relief)*, 2015.

UL 132, *Standard for Safety Relief Valves for Anhydrous Ammonia and LP-Gas*, 2016.

UL 144, *Standard for LP-Gas Regulators*, 2012, revised 2014.

UL 147A, *Standard for Nonrefillable (Disposable) Type Fuel Gas Cylinder Assemblies*, 2005, revised 2014.

UL 147B, *Standard for Nonrefillable (Disposable) Type Metal Container Assemblies for Butane*, 2016.

UL 263, *Standard for Fire Tests of Building Construction and Materials*, 2011, revised 2015.

UL 514B, *Standard for Conduit, Tubing, and Cable Fittings*, 2012, revised 2014.

UL 567, *Standard for Emergency Breakaway Fittings, Swivel Connectors, and Pipe-Connection Fittings for Petroleum Products and LP-Gas*, 2014.

UL 569, *Standard for Pigtails and Flexible Hose Connectors for LP-Gas*, 2013.

UL 651, *Standard for Schedule 40, 80, Type EB and A Rigid PVC Conduit and Fittings*, 2016.

ANSI/UL 723, *Standard for Test for Surface Burning Characteristics of Building Materials*, 2018.

UL 1337, *Outline of Investigation for LP-Gas, Natural Gas, and Manufactured Gas Devices for Engine Fuel Systems*, 2016.

UL 1660, *Standard for Liquid-Tight Flexible Nonmetallic Conduit*, 2014.

UL 1769, *Standard for Cylinder Valves*, 2015, revised 2016.

UL 2061, *Standard for Adapters and Cylinder Connection Devices for Portable LP-Gas Cylinder Assemblies*, 2015.

UL 2227, *Standard for Overfilling Prevention Devices*, 2007.

2.3.11 United Nations Economic Commission for Europe Publications. UN Economic Commission for Europe Information Services, Palais des Nations, CH-1211 Geneva 10, Switzerland.

ECE R67.01, *Agreement Concerning the Adoption of Uniform Technical Prescriptions for Wheeled Vehicles, Equipment and Parts Which Can Be Fitted and/or Be Used on Wheeled Vehicles and the Conditions for Reciprocal Recognition of Approvals Granted on the Basis of these Prescriptions*, Revision 4, 1998.

2.3.12 U.S. Government Publications. U.S. Government Publishing Office, 732 North Capitol Street, NW, Washington, DC 20401-0001.

Interstate Commerce Commission (ICC), *Rules for Construction of Unfired Pressure Vessels.*

Title 14, Code of Federal Regulations, "Aeronautics and Space."

Title 49, Code of Federal Regulations, Parts 171–180, 393, 396, and 397.

Title 49, Code of Federal Regulations, Parts 173.301(h)(3), 173.315(n), and 192.283(b).

Title 49, Code of Federal Regulations, Part 192, Appendix D, "Criteria for Cathodic Protection and Determination of Measurements."

2.3.13 Other Publications.

Merriam-Webster's Collegiate Dictionary, 11th edition, Merriam-Webster, Inc., Springfield, MA, 2003.

2.4 References for Extracts in Mandatory Sections.

NFPA 30, *Flammable and Combustible Liquids Code*, 2018 edition.
NFPA 54, *National Fuel Gas Code*, 2018 edition.
NFPA *101®*, *Life Safety Code®*, 2018 edition.

Chapter 3 Definitions

3.1 General. The definitions contained in this chapter shall apply to the terms used in this code. Where terms are not defined in this chapter or within another chapter, they shall be defined using their ordinarily accepted meanings within the context in which they are used. *Merriam-Webster's Collegiate Dictionary*, 11th edition, shall be the source for the ordinarily accepted meaning.

3.2 NFPA Official Definitions.

3.2.1* Approved. Acceptable to the authority having jurisdiction.

3.2.2* Authority Having Jurisdiction (AHJ). An organization, office, or individual responsible for enforcing the requirements of a code or standard, or for approving equipment, materials, an installation, or a procedure.

3.2.3* Code. A standard that is an extensive compilation of provisions covering broad subject matter or that is suitable for adoption into law independently of other codes and standards.

3.2.4 Labeled. Equipment or materials to which has been attached a label, symbol, or other identifying mark of an organization that is acceptable to the authority having jurisdiction and concerned with product evaluation, that maintains periodic inspection of production of labeled equipment or materials, and by whose labeling the manufacturer indicates compliance with appropriate standards or performance in a specified manner.

3.2.5* Listed. Equipment, materials, or services included in a list published by an organization that is acceptable to the authority having jurisdiction and concerned with evaluation of products or services, that maintains periodic inspection of production of listed equipment or materials or periodic evaluation of services, and whose listing states that either the equipment, material, or service meets appropriate designated standards or has been tested and found suitable for a specified purpose.

3.2.6 Shall. Indicates a mandatory requirement.

3.2.7 Should. Indicates a recommendation or that which is advised but not required.

3.3 General Definitions.

3.3.1 Actuated Liquid Withdrawal Excess-Flow Valve. See 3.3.78.1.

3.3.2 Anodeless Riser. A transition assembly used between underground polyethylene or polyamide pipe and aboveground metal piping or equipment, and terminating aboveground outside of a building.

3.3.3 ANSI. American National Standards Institute.

3.3.4 API. American Petroleum Institute.

3.3.5 API-ASME Container (or Tank). A container constructed in accordance with the pressure vessel code jointly developed by the American Petroleum Institute and the American Society of Mechanical Engineers.

3.3.6 ASME. American Society of Mechanical Engineers.

3.3.7 ASME Code. The American Society of Mechanical Engineers *Boiler and Pressure Vessel Code.*

3.3.8 ASME Container. A container constructed in accordance with the ASME Code.

N 3.3.9* Assembly Occupancy. An occupancy (1) used for a gathering of 50 or more persons for deliberation, worship, entertainment, eating, drinking, amusement, awaiting transportation, or similar uses; or (2) used as a special amusement building, regardless of occupant load. [*101,* 2018]

3.3.10* Bulk Plant. A facility that stores LP-Gas in containers of more than 4000 gal (15.2 m³) water capacity prior to further distribution as a liquid for use at other facilities.

3.3.11 Cabinet Heater. A portable unvented heater with a self-contained propane supply.

3.3.12 Cargo Tank. A container that is used to transport LP-Gas as liquid cargo that either is mounted on a conventional truck chassis or is an integral part of a cargo transporting vehicle.

3.3.13 CGA. The Compressed Gas Association.

3.3.14 Concrete Pad. A foundation consisting of solid concrete or masonry blocks, a placed concrete slab, or a poured concrete foundation.

3.3.15 Container. Any vessel, including cylinders, tanks, portable tanks, and cargo tanks, used for the transporting or storing of LP-Gases.

3.3.16 Container Appurtenances. Devices installed in container openings for safety, control, or operating purposes.

3.3.17 Container Assembly. An assembly consisting of the container and fittings for all container openings such as shutoff valves, excess-flow valves, liquid level gauging devices, pressure relief devices, and protective housings.

3.3.18 Cylinder. A portable container with a marked water capacity of 1000 lb (454 kg) or less that is designed to transport and store LP-Gas.

    3.3.18.1 *Universal Cylinder.* A cylinder that can be connected for service in either the vertical or the horizontal position so that the fixed maximum liquid level gauge, pressure relief device, and filling and withdrawal appurtenances function properly in either position.

3.3.19 Design Certification. The process by which a product is evaluated and tested by an independent laboratory to affirm that the product design complies with specific requirements.

3.3.20 Design Pressure. The maximum pressure at which the equipment or system is designed to operate.

3.3.21 Direct Injection. A fuel injection system that delivers LP-Gas fuel through a fuel injector, directly into the combustion chamber at high pressures, as opposed to the injection of fuel into the intake manifold air flow stream, upstream of and prior to the intake valve opening.

3.3.22* Dispenser. An assembly used to transfer LP-Gas into cylinders, portable and mobile containers, and vehicle fuel containers.

    3.3.22.1 *Vehicle Fuel Dispenser.* A dispenser designed to transfer LP-Gas into engine fuel and mobile containers on vehicles.

3.3.23 Dispensing System. An assembly of equipment that includes a dispenser and storage container(s) for storing and transferring LP-Gas from storage to cylinders, portable and mobile containers, and vehicle fuel containers.

3.3.24 DOT. U.S. Department of Transportation.

3.3.25 Facility Hose. A hose and its couplings permanently installed for the purpose of unloading product from cargo tank motor vehicles in nonmetered service into a bulk plant or industrial plant.

3.3.26 Filling.

    3.3.26.1 *Volumetric Method Filling.* Filling a container to not more than the maximum permitted liquid volume.

    3.3.26.2 *Weight Method Filling.* Filling containers to not more than the maximum permitted filling limit by weighing the LP-Gas in the container.

3.3.27* Fire Protection. Includes fire prevention, fire detection, and fire suppression.

△ 3.3.28 Flexible Connector. A fixed piping system component that is fabricated from a flexible material and equipped with connections at both ends.

    3.3.28.1 *Flexible Hose Connector.* A component fabricated from LP-Gas hose that is made from a material that is compatible with LP-Gas.

    3.3.28.2 *Flexible Metallic Connector.* A component fabricated from metallic material that provides liquid and vapor LP-Gas confinement and is provided with connections on both ends.

    3.3.28.3 *Metallic-Protected Flexible Hose Connector.* A flexible hose connector that is provided with a metallic material over wrap that provides mechanical protection of the inner hose but does not provide fluid confinement.

3.3.29 Fuel Rail. A manifold, pipe, or duct that connects or retains the fuel injection devices for the purpose of providing fuel supply to each injector.

3.3.30 Fuel Switching Device. A component used in some direct injections systems, which is used to switch between fuels of a bifuel powered vehicle.

3.3.31 Gallon, U.S. Standard. 1 U.S. gal = 0.833 Imperial gal = 231 in.³ = 3.785 L.

3.3.32* Gas. For the purposes of this code, liquefied petroleum gas (LP-Gas) in either the liquid or vapor state.

3.3.33* Gas-Air Mixer. A device or a system of piping and controls that mixes LP-Gas vapor with air to produce a mixed gas of a lower heating value than the LP-Gas.

3.3.34 Gauge.

    3.3.34.1 *Fixed Liquid Level Gauge.* A liquid level indicator that uses a positive shutoff vent valve to indicate that the liquid level in a container being filled has reached the point at which the indicator communicates with the liquid level in the container.

    3.3.34.2 *Fixed Maximum Liquid Level Gauge.* A fixed liquid level gauge that indicates the liquid level at which the container is filled to its maximum permitted filling limit.

3.3.34.3 *Float Gauge.* A gauge constructed with an element installed inside the container that floats on the liquid surface and transmits its position to a device outside the container to indicate the liquid level.

3.3.34.4 *Magnetic Gauge.* See 3.3.34.3, Float Gauge.

3.3.34.5 *Rotary Gauge.* A type of variable liquid level gauge that indicates the liquid level on a dial gauge installed on an ASME container by manually rotating an open ended tube inside the container, which is connected to a positive shutoff vent valve.

3.3.34.6* *Slip Tube Gauge.* A variable liquid level gauge in which a small positive shutoff valve is located at the outside end of a straight tube that is installed vertically within a container.

3.3.34.7* *Variable Liquid Level Gauge.* A device that indicates the liquid level in a container throughout a range of levels.

3.3.35* Ground Snow Load. The snow load established by ASCE/SEI 7, *Minimum Design Loads for Buildings and Other Structures*, as the 2 percent annual probability of exceedance or 50-year mean recurrence interval; also known as the "50-year ground snow load."

3.3.36 ICC. U.S. Interstate Commerce Commission.

3.3.37 Ignition Source. See 3.3.72, Sources of Ignition.

N **3.3.38 Important Building.** A building that is considered not expendable in an exposure fire. [**30,** 2018] *(See A.6.4.1.1.)*

3.3.39 Industrial Occupancy. Includes factories that manufacture products of all kinds and properties devoted to operations such as processing, assembling, mixing, packaging, finishing or decorating, and repairing.

3.3.40* Industrial Plant. A facility that stores LP-Gas in containers of water capacity more than 4000 gal (15.2 m³) for use at the facility or to distribute vapor to other facilities.

3.3.41 kPa. Absolute pressure in kilo-Pascals.

3.3.42 kPag. Gauge pressure in kilo-Pascals.

3.3.43 Leak Check. An operation performed on a gas piping system to verify that the system does not leak.

3.3.44* Liquefied Petroleum Gas (LP-Gas). Any material having a vapor pressure not exceeding that allowed for commercial propane that is composed predominantly of the following hydrocarbons, either by themselves (except propylene) or as mixtures: propane, propylene, butane (normal butane or isobutane), and butylenes.

3.3.45* Low-Emission Transfer. A method of transfer of LP-Gas liquid that limits the amount of propane released during the transfer process.

3.3.46 LP-Gas System. An assembly consisting of one or more containers with a means for conveying LP-Gas from a container to dispensing or consuming devices that incorporates components that control the quantity, flow, pressure, and physical state (liquid or vapor) of the LP-Gas.

3.3.47 Maximum Allowable Working Pressure (MAWP). The maximum pressure at which a pressure vessel is to operate as described by the ASME *Boiler and Pressure Vessel Code.*

3.3.48 Mobile Container. A container that is permanently mounted on a vehicle and connected for uses other than supplying engine fuel.

3.3.49 Mounded Container. An ASME container designed for underground service installed above the minimum depth required for underground service and covered with earth, sand, or other material, or an ASME container designed for aboveground service installed above grade and covered with earth, sand, or other material.

3.3.50 MPa. Absolute pressure in mega-Pascals.

3.3.51 MPag. Gauge pressure in mega-Pascals.

3.3.52 NFPA. National Fire Protection Association.

3.3.53 NPGA. National Propane Gas Association.

3.3.54 Overfilling Prevention Device (OPD). A device that is designed to provide an automatic means to prevent the filling of a container beyond a predetermined level.

3.3.55 Overpressure Shutoff Device. A device that shuts off the flow of LP-Gas vapor when the outlet pressure of the regulator reaches a predetermined maximum allowable pressure.

3.3.56 Permanent Installation. See 3.3.75, Stationary Installation.

3.3.57 Permitted. Allowed or acceptable, and not requiring a permit (a document granting permission) to be secured.

3.3.58 Piping Systems. Pipe, tubing, hose, and flexible rubber or metallic hose connectors with valves and fittings made into complete systems for conveying LP-Gas from one point to another in either the liquid or the vapor state at various pressures.

3.3.59 Point of Transfer. The location where connections and disconnections are made or where LP-Gas is vented to the atmosphere in the course of transfer operations.

3.3.60* Portable Container. A container designed to transport LP-Gas.

3.3.60.1 *Cargo Tank.* See 3.3.12, Cargo Tank.

3.3.60.2 *Cylinder.* See 3.3.18, Cylinder.

3.3.60.3 *Portable Tank.* A container of more than 1000 lb (454 kg) water capacity that is equipped with protected container appurtenances, is used to transport LP-Gas, and is designed and fabricated with permanently mounted skids or runners or is fabricated and installed within a full framework.

3.3.61* Portable Storage Container. A storage container that is not used to transport LP-Gas.

3.3.61.1 *Movable Fuel Storage Tender.* A non-DOT specification cargo tank that is used exclusively for agricultural purposes and is commonly known as a "farm cart."

3.3.61.2 *Porta-Pac.* An ASME container installed on wheels with retractable landing gear that is used to store LP-Gas in temporary installations and not used to transport LP-Gas.

3.3.61.3 *Skid Tank.* A container that is designed and fabricated with permanently mounted skids or runners that is not designed to transport LP-Gas.

3.3.62 Power Supply Bushing. A sealed fitting that is installed in a container opening or multifunction valve body that seals conductors passing from the inside to the outside of the pressure vessel for the purposes of supplying electrical signals or operating voltage to electrical/electronic components located inside the pressure containment area of an ASME container.

3.3.63 Pressure Relief Device. A device designed to open to prevent a rise of internal pressure in excess of a specified value.

3.3.64 Pressure Test. An operation performed to verify the gastight integrity of gas piping following its installation or modification.

3.3.65 psi. Pounds per square inch.

3.3.66 psia. Pounds per square inch absolute.

3.3.67 psig. Pounds per square inch gauge.

3.3.68 Quick Connectors. Fittings used to connect hose assemblies to piping and valves without the use of tools.

3.3.69* Refrigerated LP-Gas. LP-Gas that is cooled to temperatures below ambient to maintain the product as a liquid with a vapor pressure of 15 psig (103 kPag) or less.

3.3.70 Regulator.

3.3.70.1* *Automatic Changeover Regulator.* An integral two-stage regulator that combines two high-pressure regulators and a second-stage regulator into a single unit designed for use with multiple cylinder installations.

3.3.70.2 *First-Stage Regulator.* A pressure regulator for LP-Gas vapor service designed to reduce pressure from a container to 10 psig (69 kPag) or less.

3.3.70.3 *High-Pressure Regulator.* A pressure regulator for LP-Gas liquid or vapor service designed to reduce pressure from the container to a lower pressure in excess of 1.0 psig (6.9 kPag).

3.3.70.4 *Integral 2 psi Service Regulator.* A pressure regulator for LP-Gas vapor service that combines a high-pressure regulator and a 2 psi (14 kPag) service regulator into a single unit.

3.3.70.5 *Integral Two-Stage Regulator.* A pressure regulator for LP-Gas vapor service that combines a high-pressure regulator and a second-stage regulator into a single unit.

3.3.70.6 *Line Pressure Regulator.* A pressure regulator with no integral overpressure protection device for LP-Gas vapor service to reduce a nominal inlet pressure.

3.3.70.7 *Second-Stage Regulator.* A pressure regulator for LP-Gas vapor service designed to reduce first-stage regulator outlet pressure to the pressure required at the point of delivery.

3.3.70.8 *Single-Stage Regulator.* A pressure regulator for LP-Gas vapor service designed to reduce pressure from the container to 1.0 psig (6.9 kPag) or less.

3.3.70.9 *2 psi Regulator System.* An LP-Gas vapor delivery system that combines a first-stage regulator, a 2 psi (14 kPag) service regulator, and a line pressure regulator(s).

3.3.70.10 *2 psi Service Regulator.* A pressure regulator for LP-Gas vapor service designed to reduce first-stage regulator outlet pressure to a nominal 2 psig (14 kPag).

3.3.70.11 *Two-Stage Regulator System.* An LP-Gas vapor delivery system that combines a first-stage regulator and a second-stage regulator(s), or utilizes a separate integral two-stage regulator.

3.3.71 SCFM. Standard cubic feet per minute.

3.3.72 Sources of Ignition. Devices or equipment that, because of their modes of use or operation, are capable of providing sufficient thermal energy to ignite flammable LP-Gas vapor–air mixtures when introduced into such a mixture or when such a mixture comes into contact with them, and that will permit propagation of flame away from them.

3.3.73* Special Protection. A means of limiting the temperature of an LP-Gas container for purposes of minimizing the possibility of failure of the container as the result of fire exposure.

3.3.74 Standard Cubic Foot (SCF). The volume of gas in cubic feet at the standard atmospheric conditions at 60°F (15.6°C) and 14.7 psia (101 kPa).

3.3.75 Stationary Installation (Permanent Installation). An installation of LP-Gas containers, piping, and equipment for indefinite use at a particular location; an installation not normally expected to change in status, condition, or location.

3.3.76 Tank Heater (Indirect and Direct Types). A device used to apply heat either directly to a portion of the container surface in contact with LP-Gas liquid or indirectly by circulating LP-Gas liquid from the container to the device and then back to the container.

3.3.76.1 *Direct Gas-Fired Tank Heater.* A gas-fired device that applies heat directly to the container surface in contact with LP-Gas liquid.

3.3.77 UL. Underwriters Laboratories Inc.

3.3.78 Valve.

3.3.78.1 *Actuated Liquid Withdrawal Excess-Flow Valve.* A container valve that is opened and closed by an adapter, incorporates an internal excess-flow valve, and is used to withdraw liquid from the container.

3.3.78.2 *Emergency Shutoff Valve.* A shutoff valve incorporating thermal and manual means of closing that also provides for remote means of closing.

3.3.78.3 *Excess-Flow Valve (or Excess-Flow Check Valve).* A valve designed to close when the liquid or vapor passing through it exceeds a prescribed flow rate.

3.3.78.4 *Filler Valve.* A valve that is designed to allow liquid flow only into a container.

3.3.78.5 *Internal Excess-Flow Valve.* An excess-flow valve constructed and installed so that damage to valve parts exterior to the container does not prevent closing of the valve.

3.3.78.6* *Internal Valve.* A container primary shutoff valve that can be closed remotely, which incorporates an internal excess flow valve with the seat and seat disc located within the container so that they remain in place should external damage occur to the valve.

3.3.78.7 *Positive Shutoff Valve.* A shutoff valve that, in the closed position, does not allow the flow of product in either direction.

3.3.78.8 *Pressure Relief Valve.* A type of pressure relief device designed to both open and close to maintain internal fluid pressure.

3.3.78.8.1* *External Pressure Relief Valve.* A pressure relief valve where all the working parts are located entirely outside the container or piping.

3.3.78.8.2* *Flush-Type Full Internal Pressure Relief Valve.* An internal pressure relief valve in which the wrenching section is also within the container connection, not including a small portion due to pipe thread tolerances on makeup.

3.3.78.8.3* *Full Internal Pressure Relief Valve.* A pressure relief valve in which all working parts are recessed within a threaded connection of the valve, and the spring and guiding mechanism are not exposed to the atmosphere.

3.3.78.8.4* *Internal Spring-Type Pressure Relief Valve.* A pressure relief valve that is similar to a full internal relief valve except the wrenching pads and seating section are above the container connection in which the adjusting spring and the stem are below the seat and are not exposed to the atmosphere.

3.3.78.9 *Purge Valve.* A mechanical or electromechanical device used to permit fuel flow through the engine supply and return lines, generally on fuel injection systems, to ensure all vapor is removed from the lines prior to engine start.

3.3.79 Vaporizer. A device, other than a container, that receives LP-Gas in liquid form and adds sufficient heat to convert the liquid to a gaseous state.

3.3.79.1 *Direct-Fired Vaporizer.* A vaporizer in which heat furnished by a flame is directly applied to a heat exchange surface in contact with the liquid LP-Gas to be vaporized.

3.3.79.2 *Electric Vaporizer.* A vaporizer that uses electricity as a source of heat.

3.3.79.2.1 *Direct Immersion Electric Vaporizer.* A vaporizer wherein an electric element is immersed directly in the LP-Gas liquid and vapor.

3.3.79.2.2 *Indirect Electric Vaporizer.* An immersion-type vaporizer wherein the electric element heats an interface solution in which the LP-Gas heat exchanger is immersed or heats an intermediate heat sink.

3.3.79.3 *Indirect (or Indirect-Fired) Vaporizer.* A vaporizer in which heat furnished by steam, hot water, the ground, surrounding air, or other heating medium is applied to a vaporizing chamber or to tubing, pipe coils, or other heat exchange surface containing the liquid LP-Gas to be vaporized; the heating of the medium used is at a point remote from the vaporizer.

3.3.79.4 *Waterbath (or Immersion-Type) Vaporizer.* A vaporizer in which a vaporizing chamber, tubing, pipe coils, or other heat exchange surface containing liquid LP-Gas to be vaporized is immersed in a temperature-controlled bath of water, water-glycol combination, or other noncombustible heat transfer medium that is heated by an immersion heater not in contact with the LP-Gas heat exchange surface.

3.3.80 Vaporizing Burner (Self-Vaporizing Liquid Burner). A burner that also vaporizes liquid LP-Gas prior to burning it.

3.3.81* Vehicular Barrier Protection (VBP). A system or method to provide physical protection for LP-Gas storage areas or installations from vehicular incursion.

3.3.82 Volumetric Loading. See 3.3.26.1, Volumetric Method Filling.

3.3.83 Water Capacity. The amount of water at 60°F (16°C) required to fill a container.

Chapter 4   General Requirements

4.1 Acceptance of Equipment and Systems.

4.1.1 Systems or components assembled to make up systems shall be approved as specified in Table 4.1.1.

4.1.2 Where it is necessary to alter or repair such systems or assemblies, approved components shall be used.

4.1.3 Acceptance applies to the complete system or to the individual components of which it is comprised as specified in Table 4.1.1.

4.2 LP-Gas Odorization.

4.2.1* All LP-Gases shall be odorized prior to being loaded into a railcar or cargo tank motor vehicle by the addition of a warning agent of such character that the gases are detectable by a distinct odor to a concentration in air of not over one-fifth the lower limit of flammability.

Table 4.1.1 Containers

Containers Used	Water Capacity		Approval Applies to …
	gal	m³	
Cylinders	<120	<0.445	Container valves and connectors
			Manifold valve assemblies
			Regulators and pressure relief devices
ASME containers	≤4000	≤15.2	Container system,* including regulator, or container assembly* and regulator separately
ASME containers	>4000	>15.2	Container valves
			Container excess-flow valves, backflow check valves, or alternate means of providing this protection, such as remotely controlled internal valves
			Container gauging devices
			Regulators and container pressure relief devices

*Where necessary to alter or repair such systems or assemblies in the field in order to provide for different operating pressures, change from vapor to liquid withdrawal, or the like. Such changes are permitted to be made by the use of approved components.

Shaded text = Revisions.   Δ = Text deletions and figure/table revisions.   • = Section deletions.   **N** = New material.

4.2.2 The addition of the odorant shall be documented at the point of odorization.

4.2.3* The presence of the odorant shall be verified by sniff-testing or other means and the results documented prior to final delivery to the end-use customer.

4.2.4 Odorization shall not be required if it is harmful in the use or further processing of the LP-Gas or if such odorization will serve no useful purpose as a warning agent in such further use or processing.

4.3 Notification of Installations.

4.3.1 Stationary Installations. Plans for stationary installations utilizing storage containers with aggregate water capacity exceeding 4000 gal (15.2 m³) and all rooftop installations of ASME containers shall be submitted to the authority having jurisdiction before the installation is started by the person or company that either installs or contracts to have the containers installed. *[See also 6.22.11.1(F).]*

4.3.2 Temporary Installations.

4.3.2.1 The authority having jurisdiction shall be notified of temporary installations of the container sizes covered in 4.3.1 before the installation is started.

4.3.2.2 Where temporary installations exceed 12 months, approval shall be obtained.

4.3.3 Railcar to Cargo Tank Transfer.

4.3.3.1 Notification of intent to transfer LP-Gas directly from railcar to cargo tank shall be submitted to the authority having jurisdiction before the first transfer.

4.3.3.2 The authority having jurisdiction shall have the authority to require inspection of the site or equipment for such transfer prior to the initial transfer.

4.4* Qualification of Personnel.

4.4.1 Persons whose duties fall within the scope of this code shall be provided with training that is consistent with the scope of their job activities and that includes proper handling and emergency response procedures.

4.4.2 Persons whose primary duties include transporting LP-Gas, transferring liquid LP-Gas into or out of stationary containers, or making stationary installations shall complete training that includes the following components:

(1) Safe work practices
(2) The health and safety hazards of LP-Gas
(3) Emergency response procedures
(4) Supervised, on-the-job training
(5) An assessment of the person's ability to perform the job duties assigned

4.4.3* Refresher training shall be provided at least every 3 years.

4.4.4 Initial and subsequent refresher training shall be documented.

4.5* Ammonia Contamination.

4.5.1 LP-Gas stored or used in systems within the scope of this code shall contain less ammonia than is required to turn the color of red litmus paper to blue.

4.5.2 A test for ammonia shall be performed on the LP-Gas prior to the initial use or transfer of LP-Gas from a transportation or storage system that has been converted from ammonia service.

4.6* Minimum Requirements. For any purpose or application addressed within the scope of this code, where the minimum requirements of the code are met, additional features or components of equipment not prohibited by the code shall be permitted to be used.

△ **4.7* Portable Fire Extinguisher.** Where portable fire extinguishers are required, they shall comply with NFPA 10 and the following requirements:

(1) They shall have a minimum capacity of dry chemical with an A:B:C rating, as specified elsewhere in this code.
(2) They shall not be used to extinguish an LP-Gas pressure fire unless the source of fuel can be shut off promptly.

N **4.8 Fire Resistance Rating.** Whenever a fire resistance rating is required by this code, it shall be determined in accordance with ASTM E119, *Standard Test Methods for Fire Tests of Building Construction and Materials.*

N **4.9* Noncombustible Material.**

N **4.9.1** A material that complies with any of the following shall be considered a noncombustible material:

(1)* A material that, in the form in which it is used and under the conditions anticipated, will not ignite, burn, support combustion, or release flammable vapors when subjected to fire or heat
(2) A material that is reported as passing ASTM E136, *Standard Test Method for Behavior of Materials in a Vertical Tube Furnace at 750°C*
(3) A material that is reported as complying with the pass/fail criteria of ASTM E136 when tested in accordance with the test method and procedure in ASTM E2652, *Standard Test Method for Behavior of Materials in a Tube Furnace with a Cone-shaped Airflow Stabilizer, at 750°C*

[**101**:4.6.13.1]

Chapter 5   LP-Gas Equipment and Appliances

5.1* Scope. This chapter applies to individual components and components shop-fabricated into subassemblies, container assemblies, and complete container systems.

5.2 Containers.

5.2.1 General.

△ **5.2.1.1*** Containers shall be designed, fabricated, tested, and marked (or stamped) in accordance with the regulations of the U.S. Department of Transportation (DOT 49 CFR); Federal Aviation Administration (FAA 14 CFR); the ASME *Boiler and Pressure Vessel Code*, Section VIII, "Rules for the Construction of Unfired Pressure Vessels"; or the API-ASME *Code for Unfired Pressure Vessels for Petroleum Liquids and Gases*, except for UG-125 through UG-136.

(A) Used containers constructed to specifications of the Association of American Railroads shall not be installed.

(B) Adherence to applicable ASME Code case interpretations and addenda that have been adopted and published by ASME

180 calendar days prior to the effective date of this code shall be considered as compliant with the ASME Code.

(C) Where containers fabricated to earlier editions of regulations, rules, or codes listed in 5.2.1.1, and of the Interstate Commerce Commission (ICC) *Rules for Construction of Unfired Pressure Vessels*, prior to April 1, 1967, are used, the requirements of Section 1.4 shall apply.

5.2.1.2 Containers that have been involved in a fire and show no distortion shall be requalified for continued service before being used or reinstalled.

(A) Cylinders shall be requalified by a manufacturer of that type of cylinder or by a repair facility approved by DOT.

(B) ASME or API-ASME containers shall be retested using the hydrostatic test procedure applicable at the time of the original fabrication.

(C) All container appurtenances shall be replaced.

(D) DOT 4E specification (aluminum) cylinders and composite cylinders involved in a fire shall be permanently removed from service.

5.2.1.3 ASME paragraph U-68 or U-69 containers shall be permitted to be continued in use, installed, reinstalled, or placed back into service. Installation of containers shall be in accordance with all provisions listed in this code. *[See Section 5.2, Table 5.2.4.3, Table 5.9.2.5(A), and Annex D.]*

5.2.1.4 Containers that show excessive denting, bulging, gouging, or corrosion shall be removed from service.

5.2.1.5 Except for containers used in cargo tank vehicle service, ASME containers of 3000 gal (11.4 m³) water capacity or less used to store anhydrous ammonia shall not be converted to LP-Gas fuel service.

5.2.1.6 Repairs or alteration of a container shall comply with the regulations, rules, or code under which the container was fabricated. Repairs or alteration to ASME containers shall be in accordance with the NBBI NB23, *National Board Inspection Code*.

5.2.1.7 Field welding shall be permitted only on saddle plates, lugs, pads, or brackets that are attached to the container by the container manufacturer.

5.2.1.8 Containers for general use shall not have individual water capacities greater than 120,000 gal (454 m³).

5.2.1.9 Dispensing systems not located in LP-Gas bulk plants or industrial plants shall have an aggregate water capacity not greater than 30,000 gal (114 m³).

5.2.1.10 Heating or cooling coils shall not be installed inside storage containers.

5.2.1.11 ASME containers installed underground, partially underground, or as mounded installations shall incorporate provisions for cathodic protection and shall be coated with a material recommended for the service that is applied in accordance with the coating manufacturer's instructions.

5.2.2 Cylinders.

5.2.2.1* Cylinders shall be containers designed, constructed, tested, and marked in accordance with U.S. Department of Transportation specifications, Title 49, Code of Federal Regulations, or in accordance with a valid DOT special permit.

5.2.2.2* Cylinders shall be continued in service and transported in accordance with DOT regulations.

5.2.2.3 A cylinder with an expired requalification date shall not be refilled until it is requalified by the methods prescribed in DOT regulations.

△ **5.2.3 Cylinders Filled at the Point of Use.**

△ **5.2.3.1** Cylinders in stationary service that are filled at the point of use and, therefore, are not under the jurisdiction of DOT shall comply with one of the following criteria:

(1) They shall be requalified in accordance with DOT requirements.
(2) They shall be visually inspected within 12 years of the date of manufacture and within every 5 years thereafter, in accordance with 5.2.3.2 through 5.2.3.4.

5.2.3.2 Any cylinder that fails one or more of the criteria in 5.2.3.4 shall not be refilled or continued in service until the condition is corrected.

5.2.3.3 Personnel shall be trained and qualified to perform inspections. Training shall be documented in accordance with Section 4.4.

5.2.3.4 Visual inspection shall be performed in accordance with the following:

(1) The cylinder is checked for exposure to fire, dents, cuts, digs, gouges, and corrosion according to CGA C-6, *Standard for Visual Inspection of Steel Compressed Gas Cylinders*, except that 5.2.1.1(1) of that standard (which requires tare weight verification) shall not be part of the required inspection criteria.
(2) The cylinder protective collar (where utilized) and the foot ring are intact and are firmly attached.
(3) The cylinder is painted or coated to minimize corrosion.
(4) The cylinder pressure relief valve indicates no visible damage, corrosion of operating components, or obstructions.
(5) There is no leakage from the cylinder or its appurtenances that is detectable without the use of instruments.
(6) The cylinder is installed on a firm foundation and is not in contact with the soil.
(7) A cylinder that passes the visual examination is marked with the month and year of the examination followed by the letter E (e.g., "10-01E," indicating requalification in October 2001 by the external inspection method).
(8) The results of the visual inspection are documented, and a record of the inspection is retained for a 5-year period.

5.2.4 Container Service Pressure.

5.2.4.1 The service pressure of cylinders shall be in accordance with the regulations published under 49 CFR, "Transportation."

5.2.4.2 Cylinders shall be designed and constructed for at least a 240 psig (16 bar) service pressure.

5.2.4.3 The maximum allowable working pressure (MAWP) for ASME containers shall be in accordance with Table 5.2.4.3.

5.2.4.4 In addition to the applicable provisions for horizontal ASME containers, vertical ASME containers over 125 gal (0.5 m³) water capacity shall comply with 5.2.4.4(A) through 5.2.4.4(E).

△ Table 5.2.4.3 Maximum Vapor Pressure and Maximum Allowable Working Pressure (MAWP)

Maximum Vapor Pressure		MAWP					
		Current ASME Code[a]		Earlier Codes			
				API-ASME		ASME[b]	
At 100°F (psig)	At 37.8°C (MPag)	psig	MPag	psig	MPag	psig	MPag
80	0.6	100	0.7	100	0.7	80	0.6
100	0.7	125	0.9	125	0.9	100	0.7
125	0.9	156	1.1	156	1.1	125	0.9
150	1.0	187	1.3	187	1.3	150	1.0
175	1.2	219	1.5	219	1.5	175	1.2
215	1.5	250	1.7[c]	250	1.7[c]	200	1.4
215	1.5	312	2.2[c]	312	2.2[c]	—	—

Note: See Annex D for information on earlier ASME or API-ASME codes.
[a]ASME Code, 1949 edition, paragraphs U-200 and U-201, and all later editions. (See D.2.1.5.)
[b]All ASME codes up to the 1946 edition and paragraphs U-68 and U-69 of the 1949 edition. (See D.2.1.5.)
[c]See 5.2.4.4 and 5.2.4.5 for required MAWP for ASME engine fuel and mobile containers.

(A) Containers shall be designed to be self-supporting without the use of guy wires and shall be designed to withstand the wind, seismic (earthquake) forces, and hydrostatic test loads anticipated at the site.

(B) The MAWP (see Table 5.2.4.3) shall be the pressure at the top head, with allowance made for increased pressure on lower shell sections and bottom head due to the static pressure of the product.

(C) Wind loading on containers shall be based on wind pressures on the projected area at various height zones above ground in accordance with ASCE/SEI 7, Minimum Design Loads for Buildings and Other Structures. Wind speeds shall be based on a mean occurrence interval of 100 years.

(D) Seismic loading on containers shall be in accordance with ASCE/SEI 7, Minimum Design Loads for Buildings and Other Structures. A seismic analysis of the proposed installation shall be made that meets the approval of the authority having jurisdiction.

(E) Shop-fabricated containers shall be fabricated with lifting lugs or other means to lift the container.

5.2.4.5 ASME engine fuel containers shall have a MAWP as required in Chapter 11 or Chapter 12.

5.2.4.6* ASME mobile containers shall be in accordance with one of the following:

(1) A MAWP of 312 psig (2.2 MPag) or higher where installed in enclosed spaces of vehicles
(2) A MAWP of 312 psig (2.2 MPag) where installed outside of passenger vehicles
(3) A MAWP of 250 psig (1.7 MPag) where installed outside of nonpassenger vehicles

5.2.5 ASME Container Openings.

5.2.5.1 ASME containers shall be equipped with openings for the service for which the container is to be used.

5.2.5.2 The openings required by 5.2.5.1 shall be located either in the shell, in the heads, or in a manhole cover.

5.2.5.3* ASME containers of more than 30 gal through 2000 gal (0.1 m³ through 7.6 m³) water capacity that are designed to be filled volumetrically shall be equipped for filling into the vapor space.

5.2.5.4* ASME containers of 126 gal through 4000 gal (0.5 m³ through 15.2 m³) water capacity in other than bulk plant and industrial occupancies shall be provided with an opening for an actuated liquid withdrawal excess-flow valve with a connection not smaller than ¾ in. (19 mm) national pipe thread (NPT).

5.2.5.5* ASME containers of more than 4000 gal (15.2 m³) water capacity shall have an opening for a pressure gauge.

5.2.5.6 ASME containers in storage or use shall have pressure relief valve connections that have direct communication with the vapor space of the container.

(A) If the pressure relief valve is located within a well inside the ASME container with piping to the vapor space, the design of the well and piping shall have a flow capacity equal to or greater than that of the pressure relief valve.

(B) An enclosure that protects a pressure relief valve shall be painted, coated, or made from corrosion-resistant materials.

(C) The design of an enclosure that protects a pressure relief valve shall permit inspection of the pressure relief valve.

(D) If the pressure relief valve is located in any position other than the uppermost point of the ASME container, the connection shall be internally piped to the uppermost point practical in the vapor space of the container.

5.2.5.7* ASME containers to be filled on a volumetric basis shall be fabricated so that they can be equipped with a fixed maximum liquid level gauge(s) that is capable of indicating the maximum permitted filling level(s) in accordance with 7.4.2.3.

5.2.6 Portable Container Appurtenance Physical Damage Protection.

5.2.6.1 Cylinders shall incorporate protection against physical damage to cylinder appurtenances and immediate connections to such appurtenances when not in use by any of the following means:

(1) A ventilated cap
(2) A ventilated collar
(3) A cylinder valve providing inherent protection as defined by DOT in 49 CFR 173.301(h)(3)

5.2.6.2 Protection of appurtenances of portable containers, skid tanks, and tanks for use as cargo tanks of more than 1000 lb (454 kg) water capacity [nominal 420 lb (191 kg) propane capacity] shall comply with 5.2.6.2(A) through 5.2.6.2(C).

(A) Appurtenance protection from physical damage shall be provided by recessing, by protective housings, or by location on the vehicle.

(B) Appurtenance protection shall comply with the provisions under which the containers are fabricated.

(C) Appurtenance protection shall be secured to the container in accordance with the ASME code under which the container was designed and built.

5.2.7 Portable Storage Containers.

5.2.7.1 The legs or supports, or the lugs for the attachment of legs or supports, shall be secured to the container in accordance with the ASME code under which the container was designed and built.

5.2.7.2 The attachment of a container to either a trailer or semitrailer running gear, or the attachments to the container to make it a vehicle, so that the unit can be moved by a conventional over-the-road tractor, shall comply with the DOT requirements for cargo tank service.

5.2.7.3 Portable tank design and construction of a full framework, skids, or lugs for the attachment of skids, and protection of fittings shall be in accordance with DOT portable tank specifications. The bottom of the skids shall be not less than 2 in. (51 mm) or more than 12 in. (300 mm) below the outside bottom of the tank shell.

5.2.8 Container Marking.

5.2.8.1 Cylinders shall be marked as provided in the regulations, rules, or code under which they are fabricated.

(A) Where LP-Gas and one or more other compressed gases are to be stored or used in the same area, the cylinders shall be marked "Flammable" and either "LP-Gas," "Propane," or "Butane," or shall be marked in accordance with the requirements of 49 CFR, "Transportation."

(B) When being transported, cylinders shall be marked and labeled in accordance with 49 CFR, "Transportation."

5.2.8.2* Cylinders shall be marked with the following information:

(1) Water capacity of the cylinder in pounds
(2) Tare weight of the cylinder in pounds, fitted for service

5.2.8.3* The markings specified for ASME containers shall be on a stainless steel metal nameplate attached to the container, located to remain visible after the container is installed.

(A) The nameplate shall be attached in such a way as to minimize corrosion of the nameplate or its fastening means and not contribute to corrosion of the container.

(B) Where the container is buried, mounded, insulated, or otherwise covered so the nameplate is obscured, the information contained on the nameplate shall be duplicated and installed on adjacent piping or on a structure in a clearly visible location.

(C) Stationary ASME containers shall be marked with the following information:

(1) Service for which the container is designed (e.g., underground, aboveground, or both)
(2) Name and address of container supplier or trade name of container
(3) Water capacity of container in pounds or U.S. gallons
(4) MAWP in pounds per square inch
(5) Wording that reads "This container shall not contain a product that has a vapor pressure in excess of ___ psig at 100°F" (see Table 5.2.4.3)
(6) Outside surface area in square feet
(7) Year of manufacture
(8) Shell thickness and head thickness
(9) OL (overall length), OD (outside diameter), and HD (head design)
(10) Manufacturer's unique serial number
(11) ASME Code symbol
(12) Minimum design metal temperature "___°F at MAWP ___ psi"
(13) Type of construction "W"
(14) Degree of radiography "RT-___"

(D) In addition to the markings required by this code, nameplates on cargo tanks shall include the markings required by the ASME Code and the DOT.

5.2.8.4 Warning labels shall meet the following requirements:

(1) Warning labels shall be applied to all cylinders of 100 lb (45.4 kg) propane capacity or less that are not filled on-site.
(2) Warning labels shall include information on the potential hazards of LP-Gas.

△ **5.2.8.5** All containers that contain unodorized LP-Gas products shall be marked "NOT ODORIZED."

(A) The marking shall have a contrasting background surrounded by a rectangular red border and with red letters in the sizes shown in Table 5.2.8.5(A).

(B) The markings shall be on both ends or on both sides of a container or on both sides and the rear of cargo tanks.

5.2.9 Containers for Hot Air Balloons.

5.2.9.1 Containers for hot air balloons shall be marked to demonstrate compliance with FAA regulations.

5.2.9.2 Containers used in hot air balloons shall not be used for any other purpose.

△ Table 5.2.8.5(A) Size of "NOT ODORIZED" Marking

Water Capacity		Letter Height		Border Width	
gal	m³	in.	mm	in.	mm
≥499	≥1.89	4	100	½	13
49–498	0.19–1.88	1½	37	5/16	8
2.6–48	0.01–0.18	¾	18	¼	6
1–2.5	0.004–0.009	⅜	10	1/16	2

Shaded text = Revisions.   △ = Text deletions and figure/table revisions.   • = Section deletions.   **N** = New material.

5.3 Reserved.

5.4 Reserved.

5.5 Reserved.

5.6 Containers with Attached Supports.

5.6.1 Vertical ASME Containers. Vertical ASME containers of over 125 gal (0.5 m³) water capacity for use in permanent installations in stationary service shall be designed with steel supports that allow the container to be mounted on and fastened to concrete foundations or supports.

5.6.1.1 Steel supports shall be designed to make the container self-supporting without guy wires and to withstand the wind and seismic (earthquake) forces anticipated at the site.

5.6.1.2 Steel supports shall be protected against fire exposure with a material having a fire resistance rating of at least 2 hours.

5.6.1.3 Continuous steel skirts having only one opening of 18 in. (460 mm) or less in diameter shall have 2-hour fire protection applied to the outside of the skirt.

5.6.2 Skid Tanks. Skid tanks shall have a secure steel frame to allow transportation of the skid tank when not filled with LP-Gas.

5.6.3 Porta-Pacs.

5.6.3.1 The legs or supports, or the lugs for the attachment of legs or supports, shall be secured to the container in accordance with the ASME code under which the container was designed and built.

Δ **5.6.3.2** The ASME container shall be attached to either of the following:

(1) A trailer or semitrailer running gear, or the attachments to the container to make it a vehicle, so that the unit can be moved by a conventional over-the-road tractor.
(2) A metal frame such that the container can be moved as a trailer if wheels are added, which is approved for stationary use, or on a flat rail car.

N **5.6.3.3** Protection of appurtenances shall be in accordance with 5.2.6.

N **5.6.3.4** Movable fuel storage tenders shall be secured to the trailer support structure for the service involved.

5.7 Reserved.

5.8 Reserved.

5.9 Container Appurtenances.

5.9.1 Materials.

5.9.1.1 Container appurtenances and regulators shall be fabricated of materials that are compatible with LP-Gas and shall be resistant to the action of LP-Gas under service conditions.

(A) The following materials shall not be used:

(1) Gray cast iron
(2) Nonmetallic materials for bonnets or bodies of valves or regulators

5.9.1.2* Pressure-containing metal parts of appurtenances shall have a minimum melting point of 1500°F (816°C), except for the following:

(1) Fusible elements
(2) Approved or listed variable liquid level gauges used in containers of 3500 gal (13.2 m³) water capacity or less

5.9.1.3 Container appurtenances shall have a service pressure of at least 250 psig (1.7 MPag).

5.9.1.4 Gaskets used to retain LP-Gas in containers shall be resistant to the action of LP-Gas.

(A) Gaskets shall be made of metal or other material confined in metal having a melting point over 1500°F (816°C) or shall be protected against fire exposure.

(B) When a flange is opened, the gasket shall be replaced.

(C) Aluminum O-rings and spiral-wound metal gaskets shall be permitted.

(D) Gaskets for use with approved or listed liquid level gauges for installation on a container of 3500 gal (13.2 m³) water capacity or less shall be exempt from the minimum melting point requirement.

5.9.2 Pressure Relief Devices. See Section 5.15 for hydrostatic relief valves.

5.9.2.1* ASME containers shall be equipped with one or more pressure relief valves that are designed to relieve vapor.

5.9.2.2 Cylinders shall be equipped with pressure relief valves as required by DOT regulations.

5.9.2.2.1 The rated flow capacity of the pressure relief valve (CG-7) shall meet the requirements for a liquefied gas as defined in CGA S-1.1, *Pressure Relief Device Standards, Part 1 — Cylinders for Compressed Gases.*

5.9.2.3 Cylinders shall not be solely equipped with C-2 or CG-3 fusible plugs as defined in CGA S-1.1, *Pressure Relief Device Standards, Part 1 — Cylinders for Compressed Gases.*

5.9.2.3.1 A composite cylinder shall be permitted to be equipped with a combination device containing a pressure relief valve (CG-7) with 212°F (100°C) fuse metal (CG-3).

5.9.2.4 DOT nonrefillable metal containers shall be equipped with a pressure relief device(s) or system(s) that prevents propulsion of the container when the container is exposed to fire.

5.9.2.5 ASME containers for LP-Gas shall be equipped with direct spring-loaded pressure relief valves conforming with the applicable requirements of UL 132, *Standard for Safety Relief Valves for Anhydrous Ammonia and LP-Gas,* or other equivalent pressure relief valve standards.

(A) The start-to-leak setting of the pressure relief valves specified in 5.9.2.5, in relation to the pressure rating of the container, shall be in accordance with Table 5.9.2.5(A).

(B) Containers of 40,000 gal (151 m³) or more water capacity shall be equipped with either a spring-loaded pressure relief valve or a pilot-operated pressure relief valve, as follows:

(1) Pilot-operated relief valves shall be combined with, and controlled by, self-actuated, direct, spring-loaded pilot valves that comply with Table 5.9.2.5(A).
(2) Pilot-operated pressure relief valves shall be inspected and maintained by persons with training and experience.

Table 5.9.2.5(A) Start-to-Leak Pressure Settings of Pressure Relief Valves in Relation to Container Pressure Rating

Containers	Minimum (%)	Maximum (%)
All ASME codes prior to the 1949 edition, and the 1949 edition, paragraphs U-68 and U-69	110	125*
ASME Code, 1949 edition, paragraphs U-200 and U-201, and all ASME codes later than 1949	100	100*

*Manufacturers of pressure relief valves are allowed a plus tolerance not exceeding 10 percent of the set pressure marked on the valve.

(3) Pilot-operated pressure relief valves shall be inspected and maintained by persons with training and experience and shall be tested for operation at intervals not exceeding 5 years.

5.9.2.6 The minimum rate of discharge of pressure relief valves installed in ASME containers shall be in accordance with Table 5.9.2.6 or shall be calculated using the following formula:

[5.9.2.6]

$$F = 53.632 \times A^{0.82}$$

where:
F = flow rate (SCFM air)
A = total outside surface area of container (ft^2)

5.9.2.7 Relief valves for aboveground ASME containers shall relieve at not less than the flow rate specified in 5.9.2.6 before the pressure exceeds 120 percent of the minimum permitted start-to-leak pressure setting of the device, excluding the 10 percent tolerance in Table 5.9.2.5(A).

5.9.2.8 The flow capacity of pressure relief valves installed on underground or mounded containers shall be a minimum of 30 percent of the flow specified in Table 5.9.2.6.

5.9.2.9 Each pressure relief valve shall be plainly and permanently marked with the following:

(1) Pressure in psig (MPag) at which the valve is set to start-to-leak
(2) Rated relieving capacity in SCFM (m^3/min) air
(3) Manufacturer's name and catalog number

5.9.2.10 Shutoff valves shall not be installed between pressure relief devices and the container unless a listed pressure relief valve manifold meeting the requirements of 6.9.2.8 is used.

5.9.2.11 Pressure relief valves shall be designed to minimize the possibility of tampering.

5.9.2.12 Externally set or adjusted valves shall be provided with an approved means of sealing the adjustment.

5.9.2.13 Where used on aboveground ASME containers of 1200 gal (4.5 m^3) or less water capacity in addition to spring-loaded pressure relief valves, fusible plugs shall meet the following criteria:

Table 5.9.2.6 Pressure Relief Valve Flow Capacity as Function of Container Surface Area

Surface Area (ft^2)	Flow Rate (SCFM)	Surface Area (ft^2)	Flow Rate (SCFM)	Surface Area (ft^2)	Flow Rate (SCFM)
≤20	626	170	3620	600	10,170
25	751	175	3700	650	10,860
30	872	180	3790	700	11,550
35	990	185	3880	750	12,220
40	1100	190	3960	800	12,880
45	1220	195	4050	850	13,540
50	1330	200	4130	900	14,190
55	1430	210	4300	950	14,830
60	1540	220	4470	1000	15,470
65	1640	230	4630	1050	16,100
70	1750	240	4800	1100	16,720
75	1850	250	4960	1150	17,350
80	1950	260	5130	1200	17,960
85	2050	270	5290	1250	18,570
90	2150	280	5450	1300	19,180
95	2240	290	5610	1350	19,780
100	2340	300	5760	1400	20,380
105	2440	310	5920	1450	20,980
110	2530	320	6080	1500	21,570
115	2630	330	6230	1550	22,160
120	2720	340	6390	1600	22,740
125	2810	350	6540	1650	23,320
130	2900	360	6690	1700	23,900
135	2990	370	6840	1750	24,470
140	3080	380	7000	1800	25,050
145	3170	390	7150	1850	25,620
150	3260	400	7300	1900	26,180
155	3350	450	8040	1950	26,750
160	3440	500	8760	2000	27,310
165	3530	550	9470	—	—

For SI units, 1 ft^2 = 0.0929 m^2; 1 SCFM = 0.0283 m^3/min.
Note: Flow rate in SCFM air.

(1) They shall have a yield point between 208°F and 220°F (98°C and 104°C).
(2) They shall have a total discharge area not exceeding 0.25 in.^{2} (1.6 cm^2).
(3) They shall communicate directly with the vapor space of the container.

5.9.2.14 All cylinders used in industrial truck service (including forklift truck cylinders) shall have the cylinder's pressure relief valve replaced by a new or unused valve within 12 years of the date of manufacture of the cylinder and every 10 years thereafter.

5.9.3 Overfilling Prevention Devices.

5.9.3.1 Cylinders with 4 lb through 40 lb (1.8 kg through 18 kg) propane capacity for vapor service shall be equipped or fitted with a listed overfilling prevention device that complies with UL 2227, *Standard for Overfilling Prevention Devices*, and a fixed maximum liquid level gauge. These devices shall be either separate components or combined in the container valve assembly.

Shaded text = Revisions. Δ = Text deletions and figure/table revisions. • = Section deletions. *N* = New material.

5.9.3.2* Cylinders requalified after September 30, 1998, shall be equipped with a listed overfilling prevention device and a fixed maximum liquid level gauge, sized in accordance with 7.4.3.2(A) or Table 5.9.3.2.

5.9.3.3 Cylinders required to have an overfilling prevention device installed shall be equipped with either a CGA connection number 791 or a CGA connection number 810 as described in CGA V-1, *Standard Compressed Gas Cylinder Valve Outlet and Inlet Connections.*

5.9.3.4 The following types of cylinders shall be exempt from the requirements of 5.9.3.1 through 5.9.3.3:

(1) Cylinders used in industrial truck service
(2) Cylinders identified and used for industrial welding and cutting gases
(3) Cylinders manufactured prior to October 1, 1998, and designed for use in the horizontal position and where an overfilling prevention device is not available

5.9.3.5 Exempted horizontal cylinders shall be marked with a label to indicate that they are not equipped with an overfilling prevention device.

5.9.4 Container Valves and Other Appurtenances.

5.9.4.1 Containers of 4000 gal (15.2 m³) water capacity or less shall comply with 5.9.4.1(A) through 5.9.4.1(D).

(A) The following containers shall be permitted to be equipped with external pressure relief valves:

Table 5.9.3.2 Recommended Dip Tube Lengths for Various Cylinders

Propane Cylinder Size (lb)	Material	Cylinder I.D. (in.)	Cylinder Water Capacity (lb)	Dip Tube Lengths for Various Cylinders (in.)
4.25	Steel	8.9	10.2	2.2
5	Steel	7.8	11.9	3.0
6	Steel	7.5	15.5	3.2
10	Steel	8.9	26.1	3.6
11	Steel	8.9	26.2	3.6
11	Steel	12.0	26.2	3.0
11.5	Steel	12.0	27.3	3.2
20	Steel	12.0	47.6	4.0
25	Steel	12.0	59.7	4.8
30	Steel	12.0	71.5	4.8
40	Steel	12.0	95.3	6.5
6	Aluminum	6.0	15.0	4.8
10	Aluminum	10.0	23.6	4.0
20	Aluminum	12.0	47.6	4.8
30	Aluminum	12.0	71.5	6.0
40	Aluminum	12.0	95.2	7.0

For SI units, 1 lb = 0.454 kg; 1 in. = 25 mm.
Note: This table indicates the approximate fixed maximum liquid level gauge dip tube lengths to be used for retrofitting cylinders with valves incorporating an overfilling prevention device. This table does not cover every cylinder design or configuration. If the dip tube length that is marked on the cylinder does not appear in Table 5.9.3.2, the next longer dip tube shown in the table should be used.

(1) Underground ASME containers
(2) ASME containers originally equipped with external pressure relief valves
(3) ASME containers with 125 gal (0.5 m³) water capacity or less, having a pressure relief valve integrated as part of a multiple function valve

(B) Cylinders of less than 2 lb water capacity shall comply with Table 5.9.4.1(B).

(C) Containers 2 lb through 4000 gal water capacity shall be fitted with valves and other appurtenances in accordance with 5.9.8.1, Table 5.9.4.1(B) and the following:

(1) Shutoff, filler, check, and excess-flow valves for ASME containers shall comply with UL 125, *Standard for Flow Control Valves for Anhydrous Ammonia and LP-Gas (Other than Safety Relief).*
(2) Shutoff valves used on cylinders shall comply with UL 1769, *Standard for Cylinder Valves.*
(3) Containers greater than 125 gal through 4000 gal (0.5 m³ through 15.2 m³) water capacity shall be provided with an actuated liquid withdrawal excess-flow valve with a connection not smaller than ¾ in. NPT (19 mm), and the container connection shall not be smaller than ¾ in. NPT (19 mm).
(4) An actuated liquid withdrawal excess-flow valve shall not be required on container connections equipped for liquid withdrawal with a positive shutoff valve that is located as close to the container as practical and an excess-flow valve installed in the container connection.
(5) The actuated liquid withdrawal excess-flow valve shall not be connected for continuous use unless the valve is recommended by the manufacturer for such service.
(6) An overfilling prevention device shall not be required for engine fuel cylinders used on industrial (and forklift) trucks powered by LP-Gas or for engine fuel cylinders used on vehicles (including floor maintenance machines) having LP-Gas–powered engines mounted on them.
(7) A filler valve shall incorporate one of the following:

    (a) Double backflow check valves of the spring-loaded type
    (b) Manual shutoff valve with an internal backflow check valve of the spring-loaded type
    (c) Combination single backflow check valve of the spring-loaded type and an overfilling prevention device designed for containers

(8) Manual shutoff valves in vapor service shall be equipped with one of the following:

    (a) An orifice between the container contents and the shutoff valve outlet, not exceeding ⁵⁄₁₆ in. (8 mm) in diameter, and an approved regulator directly attached, or attached with a flexible connector, to the manual shutoff valve outlet
    (b) An excess-flow valve

(9) Overfilling prevention devices shall be required on cylinders having 4 lb through 40 lb (1.8 kg through 18 kg) propane capacity for vapor service. *(See 5.9.3.)*
(10) Cylinders greater than 40 lb through 100 lb (18 kg through 45 kg) propane capacity filled by volume shall have a fixed maximum liquid level gauge.

Shaded text = Revisions.   △ = Text deletions and figure/table revisions.   • = Section deletions.   *N* = New material.

2020 Edition

Δ **Table 5.9.4.1(B) Container Connection and Appurtenance Requirements for Containers Used in Other Than Bulk Plants and Industrial Plants**

Part	Appurtenance	1 ≤420 lb propane capacity (except DOT Spec. 39)	2 Stationary ASME containers ≤4000 gal water capacity[a]	3 DOT and ASME engine fuel and mobile containers
A	Vapor shutoff valve[b]	R (CGA 555 outlet prohibited)	R	R With internal excess-flow valve
B	Liquid shutoff valve[b]	R With CGA 555 outlet and internal excess-flow valve	R With internal excess flow valve	R With internal excess-flow valve
C	Pressure relief valve	R *(See 5.9.2.2.)*	R[c] *[See 5.9.4.1(A).]*	R With full internal or flush-type full internal pressure relief valve
D	Fixed maximum liquid level gauge	R (filled by volume) R (filled by weight, ≤40 lb and >100 lb)	R *[See 5.9.4.1(C)(10).]*	R (ASME only) *[See 5.9.4.1(C)(6).]*
E	Overfilling prevention device	R (4 lb through 40 lb) *(See 5.9.3.)*	NR	R (ASME only) *[See 5.9.4.1(C)(6).]*
F	Actuated liquid withdrawal excess-flow valve	NR	R (≥125 gal) *[See 5.9.4.1(C)(3), (4), and (5).]*	NR
G	Float gauge	NR	R (>124 gal only)	NR
H	Filler valve *[See 5.9.4.1(C)(7).]*	R (≥100 lb cylinders that are filled at the point of use)	R	R (ASME containers only)

For SI units, 1 lb = 0.454 kg; 1 gal = 0.0045 m³.
R: Required. NR: Not required.
[a]All ASME container capacities are water capacity.
[b]Where installed.
[c]Aboveground ASME containers, internal spring-type pressure relief valves can be used. See 5.9.4.1(A), 5.9.4.1(B), and 5.9.4.1(C).

(11) Full internal pressure relief valves or flush-type full internal pressure relief valves shall be installed in multiple function valves that are used with single opening cylinders used in industrial truck service and shall have the springs and guiding mechanism on the container pressure side of the seats, so that the springs and guiding mechanism shall not be exposed to the atmosphere.

(12) Multiple function valves installed on single opening cylinders used in industrial truck service shall meet the following requirements:

(a) Cylinders complying with 5.9.2.14 shall have the full internal or flush-type full internal pressure relief valve exchanged with a replacement multiple function valve that incorporates the full internal or flush-type full internal pressure relief valve as described in 5.9.4.1(C)(11) and 5.9.4.1(C)(12).

(b) The multiple function valve with the full internal or flush-type full internal pressure relief valve shall be permitted to have the means to be replaced without removing the multiple function valve from the cylinder.

(c) The multiple function valve shall incorporate an excess-flow valve installed inside the container for the liquid or vapor withdrawal service valve outlet.

(d) The multiple function valve shall incorporate a weak section on the service valve outlet connection.

(e) The multiple function valve shall incorporate an excess-flow valve installed inside the container that shall not restrict the flow to the full internal or flush-type full internal pressure relief valve.

(f) The multiple function valve shall be listed.

△ **(D)** Containers utilized in stationary service having water capacities greater than 1000 gal (3.8 m³) and not exceeding 4000 gal (15.2 m³) water capacity and utilizing a liquid withdrawal opening for liquid service shall be equipped with one of the following:

(1) An internal valve fitted for remote closure and automatic shutoff equipped with thermal activation

(2) An emergency shutoff valve fitted for remote closure and automatic shutoff, equipped with thermal activation, and installed in a line downstream close to a positive shutoff valve and an excess-flow valve installed in the container

(3) Container openings that are not compatible with internal valves shall be permitted to utilize both an excess-flow valve installed at the container and a valve complying with API 607, *Fire Test for Quarter-turn Valves and Valves Equipped with Nonmetallic Seats*, with the following features:

    (a) The valve shall be activated either hydraulically or pneumatically.

    (b) The valve shall be designed to fail in the closed position.

    (c) The valve shall be equipped for remote closure and equipped with thermal actuation.

(4) Remote actuation devices required in 5.9.4.1(D)(1), 5.9.4.1(D)(2), and 5.9.4.1(D)(3) shall be located not less than 10 ft (3.1 m) or more than 100 ft (30.5 m) along a path of egress from the liquid transfer point into the container.

(5) For existing installations, the requirements in (D) shall be complied with by January 1, 2024.

5.9.4.2 ASME containers greater than 4000 gal (15.2 m³) water capacity shall be fitted with valves and other appurtenances in accordance with 5.9.4.2(A) through 5.9.4.2(I) and Table 5.9.4.2.

(A) Vapor withdrawal openings shall be equipped with either of the following:

(1) A positive shutoff valve located as close to the container as practical and an excess-flow valve installed in the container

(2) An internal valve

(B) Liquid withdrawal openings in new installations shall be equipped with an internal valve that is fitted for remote closure and automatic shutoff using thermal (fire) actuation where the thermal element is located within 5 ft (1.5 m) of the internal valve.

(C) Liquid withdrawal openings in existing installations where the container is equipped with an internal valve that is not fitted for remote closure and automatic shutoff using thermal (fire) actuation shall be equipped for remote and thermal closure by July 1, 2003.

(D) Liquid withdrawal openings in existing installations shall be equipped with either of the following by July 1, 2011:

(1) An internal valve that is fitted for remote closure and automatic shutoff using thermal (fire) actuation where the thermal element is located within 5 ft (1.5 m) of the internal valve

△ **Table 5.9.4.2 Connection and Appurtenance Requirements for New and Existing Container Installations in Bulk Plants and Industrial Plants**

Service	>4000 gal w.c.* (>15.2 m³)	Requirements for Containers of >4000 gal w.c. (>15.2 m³) With and Without Internal Valves†	
		Without Existing Internal Valves (by 7/1/11)	With Existing Internal Valves
Vapor inlet	Option A, Option B, or Option C	See Note	See Note
Vapor outlet	Option B or Option C	See Note	See Note
Liquid inlet	Option D or Option E	Option D, Option E, Option F, or Option G	RT
Liquid outlet	Option E	Option E or Option H	RT

Option A: Positive shutoff valve installed as close as practical to a backflow check valve installed in the container.

Option B: Positive shutoff valve installed as close as practical to an excess-flow valve installed in the container and sized in accordance with 5.9.8.1(H).

Option C: Internal valve installed in the container or an excess-flow valve in accordance with 5.9.4.2(I).

Option D: Positive shutoff valve installed as close as practical to a backflow check valve designed for the intended application and installed in the container.

Option E: Internal valve installed in the container equipped for remote closure and automatic shutoff using thermal (fire) activation within 5 ft (1.5 m) of valve or an excess-flow valve in accordance with 5.9.4.2(I).

Option F: Emergency shutoff valve equipped for remote closure and automatic shutoff using thermal (fire) activation installed in the line upstream as close as practical to an existing positive shutoff valve/excess-flow valve combination.

Option G: Backflow check valve designed for the intended application and installed in the line upstream as close as practical to the existing positive shutoff valve/excess-flow valve combination.

Option H: Emergency shutoff valve equipped for remote closure and automatic shutoff using thermal (fire) activation, installed in the line downstream as close as practical to an existing positive shutoff valve/excess-flow valve combination.

RT: Equipping an existing internal valve for remote closure and automatic shutoff using thermal (fire) actuation within 5 ft (1.5 m) of the internal valve.

Note: Vapor connections on containers installed prior to the effective date of the 2001 edition of NFPA 58 are not required to be modified.

*Applicable to installations constructed on or after the effective date of this code.

†Applicable to installations constructed prior to the effective date of this code.

Shaded text = Revisions.   △ = Text deletions and figure/table revisions.   • = Section deletions.   *N* = New material.

2020 Edition

(2) An emergency shutoff valve that is installed in the line downstream as close as practical to a positive shutoff valve and an excess-flow valve installed in the container

(E) Vapor inlet openings shall be equipped with either of the following:

(1) A positive shutoff valve that is located as close to the container as practical and either a backflow check valve or an excess-flow valve installed in the container

(2) An internal valve

(F) Liquid inlet openings in new installations shall be equipped with either of the following:

(1) An internal valve that is fitted for remote closure and automatic shutoff using thermal (fire) actuation where the thermal element is located within 5 ft (1.5 m) of the internal valve

(2) A positive shutoff valve that is located as close to the container as practical and a backflow check valve that is designed for the intended application and is installed in the container

(G) Liquid inlet openings in existing installations where the container is equipped with an internal valve that is not fitted for remote closure and automatic shutoff using thermal (fire) actuation shall be equipped for remote and thermal closure by July 1, 2003.

(H) Liquid inlet openings in existing installations shall be equipped with any of the following by July 1, 2011:

(1) An internal valve that is fitted for remote closure and automatic shutoff using thermal (fire) actuation where the thermal element is located within 5 ft (1.5 m) of the internal valve

(2) An emergency shutoff valve that is installed in the line upstream as close as practical to a positive shutoff valve and an excess-flow valve installed in the container

(3) A positive shutoff valve that is located as close to the container as practical and a backflow check valve that is designed for the intended application and is installed in the container

(4) A backflow check valve that is designed for the intended application and is installed in the line upstream as close as practical to a positive shutoff valve and an excess-flow valve installed in the container

Δ **(I)** Container openings that are not compatible with internal valves shall be permitted to utilize both an excess-flow valve installed in the container and a valve complying with API 607, *Fire Test for Quarter-turn Valves and Valves Equipped with Nonmetallic Seats*, with the following features:

(1) The valve shall be activated either hydraulically or pneumatically.

(2) The valve shall be designed to fail in the closed position.

(3) The valve shall be equipped for remote closure and thermal actuation with a thermal element located within 5 ft (1.5 m) of the valve.

5.9.4.3* ASME containers over 4000 gal (15.2 m³) water capacity shall also be equipped with the following appurtenances and shall comply with Table 5.9.4.2:

(1) A fixed maximum liquid level gauge

(2) A variable liquid level gauge

(3) A pressure gauge

(4) A temperature gauge for aboveground containers only

5.9.4.4 The appurtenances specified in Table 5.9.4.1(B) shall comply with the following:

(1) Manual shutoff valves shall be designed to provide positive closure under service conditions.

(2) Excess-flow valves shall be designed to close automatically at the rated flows of vapor or liquid specified by the manufacturer.

(3) Excess-flow valves shall be designed with a bypass that shall not exceed a No. 60 drill size opening to allow equalization of pressure.

(4) Excess-flow valves of less than ½ in. NPT (13 mm) shall have a bypass that limits propane vapor flow to 10 scf/hr at 100 psig (690 kPag).

(5) Backflow check valves shall be of the spring-loaded or weight-loaded type with in-line or swing operation and shall close when the flow is either stopped or reversed.

(6) Internal valves (*see 3.3.78.6, Internal Valve*), either manually or remotely operated and designed to remain closed except during operating periods, shall be considered positive shutoff valves.

5.9.5 Liquid Level Gauging Devices.

5.9.5.1 Liquid level gauging devices shall be installed on all containers filled by volume.

5.9.5.2 The gauging devices shall be either fixed maximum liquid level gauges or variable liquid level gauges, or a combination of such devices.

5.9.5.3* Every container designed to be filled on a volumetric basis shall be equipped with a fixed maximum liquid level gauge(s) to indicate the maximum filling level(s) for the service(s) in which the container is to be filled or used. (*See 7.4.3.2.*)

5.9.5.4 ASME containers shall have permanently attached to the container adjacent to the fixed maximum liquid level gauge, or on the container nameplate, markings showing the percentage of capacity that is indicated by that gauge.

5.9.5.5 Cylinders shall have the letters DT stamped on them followed by the vertical distance (to the nearest tenth of an inch), measured from the top of the boss or coupling into which the gauge, or the cylinder valve of which it is a part, is installed to the end of the dip tube.

5.9.5.6 Cylinders equipped with a fixed maximum liquid level gauge where the dip tube is not welded to the inside of the cylinder shall be permanently marked on the cylinder collar as follows:

(1) The marking shall be the letters "DT" followed by the dip tube length to the nearest tenth of an inch.

(2) The dip tube length shall be measured from the top center of the cylinder boss or coupling where the gauge is installed to the maximum permitted filling level.

(A) Cylinders shall be marked as follows:

(1) The marking shall be the letters "DT" followed by the dip tube length to the nearest tenth of an inch.

(2) The dip tube length shall be measured from the top center of the cylinder boss or coupling where the gauge is installed to the maximum permitted filling level.

5.9.5.7 Cargo tanks and ASME containers utilizing multiple fixed liquid level gauges shall have the loading percentage (to the nearest 0.2 percent) stamped adjacent to each gauge.

5.9.5.8 Variable liquid level gauges shall comply with 5.9.5.8(A) through 5.9.5.8(D).

(A) Variable liquid level gauges installed on containers over 1200 gal (4.5 m^3) water capacity shall be marked with the maximum liquid level, in inches, metric units, or percent of capacity of the container on which they are to be installed.

(B) If temperature correction markings are provided on variable liquid level gauges on containers greater than 1200 gal (4.5 m^3) water capacity that will be used for volumetric filling as allowed by 7.4.3.2(A), 7.4.3.2(B), and 7.4.3.3, the markings shall indicate the maximum liquid level at liquid temperatures in accordance with Table 7.4.2.3(b) or Table 7.4.2.3(c). Temperature markings shall be from 20°F to 115°F (−6.7°C to 46°C), with increments not to exceed 20°F (11°C) for propane, for 50/50 butane–propane mixtures, and for butane.

(C) Dials of magnetic float gauges or rotary gauges shall indicate whether they are for cylindrical or spherical ASME containers and whether they are for aboveground or underground service.

(D) The dials of gauges for use only on aboveground containers of over 1200 gal (4.5 m^3) water capacity shall be so marked.

5.9.5.9 Variable liquid level gauges shall comply with the provisions of 7.4.3.2(B) if they are used for filling containers.

5.9.5.10 Gauging devices that vent product to the atmosphere when used shall be designed so that the vent valve maximum opening to the atmosphere is not larger than a No. 54 drill size.

5.9.6 Pressure Gauges.

5.9.6.1 Pressure gauges shall be attached directly to the container opening or to a valve or fitting that is directly attached to the container opening.

5.9.6.2 If the cross-sectional area of the opening into the container described in 5.9.6.1 is greater than that of a No. 54 drill size, an excess-flow check valve shall be provided for the container connection.

5.9.7 Other Container Connections.

5.9.7.1 Other container openings shall be equipped with any of the following:

(1) Positive shutoff valve and either an excess-flow check valve or a backflow check valve
(2) Internal valve
(3) Backflow check valve
(4) Actuated liquid withdrawal excess-flow valve, normally closed and plugged, with provision to allow for external actuation
(5) Plug, blind flange, or plugged companion flange

Δ **5.9.7.2** Any of the valves listed in 5.9.7.1(1), 5.9.7.1(2), or 5.9.7.1(3) that are not connected for service shall be plugged or capped.

5.9.8 Container Appurtenance Installation.

5.9.8.1 All container openings except those used for pressure relief devices, liquid level gauging devices, pressure gauges, filler valves, combination backflow check and excess-flow vapor return valves, actuated liquid withdrawal excess-flow valves, and plugged openings shall be equipped with internal valves or with positive shutoff valves and either excess-flow or backflow check valves.

(A) Valves in ASME containers, where excess-flow or backflow check valves are installed between the LP-Gas in the container and the shutoff valves, shall be installed either inside the container or at a point immediately outside where the line enters or leaves the container.

(B) If excess-flow and backflow check valves are installed outside the container, installation shall be made so that any strain beyond the excess-flow or backflow check valves will not cause breakage between the container and the valve.

(C) All connections that are listed in the ASME Manufacturers' Data Report for the container shall be considered part of the container.

(D) If an excess-flow valve is required for cylinders other than for mobile or engine fuel service, it shall be permitted to be located at the outlet of the cylinder shutoff valve.

(E) Shutoff valves shall be located as close to the container as practical.

(F) Shutoff valves shall be readily accessible for operation and maintenance under normal and emergency conditions.

(G) Shutoff valves either shall be located in a readily accessible position less than 6 ft (1.8 m) above ground level; shall have extension handles, stairs, ladders, or platforms for access; or shall be equipped for remote operation.

(H)* The connection or line that leads to or from any individual opening shall have a flow capacity greater than the rated flow of the excess-flow valve protecting the opening.

5.9.8.2 Valves, regulators, gauges, and other container appurtenances shall be protected against physical damage.

5.9.8.3 Valves and other appurtenances that are part of the assembly of portable multicylinder systems shall be arranged so that replacement of cylinders can be made without shutting off the flow of gas in the system.

5.9.8.4 Connections to ASME containers installed underground shall be located within a dome, housing, or manhole and shall have a cover.

(A)* Underground containers shall be installed so that all connections for hose and the point of discharge from pressure relief devices are located above the normal maximum water table.

(B) Such manholes or housings shall be ventilated.

(C) The area of ventilation openings shall equal or exceed the combined discharge areas of the pressure relief devices and other vent lines that discharge into the manhole or housing.

5.9.8.5 Container inlet and outlet connections on ASME containers of more than 2000 gal (7.6 m^3) water capacity shall be labeled either on the container service valve or on the container to designate whether they communicate with the vapor or liquid space.

5.9.8.6 Connections for pressure relief devices, liquid level gauging devices, and pressure gauges shall not be required to be labeled.

5.9.8.7 Every ASME storage container of more than 2000 gal (7.6 m^3) water capacity shall be provided with a pressure gauge.

5.9.9* Container Refurbishment. To prevent the intrusion of foreign matter and physical damage during the container refurbishment process, either of the following shall be required:

(1) The container appurtenances shall be removed and the container openings shall be protected.
(2) The container appurtenances shall be protected.

5.10 Regulators and Regulator Vents.

5.10.1 Regulators.

5.10.1.1 Pressure regulators with a maximum rated capacity of 500,000 Btu/hr (147 kW/hr), except for line pressure and appliance regulators, shall comply with UL 144, *Standard for LP-Gas Regulators*. Line pressure regulators shall comply with ANSI Z21.80/CSA 6.22, *Standard for Line Pressure Regulators*. Appliance pressure regulators shall comply with ANSI Z21.18/CSA 6.3, *Standard for Gas Appliance Pressure Regulators*.

5.10.1.2 Regulators over 500,000 Btu/hr (147 kW/hr) capacity shall be recommended by the manufacturer for use with LP-Gas.

5.10.1.3 Single-stage regulators shall have a maximum outlet pressure setting of 1.0 psig (7 kPag) and shall be equipped with one of the following (*see 6.10.1.4 for required protection from the elements*):

(1) Integral pressure relief valve on the outlet pressure side having a start-to-discharge pressure setting within the limits specified in UL 144, *Standard for LP-Gas Regulators*
(2) Integral overpressure shutoff device that shuts off the flow of LP-Gas vapor when the outlet pressure of the regulator reaches the overpressure limits specified in UL 144, *Standard for LP-Gas Regulators*, and does not open to allow flow of gas until it has been manually reset

5.10.1.4 Second-stage regulators and integral two-stage regulators shall be equipped with one of the following (*see 6.10.1.4 for required protection from the elements*):

(1) An integral pressure relief valve on the outlet pressure side having a start-to-discharge pressure setting within the limits specified in UL 144, *Standard for LP-Gas Regulators*, that limits the outlet pressure of the second-stage regulator to 2.0 psig (14 kPag) or less when the regulator seat disc is removed and the inlet pressure to the regulator is 15.0 psig (103.5 kPag), as specified in UL 144, *Standard for LP-Gas Regulators*
(2) An integral overpressure shutoff device that shuts off the flow of LP-Gas vapor when the outlet pressure of the regulator reaches the overpressure limits specified in UL 144, *Standard for LP-Gas Regulators*, and does not open to allow flow of gas until it has been manually reset

△ **5.10.1.5** Second-stage regulators with a rated capacity of more than 500,000 Btu/hr (147 kW/hr) shall either comply with UL 144, *Standard for LP-Gas Regulators*, with respect to an integral pressure relief device or an overpressure shutoff device, or shall have a separate overpressure protection device complying with 5.9.2 of NFPA 54. The overpressure protection devices shall limit the outlet pressure of the regulator to 2.0 psig (14 kPag) or less when the regulator seat disc is removed and the inlet pressure to the regulator is 15.0 psig (103.5 kPag).

5.10.1.6 Integral two-stage regulators shall be provided with a means to determine the outlet pressure of the high-pressure regulator portion of the integral two-stage regulator.

5.10.1.7 Automatic changeover regulators shall be exempt from the requirement in 5.10.1.6.

5.10.1.8 Integral two-stage regulators shall not incorporate an integral pressure relief valve in the high-pressure regulator portion of the unit.

5.10.1.9 First-stage regulators shall incorporate an integral pressure relief valve having a start-to-discharge setting within the limits specified in UL 144, *Standard for LP-Gas Regulators*.

5.10.1.10 High-pressure regulators with a rated capacity of more than 500,000 Btu/hr (147 kW/hr) where permitted to be used in two-stage systems shall incorporate an integral pressure relief valve or shall have a separate relief valve.

5.10.1.11 First-stage regulators shall have an outlet pressure setting up to 10.0 psig (69 kPag) in accordance with UL 144, *Standard for LP-Gas Regulators*.

5.10.1.12 First-stage regulators with a rated capacity of more than 500,000 Btu/hr (147 kW/hr) shall be permitted to have a separate pressure relief valve.

5.10.1.13 Regulators shall be designed to drain condensate from the regulator spring case when the vent is directed vertically down.

△ **5.10.1.14** Two psig (14 kPag) service regulators and integral 2 psig (14 kPag) regulators shall have a maximum outlet pressure setting of 2.5 psi (17 kPag) and shall be equipped with one of the following:

(1) An integral pressure relief valve on the outlet pressure side having a start-to-discharge pressure setting within the limits specified in UL 144, *Standard for LP-Gas Regulators*, that limits the outlet pressure of the 2 psig (14 kPag) service regulator to 5.0 psig (34.5 kPag) or less when the seat disc is removed and the inlet pressure to the regulator is 15.0 psig (103.5 kPag), as specified in UL 144
(2) An integral overpressure shutoff device that shuts off the flow of LP-Gas vapor when the outlet pressure of the regulator reaches the overpressure limits specified in UL 144 and does not open to allow flow of LP-Gas vapor until it has been manually reset

5.10.2 Pressure Regulators. (Reserved)

5.10.3* Pipe for Regulator Venting.

5.10.3.1 Pipe or tubing used to vent regulators shall be one of the following:

(1) Metal pipe and tubing in accordance with 5.11.3
(2) PVC conduit meeting the requirements of UL 651, *Standard for Schedule 40, 80, Type EB and A Rigid PVC Conduit and Fittings*
(3) Flexible conduit meeting the requirements of UL 1660, *Standard for Liquid-Tight Flexible Nonmetallic Conduit*, with nonmetallic fittings meeting the requirements of UL 514B, *Standard for Conduit, Tubing, and Cable Fittings*
(4) Flexible conduit meeting the requirement of UL 1660, *Standard for Liquid-Tight Flexible Nonmetallic Conduit*, with metallic or nonmetallic fittings as part of a manufactured assembly

5.10.3.2 Other PVC piping materials and polyethylene and polyamide pipe and tubing shall not be permitted to be used to vent regulators.

5.11 Piping (Including Hose), Fittings, and Valves.

5.11.1 General.

5.11.1.1 Material specifications for piping, tubing, fittings, valves (including hydrostatic relief valves), hose, hose connections, and flexible connectors shall be in accordance with Section 5.11.

△ **5.11.1.2** Piping, tubing, fittings, and valves used to supply equipment and appliances within the scope of NFPA 54 shall comply with that code.

5.11.1.3 Pipe and tubing shall comply with one of the following requirements:

(1) Pipe and tubing shall comply with 5.11.3.
(2) Pipe and tubing shall be recommended for that service by the manufacturer and shall be approved.

5.11.1.4 Piping that can contain liquid LP-Gas and that can be isolated by valving and that requires hydrostatic relief valves, as specified under Section 6.15, shall have an operating pressure of 350 psig (2.4 MPag) or a pressure that is equivalent to the maximum discharge pressure of any pump or other source feeding the fixed piping system if it is greater than 350 psig (2.4 MPag).

5.11.2 Reserved.

5.11.3 Pipe and Tubing.

△ **5.11.3.1** Pipe shall be wrought iron or steel (black or galvanized), brass, copper, polyamide, polyethylene, or austenitic stainless steel and shall comply with the following:

(1) Wrought iron: ASME B36.10M, *Welded and Seamless Wrought Steel Pipe*
(2) Steel pipe: ASTM A53/A53M, *Standard Specification for Pipe, Steel, Black and Hot-Dipped, Zinc-Coated, Welded and Seamless*
(3) Steel pipe: ASTM A106/A106M, *Standard Specification for Seamless Carbon Steel Pipe for High-Temperature Service*
(4) Brass pipe: ASTM B43, *Standard Specification for Seamless Red Brass Pipe, Standard Sizes*
(5) Copper pipe: ASTM B42, *Standard Specification for Seamless Copper Pipe, Standard Sizes*
(6) Polyamide pipe: ASTM F2945, *Standard Specification for Polyamide 11 Gas Pressure Pipe, Tubing, and Fittings*, recommended by the manufacturer for use with LP-Gas
(7) Polyethylene pipe: ASTM D2513, *Standard Specification for Polyethylene (PE) Gas Pressure Pipe, Tubing, and Fittings*, recommended by the manufacturer for use with LP-Gas
(8) Stainless pipe: ASTM A312/A312M, *Standard Specification for Seamless, Welded, and Heavily Cold Worked Austenitic Stainless Steel Pipes*

5.11.3.2 Tubing shall be steel, stainless steel, brass, copper, polyamide, or polyethylene *(see 6.11.4)* and shall comply with the following:

(1) Brass tubing: ASTM B135/B135M, *Standard Specification for Seamless Brass Tube*
(2) Copper tubing:
    (a) Type K or L: ASTM B88, *Standard Specification for Seamless Copper Water Tube*
    (b) ASTM B280, *Standard Specification for Seamless Copper Tube for Air Conditioning and Refrigeration Field Service*

(3) Polyamide tubing: ASTM F2945, *Standard Specification for Polyamide 11 Gas Pressure Pipe, Tubing, and Fittings*, and shall be recommended by the manufacturer for use with LP-Gas
(4) Polyethylene tubing: ASTM D2513, *Standard Specification for Polyethylene (PE) Gas Pressure Pipe, Tubing, and Fittings*, and shall be recommended by the manufacturer for use with LP-Gas
(5) Corrugated stainless steel tubing: ANSI/CSA 6.26 (LC1), *Interior Fuel Gas Piping Systems Using Corrugated Stainless Steel Tubing*

5.11.4 Fittings for Metallic Pipe and Tubing.

5.11.4.1 Fittings shall be steel, austenitic stainless steel, brass, copper, malleable iron, or ductile (nodular) iron.

5.11.4.2 Pipe fittings shall have a minimum pressure rating as specified in Table 5.11.4.2 and shall comply with the following:

(1) Cast-iron pipe fittings shall not be used.
(2) Brazing filler material shall have a melting point that exceeds 1000°F (538°C).

5.11.4.3 Metal tube fittings shall have a minimum pressure rating as specified in Table 5.11.4.2.

5.11.5 Fittings for Polyethylene and Polyamide Pipe and Tubing.

5.11.5.1* Joints in polyamide and polyethylene pipe and polyethylene tubing shall be made by heat fusion, by compression-type mechanical fittings, or by factory-assembled transition fittings.

5.11.5.2 Polyethylene pipe shall not be joined by a threaded or miter joint.

5.11.5.3 Polyamide and polyethylene fusion fittings shall be recommended by the manufacturer for use with LP-Gas and shall conform to one of the following:

(1) ASTM D2683, *Standard Specification for Socket-Type Polyethylene Fittings for Outside Diameter-Controlled Polyethylene Pipe and Tubing*
(2) ASTM D3261, *Standard Specification for Butt Heat Fusion Polyethylene (PE) Plastic Fittings for Polyethylene (PE) Plastic Pipe and Tubing*

Table 5.11.4.2 Service Pressure Rating of Pipe, Tube Fittings, and Valves

Service	Minimum Pressure
Higher than container pressure	350 psig (2.4 MPag) or the MAWP, whichever is higher, or 400 psig (2.8 MPag) water, oil, and gas (WOG) rating
LP-Gas liquid or vapor at operating pressure over 125 psig (0.9 MPag) and at or below container pressure	250 psig (1.7 MPag)
LP-Gas vapor at operating pressure of 125 psig (0.9 MPag) or less	125 psig (0.9 MPag)

(3)   ASTM F1055, *Standard Specification for Electrofusion Type Polyethylene Fittings for Outside Diameter Controlled Polyethylene and Crosslinked Polyethylene (PEX) Pipe and Tubing*

(4)   ASTM F1733, *Standard Specification for Butt Heat Fusion Polyamide (PA) Plastic Fitting for Polyamide (PA) Plastic Pipe and Tubing*

5.11.5.4 Installation instructions specific to the type and grade of polyethylene being joined shall be provided with heat fusion fittings.

5.11.5.5* Mechanical fittings for polyethylene gas piping shall comply with Category 1 of ASTM D2513, *Standard Specification for Polyethylene (PE) Gas Pressure Pipe, Tubing and Fittings,* or ASTM F1948, *Standard Specification for Metallic Mechanical Fittings for Use on Outside Diameter Controlled Thermoplastic Gas Distribution Pipe and Tubing,* and 5.11.5.5(A) through 5.11.5.5(C).

(A) Mechanical joints shall be tested and recommended by the manufacturer for use with polyethylene pipe and tubing.

(B) Compression-type mechanical fittings shall include a rigid internal tubular stiffener, other than a split tubular stiffener, to support the pipe.

(C) Gasket material in the fitting shall be resistant to the action of LP-Gas and shall be compatible with the polyamide or polyethylene pipe material.

5.11.5.6 Mechanical fittings for ASTM F2945, *Standard Specification for Polyamide 11 Gas Pressure Pipe, Tubing, and Fittings,* PA11 gas piping shall comply with Category 1 of ASTM F2145, *Standard Specification for Polyamide 11 (PA11) and Polyamide 12 (PA12) Mechanical Fittings for Use on Outside Diameter Controlled Polyamide 11 and Polyamide 12 Pipe and Tubing,* or ASTM F1948, *Standard Specification for Metallic Mechanical Fittings for Use on Outside Diameter Controlled Thermoplastic Gas Distribution Pipe and Tubing.*

5.11.5.7 Anodeless risers shall comply with 5.11.5.7(A) through 5.11.5.7(E).

(A) The metal-gas carrying portion of the anodeless riser after the transition shall have a wall thickness equal to Schedule 40 pipe.

(B) Factory-assembled anodeless risers shall be recommended for LP-Gas use and shall be leak tested by the manufacturer in accordance with written procedures.

(C) Field-assembled anodeless risers with service head adapter transition fittings shall be equipped with moisture seals and shall be recommended for LP-Gas use by the manufacturer for installation at the aboveground termination of the riser.

Δ (D) Polyethylene and Polyamide 11 field-assembled anodeless risers shall be design certified to meet the requirements of ASTM F2905, *Standard Specification for Field-assembled Anodeless Riser Kits for Use on Outside Diameter Controlled Polyethylene and Polyamide-11 (PA11) Gas Distribution Pipe and Tubing.*

(E) The manufacturer shall provide the user qualified installation instructions as prescribed by U.S. Department of Transportation, 49 CFR 192.283(b).

5.11.6 Hose, Quick Connectors, Hose Connections, and Flexible Connectors.

5.11.6.1 Hose, hose connections, and flexible connectors *(see 3.3.28, Flexible Connector)* shall be fabricated of materials that are resistant to the action of LP-Gas both as liquid and vapor.

5.11.6.2 When wire braid is used for reinforcement, it shall be of corrosion-resistant material such as stainless steel.

5.11.6.3 Hose and quick connectors conveying LP-Gas at pressures of 5 psig (34 kPag) and less shall be approved.

5.11.6.4 Hose, hose connections, and flexible connectors used for conveying LP-Gas liquid or vapor at pressures in excess of 5 psig (34 kPag), and as provided in Section 6.22 regardless of the pressure, shall comply with 5.11.6.4(A) through 5.11.6.4(E).

(A) Hose shall be designed for a working pressure of at least 350 psig (2.4 MPag), with a safety factor of 5 to 1 and comply with UL 569, *Standard for Pigtails and Flexible Hose Connectors for LP-Gas,* or UL 21, *Standard for LP-Gas Hose.*

(B) Hose shall be continuously marked to provide at least the following information:

(1)   LP-GAS HOSE or LPG HOSE
(2)   Maximum working pressure
(3)   Manufacturers' name or coded designation
(4)   Month or quarter and year of manufacture
(5)   Product identification

(C) Hose assemblies, after the application of couplings, shall have a design capability of not less than 700 psig (4.8 MPag).

(D) If a pressure test is performed, such assemblies shall be pressure tested at 120 percent of the maximum working pressure [350 psig (2.4 MPag) minimum] of the hose.

(E) Hose assemblies shall be leak tested at the time of installation at not less than the operating pressure of the system in which they are installed.

5.11.6.5 Hoses at a pressure of 5 psig (34 kPag) or less in agricultural buildings not normally occupied by the public shall be designed for the working pressure of the system and shall be constructed of material resistant to the action of LP-Gas.

Δ 5.11.6.6 Hoses or flexible connectors used to supply LP-Gas to equipment or appliances shall be installed in accordance with the provisions of 6.11.6 and 6.23.4.

5.12 Reserved.

5.13 Internal Valves. (Reserved)

5.14 Valves Other Than Container Valves.

5.14.1 Materials.

5.14.1.1 Pressure-containing metal parts of valves shall be of steel, ductile (nodular) iron, malleable iron, or brass.

5.14.1.2 Ductile iron shall meet the requirements of ASTM A395/A395M, *Standard Specification for Ferritic Ductile Iron Pressure-Retaining Castings for Use at Elevated Temperatures,* or equivalent.

5.14.1.3 Malleable iron shall meet the requirements of ASTM A47/A47M, *Standard Specification for Ferritic Malleable Iron Castings,* or equivalent.

5.14.1.4 All materials used, including valve seat discs, packing, seals, and diaphragms, shall be resistant to the action of LP-Gas under service conditions.

5.14.2 Valves in Piping Systems.

5.14.2.1 Valves shall have a service pressure rating as specified in Table 5.11.4.2.

5.14.2.2 Manual shutoff valves, emergency shutoff valves, excess-flow check valves, and backflow check valves used in piping systems shall comply with the provisions for container valves. *(See 5.9.4.)*

5.14.2.3 Emergency shutoff valves shall be approved and shall incorporate all of the following means of closing:

(1) Automatic shutoff through thermal (fire) actuation
(2) Manual shutoff from a remote location
(3) Manual shutoff at the installed location

N 5.14.2.4 Excess-flow check valves shall have a flow capacity in accordance with 5.9.8.1(H).

5.14.2.5 Where fusible elements are used, they shall have a melting point not exceeding 250°F (121°C).

△ 5.14.2.6 Plastic valves in polyethylene piping systems shall be manufactured from thermoplastic materials listed in ASTM D2513, *Standard Specification for Polyethylene (PE) Gas Pressure Pipe, Tubing, and Fittings,* and shall comply with ASTM D2513 and ASME B16.40, *Manually Operated Thermoplastic Gas Shutoffs and Valves in Gas Distribution Systems.*

△ 5.14.2.7 Valves in polyamide piping systems shall be manufactured from thermoplastic materials listed in ASTM F2945, *Standard Specification for Polyamide 11 Gas Pressure Pipe, Tubing, and Fittings,* which have been shown to be resistant to the action of LP-Gas and comply with ASME B16.40, *Manually Operated Thermoplastic Gas Shutoffs and Valves in Gas Distribution Systems.*

5.14.2.8 Metallic valves in polyethylene and polyamide piping systems shall be protected to minimize corrosion in accordance with Section 6.19.

5.14.2.9 Valves shall be recommended for LP-Gas service by the manufacturer.

5.15 Hydrostatic Relief Valves.

5.15.1 Hydrostatic relief valves designed to relieve the hydrostatic pressure that can develop in sections of liquid piping between closed shutoff valves shall have pressure settings not less than 400 psig (2.8 MPag) or more than 500 psig (3.5 MPag), unless installed in systems designed to operate above 350 psig (2.4 MPag).

5.15.2 Hydrostatic relief valves for use in systems designed to operate above 350 psig (2.4 MPag) shall have settings not less than 110 percent or more than 125 percent of the system design pressure.

5.16 Reserved.

5.17 Reserved.

5.18 Reserved.

5.19 Reserved.

5.20 Equipment.

5.20.1 Pressure-Containing Metal Parts.

5.20.1.1 This section shall apply to pressure-containing metal parts of LP-Gas equipment.

5.20.1.2 The service pressure rating of equipment shall be in accordance with Table 5.20.1.2.

5.20.1.3 Equipment shall be fabricated of materials that are compatible with LP-Gas under service conditions and shall be in accordance with Table 5.20.1.3.

△ (A) Pressure-containing metal parts shall be made from the following materials:

(1) Steel
(2) Ductile (nodular) iron (ASTM A395/A395M, *Standard Specification for Ferritic Ductile Iron Pressure-Retaining Castings for Use at Elevated Temperatures,* or ASTM A536, *Standard Specification for Ductile Iron Castings,* Grade 60-40-18 or 65-45-12)
(3) Malleable iron (ASTM A47/A47M, *Standard Specification for Ferritic Malleable Iron Castings*)
(4) Higher strength gray iron (ASTM A48/A48M, *Standard Specification for Gray Iron Castings,* Class 40B)
(5) Brass
(6) Materials equivalent to 5.20.1.3(A)(1) through 5.20.1.3(A)(5) in melting point, corrosion resistance, toughness, and strength

(B) Cast iron shall not be used as a material of construction for strainers or flow indicators.

(C) Aluminum shall be used only for cylinders, gaskets, regulators, meters, and indirect electric vaporizers.

Table 5.20.1.2 Service Pressure Rating

Fluid	Pressure	Equipment Design Pressure
LP-Gas vapor	≤20 psig (≤138 kPag)	Maximum anticipated pressure
	20 psig–125 psig (138 kPag–0.9 MPag)	125 psig (0.9 MPag)
	>125 psig (>0.9 MPag)	250 psig (1.7 MPag) or the anticipated pressure, whichever is higher
LP-Gas liquid	≤250 psig (≤1.7 MPag)	250 psig (1.7 MPag)
	>250 psig (>1.7 MPag)	350 psig (2.4 MPag) or the anticipated pressure, whichever is higher

Shaded text = Revisions.   △ = Text deletions and figure/table revisions.   • = Section deletions.   N = New material.

2020 Edition

Δ **Table 5.20.1.3 Materials for Equipment Used in LP-Gas Service**

Equipment Material	Service Condition
Steel Ductile (nodular) iron (ASTM A395/A395M, *Standard Specification for Ferritic Ductile Iron Pressure-Retaining Castings for Use at Elevated Temperatures,* or ASTM A536, *Standard Specification for Ductile Iron Castings,* Grade 60–40–18 or 65–45–12) Malleable iron (ASTM A47/A47M, *Standard Specification for Ferritic Malleable Iron Castings*) Higher strength gray iron (ASTM A48/A48M, *Standard Specification for Gray Iron Castings,* Class 40B) Brass Materials equivalent to 5.20.1.3(A)(1) through 5.20.1.3(A)(5) in melting point, corrosion resistance, toughness, and strength	Pressure-containing metal parts
Cast iron	Not to be used as a material of construction for strainers or flow indicators
Aluminum	For approved meters, approved regulators, and indirect vaporizers
Zinc [ASTM B86, *Standard Specification for Zinc and Zinc-Aluminum (ZA) Alloy Foundry and Die Castings*]	For approved regulators
Nonmetallic materials	Not to be used for upper or lower casings of regulators

(D) Zinc shall be used for approved regulators only, complying with ASTM B86, *Standard Specification for Zinc and Zinc-Aluminum (ZA) Alloy Foundry and Die Castings.*

(E) Nonmetallic materials shall not be used for upper or lower casings of regulators.

5.20.2 Pumps. Pumps shall be designed for LP-Gas service.

5.20.2.1 The maximum design pressure rating for pumps shall be based upon the maximum differential pressure produced and shall be in accordance with Table 5.20.2.1.

Table 5.20.2.1 Maximum Allowable Working Pressure for Pumps and Bypass Valves

Maximum Differential Pressure Produced (psi)	Equipment Design Pressure Rating (psig)
≤125	350
>125 and ≤150	375
>150 and ≤200	400
>200	200 + maximum differential pressure

For SI units, 1 psi = 6.895 kPa.

5.20.2.2 Pumps that produce a differential pressure greater than 125 psi (0.9 MPa) shall be marked to indicate that a bypass valve is required in the piping system. *(See 6.20.2.3.)*

5.20.3 Bypass Valves.

5.20.3.1 Bypass valves shall have a maximum design pressure in accordance with Table 5.20.2.1.

5.20.3.2 If a bypass valve is installed in the system, it shall have a flow capacity equal to or greater than the pump in the system at the specified differential pressure.

5.20.4 Compressors.

5.20.4.1 Compressors shall be designed for LP-Gas service.

5.20.4.2 Compressors shall be constructed or shall be equipped with auxiliary devices to limit the suction pressure to the maximum for which the compressor is designed.

5.20.4.3 Compressors shall be constructed or shall be equipped with auxiliary devices to prevent the entrance of LP-Gas liquid into the compressor suction.

5.20.4.4 Portable compressors used with temporary connections shall not require means to prevent liquid entrance into the compressor suction.

5.20.5 Reserved.

5.20.6 Meters.

5.20.6.1 Vapor meters of the tin or brass case type of soldered construction shall not be used at pressures in excess of 1 psig (7 kPag).

5.20.6.2 Vapor meters of the die cast or iron case type shall not be used at any pressure higher than the working pressure for which they are designed and marked.

5.20.7 Engines. Engines used to drive portable pumps and compressors shall be equipped with exhaust system spark arresters and shielded ignition systems.

5.20.8 Sight Flow Indicators. Where installed, sight flow indicators shall either be the simple observation type or be combined with a backflow check valve.

5.21 Reserved.

5.22 Reserved.

5.23 Appliances.

5.23.1 New residential, commercial, and industrial LP-Gas consuming appliances shall be approved.

Shaded text = Revisions.   Δ = Text deletions and figure/table revisions.   • = Section deletions.   **N** = New material.

5.23.2 Any appliance originally manufactured for operation with a gaseous fuel other than LP-Gas shall not be used with LP-Gas unless it is converted to use LP-Gas and is tested for performance with LP-Gas before being placed into use.

5.23.3 Unattended heaters used inside buildings for animal or poultry production or care shall be equipped with approved automatic devices to shut off the flow of gas to the main burners and to pilots, if used, in the event of flame extinguishment or combustion failure.

5.23.4 Approved automatic devices to shut off the flow of gas to the main burners and pilots shall not be required in structures without enclosing walls with the approval of the authority having jurisdiction.

5.23.5 Appliances using vaporizing burners shall comply with 5.24.5.

5.23.6* Appliances used in mobile homes and recreational vehicles shall be approved for such service.

5.23.7* LP-Gas appliances used on commercial vehicles shall be approved for the service.

(A) Gas-fired heating appliances and water heaters shall be equipped with automatic devices designed to shut off the flow of gas to the main burner and the pilot in the event the pilot flame is extinguished.

(B) Catalytic heating appliances shall be equipped with an approved automatic device to shut off the flow of gas in the event of combustion failure.

(C) Gas-fired heating appliances and water heaters to be used in vehicles intended for human occupancy shall be designed for complete separation of the combustion system and the living space.

(D) If the separation between the combustion system and the living space is not integral with the appliance, it shall be provided in accordance with installation requirements in 6.26.7.5.

5.24 Vaporizers, Tank Heaters, Vaporizing Burners, and Gas-Air Mixers.

5.24.1 Reserved.

5.24.2 Indirect Vaporizers.

5.24.2.1 Indirect vaporizers shall be constructed in accordance with the applicable provision of the ASME Code for a MAWP of 250 psig (1.7 MPag) and shall be permanently and legibly marked with the following:

(1) Marking required by the ASME Code
(2) Maximum allowable working pressure and temperature for which designed
(3) Name of the manufacturer

5.24.2.2 Indirect vaporizers that have an inside diameter of 6 in. (152 mm) or less are exempt from the ASME Code and shall not be required to be marked. They shall be constructed for a MAWP of 250 psig (1.7 MPag).

5.24.2.3 Indirect vaporizers shall be provided with an automatic means to prevent the passage of liquid through the vaporizer to the vapor discharge piping.

5.24.2.4 Indirect vaporizers, including atmospheric-type vaporizers using heat from the surrounding air or the ground and of more than 1 qt (0.9 L) capacity, shall be equipped with a

spring-loaded pressure relief valve providing a relieving capacity in accordance with 5.24.9. Fusible plug devices shall not be used.

5.24.2.5 Indirect atmospheric-type vaporizers of less than 1 qt (0.9 L) capacity shall not be required to be equipped with pressure relief valves but shall be installed in accordance with 6.24.2.11.

5.24.3 Direct-Fired Vaporizers.

5.24.3.1 Design and construction of direct-fired vaporizers shall be in accordance with the applicable requirements of the ASME Code for the working conditions to which the vaporizer will be subjected, and the vaporizer shall be permanently and legibly marked with the following:

(1) Markings required by the ASME Code
(2) Maximum vaporizing capacity in gallons per hour
(3) Rated heat input in Btus per hour
(4) Name or symbol of the manufacturer

5.24.3.2 Direct-fired vaporizers shall be equipped with a spring-loaded pressure relief valve that provides a relieving capacity in accordance with 5.24.9.

5.24.3.3 The relief valve shall be located so as not to be subject to temperatures in excess of 140°F (60°C). Fusible plug devices shall not be used.

5.24.3.4 Direct-fired vaporizers shall be provided with automatic means to prevent the passage of liquid from the vaporizer to its vapor discharge piping.

5.24.3.5 A means for manually turning off the gas to the main burner and pilot shall be provided.

5.24.3.6 Direct-fired vaporizers shall be equipped with an automatic safety device to shut off the flow of gas to the main burner if the pilot light is extinguished.

5.24.3.7 If the pilot flow exceeds 2000 Btu/hr (2 MJ/hr), the safety device shall also shut off the flow of gas to the pilot.

5.24.3.8 Direct-fired vaporizers shall be equipped with a limit control to prevent the heater from raising the product pressure above the design pressure of the vaporizer equipment, and to prevent raising the pressure within the storage container above the pressure specified in the first column of Table 5.2.4.3 that corresponds with the design pressure of the container (or its ASME Code equivalent). *(See notes to Table 5.2.4.3.)*

5.24.4 Tank Heaters.

5.24.4.1 Tank heaters shall be approved for the application and shall be used according to the manufacturer's instructions.

5.24.4.2 Tank heaters shall be approved and shall be permanently and legibly marked with the following:

(1) Rated input to the burner in Btus per hour
(2) Maximum vaporizing capacity in gallons per hour
(3) Name or symbol of the manufacturer

5.24.4.3 Manufacturer's instructions for tank heaters shall provide direction for their use for heating LP-Gas containers.

5.24.4.4 Tank heaters shall be equipped with a limit control to prevent the heater from raising the pressure in the storage container to more than 75 percent of the pressure shown in the first column of Table 5.2.4.3 that corresponds with the

MAWP of the container (or its ASME *Boiler and Pressure Vessel Code* equivalent).

5.24.4.5 Tank heaters of the electric immersion type shall be automatically de-energized when the liquid level falls below the top of the heater.

5.24.4.6 Devices that cannot apply a temperature in excess of 90°F (32°C) shall not be required to comply with 5.24.4.4 and 5.24.4.5.

5.24.4.7 Direct-type tank heaters shall be designed such that the heater can be removed for inspection of the entire container.

5.24.4.8 Direct gas-fired tank heaters shall be designed exclusively for outdoor aboveground use.

5.24.4.9 Direct gas-fired tank heaters shall be designed such that there is no direct flame impingement upon the container.

5.24.4.10 Fuel gas supply connections to direct gas-fired tank heaters originating in the vapor space of the container shall be provided with a manually operated shutoff valve at the heater.

5.24.4.11 Heater control systems shall be equipped with an automatic safety shutoff valve of the manual reset type arranged to shut off the flow of gas to both the main and pilot burners if the pilot flame is extinguished.

5.24.4.12 Where installed on containers exceeding 1000 gal (3.8 m³) water capacity, the heater control system shall include a valve to automatically shut off the flow of gas to both the main and pilot burners if the container becomes empty of liquid.

5.24.5 Vaporizing Burners.

5.24.5.1 Section 5.24 shall not apply to engine fuel vaporizers or to integral vaporizer burners, such as those used with weed burning equipment and tar kettles.

5.24.5.2 Vaporizing burners shall be constructed with a pressure rating of 250 psig (1.7 MPag), with a safety factor of 5 to 1.

5.24.5.3 The vaporizing burner or the appliance in which it is installed shall be permanently and legibly marked with the following:

(1) Maximum burner input in Btus per hour
(2) Name or symbol of the manufacturer

5.24.5.4 Vaporizing coils or jackets shall be made of ferrous metals or high-temperature alloys.

5.24.5.5 The vaporizing section shall be protected by a relief valve, located where it will not be subject to temperatures in excess of 140°F (60°C), and with a pressure setting sufficient to protect the components involved but not lower than 250 psig (1.7 MPag).

5.24.5.6 The relief valve discharge shall be directed upward and away from the component parts of the vaporizing burner. Fusible plug devices shall not be used.

5.24.5.7 A valve shall be provided to turn off the gas supply to the main burner and the pilot.

5.24.5.8 Vaporizing burners shall be provided with an automatic safety device to shut off the flow of gas to the main burner and pilot in the event the pilot is extinguished.

5.24.5.9* Dehydrators and dryers utilizing vaporizing burners shall be equipped with automatic devices both upstream and downstream of the vaporizing section. These devices shall be installed and connected to shut off in the event of excessive temperature, flame failure, and, if applicable, insufficient airflow.

5.24.5.10 Pressure-regulating and control equipment shall be so located or so protected to prevent its exposure to temperatures above 140°F (60°C), unless designed and recommended for use at a higher temperature by the manufacturer.

5.24.5.11 Pressure-regulating and control equipment located downstream of the vaporizing section shall be designed to withstand the maximum discharge temperature of hot vapor.

5.24.6 Waterbath Vaporizers.

5.24.6.1 The vaporizing chamber, tubing, pipe coils, or other heat exchange surface containing the LP-Gas to be vaporized, hereinafter referred to as heat exchanger, shall be constructed in accordance with the applicable provisions of the ASME Code for a MAWP of 250 psig (1.7 MPag) and shall be permanently and legibly marked with the following:

(1) Marking required by the ASME Code
(2) MAWP and temperature for which the heat exchanger is designed
(3) Name or symbol of the manufacturer

5.24.6.2 Heat exchangers for waterbath vaporizers that have an inside diameter of 6 in. (150 mm) or less are exempt from the ASME Code and shall not be required to be marked.

5.24.6.3 Heat exchangers for waterbath vaporizers shall be provided with automatic control to prevent the passage of liquid through the heat exchanger to the vapor discharge piping. This control shall be integral with the vaporizer.

5.24.6.4 Heat exchangers for waterbath vaporizers shall be equipped with a spring-loaded pressure relief valve that provides a relieving capacity in accordance with 5.24.9. Fusible plug devices shall not be used.

5.24.6.5 Waterbath sections of waterbath vaporizers shall be designed to prevent pressure from exceeding the design pressure.

5.24.6.6 The immersion heater that provides heat to the waterbath shall be installed so as not to contact the heat exchanger.

5.24.6.7 A control to limit the temperature of the waterbath shall be provided.

5.24.6.8 Gas-fired immersion heaters shall be equipped with an automatic safety device to shut off the flow of gas to the main burner and pilot in the event of flame failure.

5.24.6.9 Gas-fired immersion heaters with an input of 400,000 Btu/hr (422 MJ/hr) or more shall be equipped with an electronic flame safeguard and with programming to provide for prepurge prior to ignition, proof of pilot before the main burner valve opens, and full shutdown of the main gas valve and pilot upon flame failure.

5.24.6.10 The heat source shall be shut off if the level of the heat transfer medium falls below the top of the heat exchanger.

5.24.7 Reserved.

5.24.8 Gas-Air Mixers.

5.24.8.1 Gas-air mixers shall be designed for the air, vapor, and mixture pressures to which they are subjected.

5.24.8.2 Gas-air mixers that are capable of producing combustible mixtures shall be equipped with safety interlocks on both the LP-Gas and air supply lines to shut down the system if combustible limits are approached.

5.24.8.3 In addition to the interlocks required in 5.24.8.2, a method shall be provided to prevent air from accidentally entering gas distribution lines without LP-Gas being present. Gas-mixing control valves installed in the air and LP-Gas supply lines that fail closed when actuated by safety trip devices shall meet this requirement.

5.24.8.4 Backflow check valves shall be installed in the air and LP-Gas supply lines close to the mixer to minimize the possibility of backflow of gas into the air supply lines or of air into the LP-Gas system. Gas-mixing control valves installed in the air and LP-Gas supply lines that fail closed when actuated by safety trip devices shall meet this requirement.

5.24.8.5 Gas-air mixers that utilize the kinetic energy of the LP-Gas vapor to entrain air from the atmosphere, and are so designed that maximum air entrained is less than 85 percent of the mixture, shall comply with the following:

(1) They shall be exempt from the interlock provisions in 5.24.8.2 through 5.24.8.4.
(2) They shall be equipped with a backflow check valve at the air intake to prevent the escape of gas to atmosphere when shut down.

5.24.8.6 Gas-air mixers of the type specified in 5.24.8.5 receiving air from a blower, compressor, or any source of air other than directly from the atmosphere shall prevent air without LP-Gas, or mixtures of air and LP-Gas within the flammable range, from entering the gas distribution system accidentally.

5.24.9 Vaporizer Pressure Relief Valve.

5.24.9.1 The minimum rate of discharge in cubic feet of air per minute for pressure relief valves for LP-Gas vaporizers, either of the indirect type or direct-fired type, shall comply with 5.24.9.2 through 5.24.9.4.

5.24.9.2 Based on conservative heat transfer calculations (assuming that the vaporizing chamber is liquid full), the maximum vapor generating capacity (rate) shall be determined when maximum heat is available. That vapor rate shall be converted to an equivalent air rate.

5.24.9.3 If the vaporizer is direct fired or if a substantial exterior surface is in contact with the LP-Gas, the sum of the vaporizer surface and the LP-Gas wetted exterior surface shall be used in conjunction with Table 5.9.2.6 to determine the required relief valve capacity.

5.24.9.4 The minimum rate of discharge in cubic feet of air per minute for pressure relief valves for LP-Gas vaporizers of either the indirect type or direct-fired type shall be at least 150 percent of the rated vaporizing capacity.

5.25 Reserved.

5.26 Reserved.

5.27 Vehicle Fuel Dispensers.

5.27.1 Vehicle fuel dispensers shall have a maximum design pressure rating equal to or greater than the maximum discharge pressure from the pump and bypass valve, if provided.

5.27.2 The maximum design pressure and all equipment downstream from the pump shall be in accordance with Table 5.20.2.1.

Chapter 6   Installation of LP-Gas Systems

6.1 Scope.

6.1.1* Application. This chapter applies to the following:

(1) Location and field installation of LP-Gas systems that use components, subassemblies, container assemblies, and container systems that are fabricated in accordance with Chapter 5
(2) Location of containers and liquid transfer systems
(3) Installation of container appurtenances and regulators
(4) Installation of piping (including flexible connectors and hose), hydrostatic relief valves, and piping service limitations
(5) Installation of equipment
(6) Testing of piping systems
(7) Location of containers not connected for use

6.1.2 Nonapplication. This chapter does not apply to the following:

(1) Refrigerated containers
(2) Installation of systems used in the highway transportation of LP-Gas

6.1.3* Additional Features. For any purpose or application addressed within the scope of this chapter, if the requirements of the chapter are met, any or all additional features or components of equipment not prohibited by the chapter shall be permitted to be used.

6.2 Location of Containers.

6.2.1 LP-Gas containers shall be located outside of buildings unless they are specifically allowed to be located inside of buildings.

6.2.2 LP-Gas containers shall be allowed in buildings only for the following applications:

(1) Cylinders as specifically provided for in Section 6.22
(2) Containers of less than 125 gal (0.5 m^3) water capacity for the purposes of being filled in buildings or structures complying with Chapter 10
(3) Containers on LP-Gas vehicles complying with, and parked or garaged in accordance with, Chapter 9
(4) Containers used with LP-Gas portable engine fuel systems complying with 11.13.1
(5) Containers used with LP-Gas stationary engine fuel systems complying with Section 6.28
(6) Containers used with LP-Gas–fueled industrial trucks complying with 11.11.4
(7) Containers on LP-Gas–fueled vehicles garaged in accordance with Section 11.14

(8) Cylinders awaiting use, resale, or exchange when stored in accordance with Sections 8.2 and 8.3

6.3 Location of Containers Not Connected for Use.

6.3.1 Cylinders awaiting use, resale, or exchange shall be stored in accordance with Chapter 8.

6.3.2 ASME containers of 4,000 gal (15.2 m³) or less that have been removed from service but that contain LP-Gas shall be stored outside of buildings in accordance with either (1) or (2):

(1) Containers shall be located either at a bulk plant or in an approved area.

(2) Containers not complying with (1) shall comply with the following:

    (a) Containers shall be located in a manner that will minimize exposure to physical damage.

    (b) Containers shall be oriented so that the pressure relief valve remains in communication with the vapor space.

    (c) Containers shall not be located on roofs of buildings.

    (d) Valve outlets on ASME containers shall be plugged or capped.

    (e) Where screw-on-type caps or collars are utilized on ASME containers, they shall be in place whenever this type of container is stored regardless of the fill level of the container.

    (f) The location of ASME containers shall comply with the "Aboveground Containers" column and the "Between Containers" column of Table 6.4.1.1 with respect to important buildings and lines of adjoining property that can be built upon.

    (g) Where the provisions of (f) are impractical, alternative storage locations for containers shall be approved by the authority having jurisdiction.

6.4 Container Separation Distances.

6.4.1 Aboveground Containers.

6.4.1.1* Containers installed outside of buildings, whether of the portable type replaced on a cylinder exchange basis or permanently installed and refilled at the installation, shall be located with respect to the adjacent containers, important building, group of buildings, or line of adjoining property that can be built upon, in accordance with Table 6.4.1.1, Table 6.5.1.2, 6.4.1.2 through 6.4.1.3, 6.4.3, 6.4.4.1 through 6.4.4.4, and 6.5.3.6 through 6.5.3.11.

6.4.1.2 When the provisions of 6.30.3 through 6.30.5 are met, the minimum distance from an ASME container to a building or adjoining property line that can be built upon shall be reduced by one-half for ASME containers of 2001 gal through 30,000 gal (7.6 m³ through 114 m³) water capacity.

6.4.1.3 The 25 ft (7.6 m) minimum distance from aboveground ASME containers of 501 gal through 2000 gal (1.9 m³ through 7.6 m³) water capacity to buildings, a group of buildings, or the line of adjoining property that can be built upon shall be reduced to 10 ft (3 m) for a single ASME container of 1200 gal (4.5 m³) or less water capacity where such container is at least 25 ft (7.6 m) from any other LP-Gas container of more than 125 gal (0.5 m³) water capacity.

6.4.2 Underground or Mounded ASME Containers.

6.4.2.1 Minimum distances for underground or mounded ASME containers of 2001 gal through 30,000 gal (7.6 m³ through 114 m³) water capacity, incorporating all the provisions of Section 6.30, shall be reduced to 10 ft (3 m).

6.4.2.2 Distances for all underground and mounded ASME containers shall be measured from the container surface.

Table 6.4.1.1 Separation Distances Between Containers, Important Buildings, and Line of Adjoining Property That Can Be Built Upon

Water Capacity per Container		Minimum Distances						
		Mounded or Underground Containers[a]		Aboveground Containers		Between Containers[b]		
gal	m³	ft	m	ft	m	ft	m	
<125[c]	<0.5[c]	10	3	0[d]	0[d]	0	0	
125–250	0.5–1.0	10	3	10	3	0	0	
251–500	>1.0–1.9	10	3	10	3	3	1	
501–2,000	>1.9–7.6	10	3	25[e]	7.6	3	1	
2,001–30,000	>7.6–114	50	15	50	15	5	1.5	
30,001–70,000	>114–265	50	15	75	23			
70,001–90,000	>265–341	50	15	100	30	¼ of sum of		
90,001–120,000	>341–454	50	15	125	38	diameters of		
120,001–200,000	>454–757	50	15	200	61	adjacent		
200,001–1,000,000	>757–3,785	50	15	300	91	containers		
>1,000,000	>3,785	50	15	400	122			

[a]See 6.4.2.1.
[b]See 6.4.4.5.
[c]See 6.4.4.4.
[d]See 6.4.4.1, 6.4.4.2, 6.4.4.3, and 6.4.4.4.
[e]See 6.4.1.3.

Shaded text = Revisions. △ = Text deletions and figure/table revisions. • = Section deletions. **N** = New material.

6.4.2.3 No part of an underground or mounded ASME container shall be less than 10 ft (3 m) from a building or line of adjoining property that can be built upon.

N **6.4.3 Multiple Containers Less Than 125 gal (0.5 m³) Individual Water Capacity.** Multiple containers, each having a water capacity less than 125 gal (0.5 m³) and installed in an above-ground group as a manifolded single service or as individual services, shall comply with the following:

(1) Where the aggregate water capacity of all containers in any group is 500 gal (1.9 m³) or less, the minimum separation distances required by Table 6.4.1.1 for each container shall be 0 ft (0 m) for each container in the group from an important building or line of adjoining property that can be built upon.

(2) Where the aggregate water capacity of all containers in the group is greater than 500 gal (1.9 m³), the minimum separation distances in Table 6.4.1.1 for each container shall be based on the aggregate capacity.

(3) There shall be no separation required between individual containers within the group.

(4)* For the application of 6.4.3(1) and 6.4.3(2), the number of containers in a single group is determined by the number of containers that are less than 10 ft (3 m) from any other container in the group.

6.4.4 Separation Distance Between Container Pressure Relief Valve and Building Openings.

6.4.4.1 Cylinders shall not be located and installed underneath any building unless the space is open to the atmosphere for 50 percent of its perimeter or more.

6.4.4.2 ASME containers of less than 125 gal (0.5 m³) water capacity shall be located and installed so that the discharge from pressure relief devices shall not terminate in or beneath any building.

6.4.4.3* The distance measured horizontally from the point of discharge of a container pressure relief valve to any building opening below the level of such discharge shall be in accordance with Table 6.4.4.3.

6.4.4.4 The distance measured in any direction from the point of discharge of a container pressure relief valve, vent of a fixed maximum liquid level gauge on a container, and the container filling connection to exterior sources of ignition, openings into direct-vent (sealed combustion system) appliances, and mechanical ventilation air intakes shall be in accordance with Table 6.4.4.3.

6.4.4.5 Access at the ends or sides of individual underground containers having a water capacity of 125 gal (0.5 m³) or more shall be provided in multicontainer installations to facilitate working with cranes or hoists.

6.5 Other Container Location Requirements.

6.5.1 ASME Multicontainer Requirements.

6.5.1.1 Where storage containers having an aggregate water capacity of more than 4000 gal (15.2 m³) are located in heavily populated or congested areas, the siting provisions of 6.4.1.1 and Table 6.4.1.1 shall be permitted to be modified as indicated by the fire safety analysis described in 6.29.3.

6.5.1.2 Aboveground multicontainer installations comprised of ASME containers having an individual water capacity of 12,000 gal (45 m³) or more and installed for use in a single location shall be limited to the number of containers in one group, with each group separated from the next group in accordance with the degree of fire protection provided in Table 6.5.1.2.

Table 6.5.1.2 Maximum Number of Containers in a Group and Their Separation Distances

Fire Protection Provided by	Maximum Number of Containers in One Group	Minimum Separation Between Groups	
		ft	m
Hose streams only (see 6.5.1.2 and 6.29.3.1)	6	50	15
Fixed monitor nozzles per 6.29.6.3	6	25	7.6
Fixed water spray per 6.29.6.1	9	25	7.6
Insulation per 6.29.5.1	9	25	7.6

6.5.1.3 Where the provisions of 6.30.3 and 6.30.4 are met, the minimum separation distance between groups of ASME containers protected by hose stream only shall be one-half the distances required in Table 6.5.1.2.

△ **Table 6.4.4.3 Separation Distance Between Container Pressure Relief Valve and Building Openings**

Container Type	Exchange or Filled at Point of Use	Distance Horizontally from Relief Valve Discharge to Opening Below Discharge		Discharge from Relief Valve, Vent Discharge, and Filling Connection to Exterior Source of Ignition, Openings into Direct-Vent Appliances, and Mechanical Ventilation Air Intakes	
		ft	m	ft	m
Cylinder	Exchange	3	0.9	5	1.5
Cylinder	Filled at the point of use	3	0.9	10	3.0
ASME	Filled at the point of use	5	1.5	10	3.0

6.5.2 Underground and Mounded ASME Containers.

6.5.2.1 Underground or mounded ASME containers shall be located in accordance with 6.5.2.2 and 6.5.2.3.

6.5.2.2 Underground or mounded containers shall be located outside of any buildings.

6.5.2.3 Buildings shall not be constructed over any underground or mounded containers.

6.5.2.4 The sides of adjacent containers shall be separated in accordance with Table 6.4.1.1 but shall not be separated by less than 3 ft (1 m).

6.5.2.5 Where containers are installed parallel with ends in line, the number of containers in one group shall not be limited.

6.5.2.6 Where more than one row of containers is installed, the adjacent ends of the containers in each row shall be separated by not less than 10 ft (3 m).

6.5.3 Additional Container Installation Requirements.

6.5.3.1 Additional container installation requirements shall comply with 6.5.3.2 through 6.5.3.13 and 6.5.4.

6.5.3.2 Containers shall not be stacked one above the other.

6.5.3.3* Combustible materials shall not accumulate or be stored within 10 ft (3 m) of a container.

6.5.3.4* The area under containers shall be graded or shall have dikes or curbs installed so that the flow or accumulation of flammable liquids with flash points below 200°F (93.4°C) is prevented.

6.5.3.5* LP-Gas containers shall be located at least 10 ft (3 m) from the centerline of the wall of diked areas containing Class I flammable or Class II combustible liquids.

6.5.3.6 The minimum horizontal separation between aboveground LP-Gas containers and aboveground tanks containing liquids having flash points below 200°F (93.4°C) shall be 20 ft (6 m).

6.5.3.7 The requirements of 6.5.3.6 shall not apply where LP-Gas containers of 125 gal (0.5 m³) or less water capacity are installed adjacent to fuel oil supply tanks of 660 gal (2.5 m³) or less capacity.

6.5.3.8 No horizontal separation shall be required between aboveground LP-Gas containers and underground tanks containing flammable or combustible liquids installed in accordance with NFPA 30.

6.5.3.9* The minimum separation between LP-Gas containers and oxygen or gaseous hydrogen containers shall be in accordance with NFPA 55.

6.5.3.10 Where protective structures having a minimum fire resistance rating of 2 hours interrupt the line of sight between uninsulated portions of the oxygen or hydrogen containers and the LP-Gas containers, no minimum distance shall apply.

6.5.3.11 The minimum separation between LP-Gas containers and liquefied hydrogen containers shall be in accordance with NFPA 55.

6.5.3.12 Where LP-Gas cylinders are to be stored or used in the same area with other compressed gases, the cylinders shall be marked to identify their content in accordance with CGA C-7, *Guide to Classification and Labeling of Compressed Gases*.

6.5.3.13 An aboveground LP-Gas container and any of its parts shall not be located within 6 ft (1.8 m) of a vertical plane beneath overhead electric power lines that are over 600 volts, nominal.

6.5.3.14 The minimum separation distances specified in Table 6.4.1.1 between containers and buildings of noncombustible construction devoted exclusively to gas manufacturing and distribution operations shall be reduced to 10 ft (3 m).

6.5.4* Structure Requirements.

Δ 6.5.4.1 Structures such as fire walls, fences, earth or concrete barriers, and other similar structures shall be permitted around installed nonrefrigerated containers in accordance with all of the following:

(1) Clearance shall be provided around the container for inspection and maintenance.
(2) The structure shall be open on at least one side that includes the longest dimension of the container.
(3) The top of the container shall be capable of being wetted by an emergency response hose stream.

6.5.4.2 Structures used to prevent flammable or combustible liquid accumulation or flow shall be permitted in accordance with 6.5.3.4.

6.5.4.3 Structures between LP-Gas containers and gaseous hydrogen containers shall be permitted in accordance with 6.5.3.10.

6.5.4.4 Structures such as fences shall be permitted in accordance with 6.21.4.

6.6 Installation of Containers with Attached Supports.

6.6.1 Installation of Vertical Containers. Installation of portable storage containers shall be in accordance with 6.6.3.

6.6.2 Installation of Skid Tanks.

6.6.2.1 Temporary installation of skid tanks shall be located on concrete foundations, concrete pads, or crushed stone.

6.6.2.2 Permanent installation of skid tanks shall be in accordance with 6.8.3, except that the maximum elevation of a skid tank with non-fireproofed steel supports above the concrete foundation is 18 in. (46 cm).

6.6.2.3 Interconnection of skid tanks and portable storage tanks shall be in accordance with 6.8.3.2.

6.6.3 Installation of Porta-Pacs.

6.6.3.1 Single containers constructed as portable storage containers for temporary stationary service in accordance with 5.6.1.2 shall be placed on concrete pads, paved surfaces, or firm earth for such temporary service (not more than 12 months at a given location).

6.6.3.2 The surface on which the containers are placed shall be level.

6.6.3.3 Combustible materials shall not accumulate or be stored within 10 ft (3 m) of a container.

6.6.3.4 Flexibility shall be provided in the connecting piping in accordance with 6.11.6.

6.6.3.5 Where portable storage containers are installed at isolated locations with the bottoms of the skids or runners above the ground, either fire-resistive supports shall be provided or non–fire-resistive supports shall be permitted when all the following conditions are met:

(1) The height of the outside bottom of the container does not exceed 5 ft (1.5 m) above the ground.
(2) The approval of the authority having jurisdiction is obtained.

6.7 Location of Transfer Operations.

6.7.1 Transfer of Liquids.

6.7.1.1* Liquid shall be transferred into containers, including containers mounted on vehicles, only outdoors or in structures specially designed for such purpose.

6.7.1.2 The transfer of liquid into containers mounted on vehicles shall not take place within a building but shall be permitted to take place under a weather shelter or canopy. (See 6.27.3.4.)

6.7.1.3 Structures housing transfer operations or converted for such use after December 31, 1972, shall comply with Chapter 10.

6.7.1.4 The transfer of liquid into containers on the roofs of structures shall be permitted, provided that the installation conforms to the requirements specified in 6.8.7 and 6.22.11.

6.7.1.5 The transfer hose shall not be routed in or through any buildings except those specified in 6.7.1.3.

6.7.1.6 Filling of containers located outdoors in stationary installations in accordance with Section 6.4 shall be permitted to be filled at that location.

6.7.2 Container Point of Transfer Location Requirements.

6.7.2.1* If the point of transfer of containers located outdoors in stationary installations is not located at the container, it shall be located in accordance with Table 6.7.2.1.

6.7.2.2 Containers not located in stationary installations shall be filled at a location determined by the point of transfer in accordance with Table 6.7.2.1.

6.7.3 Separation Distance from Point of Transfer.

6.7.3.1 If the point of transfer is a component of a system covered by Section 6.26 or Chapter 11, the requirements of parts A, B, and C of Table 6.7.2.1 shall not apply to the structure containing the point of transfer.

△ **Table 6.7.2.1 Distance Between Point of Transfer and Exposures**

Part	Exposure	Minimum Horizontal Distance	
		ft	m
A	Buildings,[a] mobile homes, recreational vehicles, and modular homes with at least 1-hour fire-rated walls	10	3.1
B	Buildings[a] with other than at least 1-hour fire-rated walls	25[b]	7.6[b]
C	Building wall openings or pits at or below the level of the point of transfer	25[b]	7.6[b]
D	Line of adjoining property that can be built upon	25[b]	7.6[b]
E	Outdoor places of public assembly, including schoolyards, athletic fields, and playgrounds	50[b]	15[b]
F	Public ways, including public streets, highways, thoroughfares, and sidewalks		
	(1) From points of transfer of LP-Gas dispensing systems	10	3.1
	(2) From other points of transfer	25[b]	7.6[b]
G	Driveways[c]	5	1.5
H	Mainline railroad track centerlines	25	7.6
I	Containers[d] other than those being filled	10	3.1
J	Flammable and Class II combustible liquid[e] dispensers and the fill connections of containers	10[b]	3.1[b]
K	Flammable and Class II combustible liquid[e] aboveground containers and filling connections of underground containers	20	6.1
L	Stored or accumulated combustible materials	10	3.1

[a]For the purpose of this table, buildings also include structures such as tents and box trailers at construction sites.
[b]See 6.7.3.4.
[c]Not applicable to driveways and points of transfer at vehicle fuel dispensers.
[d]Not applicable to filling connections at the storage container or to vehicle fuel dispenser units of 4000 gal (15.2 m³) water capacity or less when used for filling containers not mounted on vehicles.
[e]NFPA 30 defines Class I flammable liquids as including those having a flash point below 100°F (37.8°C) and having a vapor pressure not exceeding 40 psia (276 kPa) at 100°F (37.8°C). NFPA 30 defines Class II combustible liquids as including those having a flash point at or above 100°F (37.8°C) and below 140°F (60°C).

Δ **6.7.3.2** If LP-Gas is vented to the atmosphere under the conditions stipulated in 7.3.1.1(4), the distances in Table 6.7.2.1 shall be doubled.

6.7.3.3 If the point of transfer is housed in a structure complying with Chapter 10, and the common walls comply with 10.2.1, separation distances in Table 6.7.2.1 shall not be required where the common walls comply with 10.3.1.3.

6.7.3.4 The distances in Table 6.7.2.1, parts B, C, D, E, F(2), and J, shall be reduced by one-half where the system incorporates the provisions of low-emission transfer as provided in 6.30.5.

6.8 Installation of Containers.

6.8.1 General Requirements.

6.8.1.1 Containers shall be positioned so that the pressure relief valve is in direct communication with the vapor space of the container.

6.8.1.2 LP-Gas containers or systems that are installed within 10 ft (3 m) of public vehicular thoroughfares shall be provided with a means of vehicular barrier protection.

6.8.1.3 Field welding on containers shall be limited to nonpressure parts such as saddle plates, wear plates, or brackets installed by the container manufacturer.

6.8.1.4* Aboveground containers shall be painted.

6.8.1.5 Containers shall be installed so that all container operating appurtenances are accessible.

6.8.1.6 Where necessary to prevent flotation due to possible high flood waters around aboveground or mounded containers, or high water table for those underground and partially underground, containers shall be securely anchored.

6.8.1.7 ASME containers that have liquid interconnections shall be installed so that the maximum permitted filling level of each container is at the same elevation.

6.8.2 Installation of Cylinders.

6.8.2.1 Cylinders shall be installed only aboveground and shall be set upon a firm foundation or otherwise be firmly secured. *(See 6.8.2.2.)*

6.8.2.2 The cylinder shall not be in contact with the soil.

6.8.2.3 Flexibility shall be provided in the connecting piping. *(See 6.8.2.4.)*

6.8.2.4 Where flexible connectors are used, they shall comply with 6.11.6.

6.8.3 Installation of Horizontal Aboveground ASME Containers.

6.8.3.1 Horizontal ASME containers designed for permanent installation in stationary aboveground service shall be placed on masonry or other noncombustible structural supports located on concrete or masonry foundations with the container supports.

(A) Where saddles are used to support the container, they shall allow for expansion and contraction and prevent an excessive concentration of stresses.

(B) Where structural steel supports are used, they shall comply with 6.8.3.2.

(C) Containers of more than 4000 gal (15.2 m³) water capacity shall be provided with concrete or masonry foundations formed to fit the container contour or, if furnished with saddles in compliance with Table 6.8.3.2(A), shall be placed on flat-topped foundations.

(D) Containers of 4000 gal (15.2 m³) water capacity or less shall be installed either on concrete or masonry foundations formed to fit the container contour or in accordance with 6.8.3.1(E).

(E) Containers of 4000 gal (15.2 m³) water capacity or less and equipped with attached supports complying with Table 6.8.3.2(A) shall be installed on a fire-resistive foundation if the bottoms of the horizontal members of the container saddles, runners, or skids are more than 12 in. (300 mm) above grade.

(F) Containers of 4000 gal (15.2 m³) water capacity or less installed with combined container-pump assemblies on a common base complying with Table 6.8.3.2(A) shall be placed either on paved surfaces or on concrete pads at ground level within 4 in. (100 mm) of ground level.

6.8.3.2 Support of horizontal ASME containers shall comply with 6.8.3.2(A) through 6.8.3.2(C).

(A) Horizontal ASME containers with attached supports and designed for permanent installation in stationary service shall be installed in accordance with 6.8.3.2(B).

(B) Steel supports shall be protected against fire exposure with a material having a fire resistance rating of at least 2 hours if the height limits specified in Table 6.8.3.2(A) are exceeded.

(C) Horizontal ASME containers of 4000 gal (15.2 m³) or less, on foundations in their installed condition, shall meet the following conditions:

(1) Structurally support the containers when subject to deteriorating environmental effects including, but not limited to, ambient temperature of −40°F to 150°F (−40°C to 66°C) or local conditions if outside this range, ultraviolet rays, radiant heat from fires, and moisture

(2) Be of either noncombustible or self-extinguishing material (per the definition in 3.3.161 of NFPA 99)

6.8.3.3 Where a single ASME container complying with Table 6.8.3.2(A) is installed in isolated locations with non-fireproofed steel supports resting on concrete pads or footings and the outside bottom of the container shell is not more than 5 ft (1.5 m) above the ground level, the approval of the authority having jurisdiction shall be obtained.

6.8.3.4 The part of an ASME container in contact with saddles, foundations, or masonry shall be coated or protected to minimize corrosion.

6.8.3.5 In locations where the snow depth, based on the ground snow load, is more than the height of aboveground containers, excluding the dome cover, both of the following requirements shall apply:

(1) A stake or other marking shall be installed higher than the snow depth based on the ground snow load.

(2) The container shall be installed to prevent its movement resulting from snow accumulation.

△ Table 6.8.3.2(A) Installation of Permanently Installed Horizontal ASME Containers with Attached Supports

Container Size		Attached Support	Height of Container Bottom
gal	m³		
≥4000	≥15.2	Non-fireproofed steel on flat-topped concrete foundations	6 in. (150 mm) maximum above concrete foundations
≤4000	≤15.2	Non-fireproofed steel on masonry or concrete foundations more than 12 in. (300 mm) above the ground	2 in. to 12 in. (51 mm to 300 mm) above concrete foundation
≤4000	≤15.2	Non-fireproofed steel on paved surfaces or concrete pads within 4 in. (100 mm) of the ground	24 in. (610 mm) maximum above paved surface or top of concrete pads
≤4000	≤15.2	Foundations or supports for horizontal LP-Gas containers per 6.8.3.2(B)	24 in. (610 mm) maximum above paved surface

6.8.3.5.1* Snow depth (ft), based on the ground snow load (lb/ft²) and snow density (lb/ft³), shall be determined as follows:

$$\text{Snow depth} = (\text{ground snow load}) / (\text{snow density}) \qquad \text{[6.8.3.5.1a]}$$

△

$$\text{Snow density} = (0.13 \times \text{ground snow load}) + 14 \qquad \text{[6.8.3.5.1b]}$$

6.8.3.5.2 Where the calculation in Equation 6.8.3.5.1b results in a value greater than 30 lb/ft³, 30 lb/ft³ shall be used in Equation 6.8.3.5.1a.

6.8.3.6 If the container is mounted on or is part of a vehicle in accordance with 5.2.7.2, the unit shall be located in accordance with 6.4.1.1.

(A) The surface on which the vehicle is parked shall be level and, if not paved, shall be able to support heavy vehicular traffic and shall be clear of dry grass, weeds, and other combustible material within 10 ft (3 m) of the container.

(B) Flexibility shall be provided in the connecting piping in accordance with 6.11.6.

6.8.3.7 Portable tanks of 4000 gal (15.2 m³) water capacity or less that comply with 5.2.7.3 shall be installed in accordance with 6.8.3.1(E).

6.8.4 Installation of Vertical ASME Containers.

6.8.4.1 Vertical ASME containers of 125 gal (0.5 m³) water capacity or less shall be installed in accordance with 6.8.2.

6.8.4.2 Vertical ASME containers of 125 gal (0.5 m³) water capacity or less shall not be in contact with the soil.

6.8.4.3 Vertical ASME containers of over 125 gal (0.5 m³) water capacity designed for permanent installation in stationary aboveground service shall be installed on reinforced concrete or steel structural supports on reinforced concrete foundations

that are designed to meet the loading provisions established in 5.2.4.4.

6.8.4.4 The requirements in 6.8.4.5 through 6.8.4.7 shall also apply to the installation of vertical ASME containers greater than 125 gal (0.5 m³) water capacity.

6.8.4.5 Steel supports shall be protected against fire exposure with a material that has a fire resistance rating of at least 2 hours, except that continuous steel skirts that have only one opening that is 18 in. (460 mm) or less in diameter shall have fire protection applied to the outside of the skirts.

6.8.4.6 Vertical ASME containers used in liquid service shall not be manifolded to horizontal ASME containers.

6.8.4.7 Vertical ASME containers of different dimensions shall not be manifolded together.

6.8.5 Temporary Container Installations.

△ **6.8.5.1** Single containers constructed as portable storage containers for temporary stationary service in accordance with 5.2.7 shall be placed on concrete pads, paved surfaces, or firm earth for such temporary service (not more than 12 months at a given location).

6.8.5.2 The surface on which the containers are placed shall be level and, if not paved, shall be clear of dry grass, weeds, and other combustible material within 10 ft (3 m) of the container.

6.8.5.3 Flexibility shall be provided in the connecting piping in accordance with 6.11.6.

6.8.5.4 Where portable storage containers are installed at isolated locations with the bottoms of the skids or runners above the ground, either fire-resistive supports shall be provided or non–fire-resistive supports shall be permitted when all the following conditions are met:

(1) The height of the outside bottom of the container does not exceed 5 ft (1.5 m) above the ground.
(2) The approval of the authority having jurisdiction is obtained.

6.8.6 Installation of Underground and Mounded Containers.

6.8.6.1* ASME container assemblies intended for underground installation, including interchangeable aboveground–underground container assemblies, shall be installed underground in accordance with 6.8.6.1(A) through 6.8.6.1(M).

(A) The shell of containers installed in areas with no vehicular traffic shall be installed at least 6 in. (150 mm) below grade.

(B) At installations within 10 ft (3 m) of a public vehicular thoroughfare or designated parking location, the shell of a noninterchangeable underground container shall be installed 18 in. (460 mm) below grade or vehicular barrier protection shall be provided.

(C) Installations within 10 ft (3 m) of a public vehicular thoroughfare or designated parking location shall be provided with vehicular barrier protection for the container's fitting housing, housing cover, container connections, and piping.

(D) Approved interchangeable aboveground–underground container assemblies installed underground shall not be placed with the container shell more than 12 in. (300 mm) below grade.

(E) The installation of a buried container shall include protection for the container and piping against physical damage from vehicular traffic.

(F) Prior to digging, the location of underground and mounded containers and piping in the vicinity of construction and excavation activities shall be determined and the installation shall be protected from damage.

(G) Where a container is to be abandoned underground, the following procedure shall be followed:

(1) As much liquid LP-Gas as practical shall be removed through the container liquid withdrawal connection.
(2)* As much of the remaining LP-Gas vapor as practical shall be removed through a vapor connection.
(3) The vapor shall be either recovered, burned, or vented to the atmosphere.
(4) Where only vapor LP-Gas at atmospheric pressure remains in the container, the container shall be filled with water, sand, or foamed plastic or shall be purged with an inert gas.
(5) If purged, the displaced vapor shall be either recovered, burned, or vented to the atmosphere.

(H)* The discharge of the regulator vent shall be above the highest probable water level.

(I)* A corrosion protection system shall be installed on new installations of underground steel containers, unless technical justification is provided to and is approved by the authority having jurisdiction. The corrosion protection system shall include the following:

(1) A container coating complying with 5.2.1.11
(2) A cathodic protection system that consists of a sacrificial anode(s) or an impressed current anode
(3) A means to test the performance of the cathodic protection system in accordance with 6.19.3

(J) Prior to burial, the container shall be visually examined for damage to the coating. Damaged areas shall be repaired with a coating recommended for underground service and compatible with the existing coating.

(K)* Containers shall be set level and shall be surrounded by earth or sand firmly tamped in place.

(L)* Where electrical isolation is provided between buried metallic piping and an underground container, the dielectric connection shall comply with the applicable requirements of Section 5.11 or shall be listed.

(M) Backfill shall be free of rocks and abrasives.

6.8.6.2 Partially underground, unmounded ASME containers shall be installed in accordance with 6.8.6.2(A) through 6.8.6.2(F).

△ **(A)** The portion of the container below the surface of the ground, and for a vertical distance of at least 3 in. (75 mm) above that surface, shall comply with the corrosion protection requirements of 6.8.6.1(I) through 6.8.6.1(J).

(B) The aboveground portion of the container shall be painted to comply with 6.8.1.4.

(C) Containers shall be set level and shall be surrounded by earth or sand firmly tamped in place.

(D) Backfill shall be free of rocks and abrasives.

(E) Spacing provisions shall be as specified for aboveground containers in 6.4.1.1 and Table 6.4.1.1.

(F) The container shall be located so as not to be subject to vehicular damage or shall be protected against such damage.

6.8.6.3 Mounded containers shall be installed in accordance with 6.8.6.3(A) through 6.8.6.3(F).

(A)* Mounding material shall be earth, sand, or other noncombustible, noncorrosive materials and shall provide a minimum thickness of cover for the container of at least 1 ft (0.3 m).

(B) A protective cover shall be provided on top of mounding materials subject to erosion.

(C) Container valves and appurtenances shall be accessible for operation or repair, without disturbing mounding material.

(D) Where containers are mounded and the bottom of the container is 30 in. (0.76 m) or more above the surrounding grade, access to bottom connections shall be provided by an opening or tunnel with a 4 ft (1.2 m) minimum diameter and a 3 ft (0.9 m) minimum clear area.

(E) Bottom connections that extend beyond the mound shall be part of the ASME container or shall be installed in compliance with the ASME Code and shall be designed for the forces that can act on the connections.

(F) Mounded containers shall comply with the corrosion protection requirements of 6.8.6.1(I) and 6.8.6.1(J).

6.8.7 Installation of Containers on Roofs of Buildings.

6.8.7.1 Installation of containers on roofs of buildings shall be prohibited, unless approved by the authority having jurisdiction and the fire department.

6.8.7.2 Where the authority having jurisdiction and the fire department have approved an installation of a container, it shall comply with 6.8.7.2(A) through 6.8.7.2(S).

(A) The building shall be of Type I, 443 or 332, or Type II, 222, construction as specified in NFPA 220.

(B) LP-Gas containers installed on roofs shall be of 2000 gal (7.6 m³) water capacity or less.

(C) The aggregate water capacity of LP-Gas containers installed on the roof or terrace of a building shall meet the following criteria:

(1) It shall not exceed 4000 gal (15.2 m³) in one location.
(2) Additional installations on the same roof or terrace shall be located at least 50 ft (15 m) apart.

(D) An ASME container installed on the roof of a building shall always be filled by two operators, one at the controls of the vehicle supplying LP-Gas and another at the controls of the container.

(E) Containers shall be installed in external locations only.

(F) Where a fill line to the container is required, it shall be located entirely outside the building.

(G) The fill connection shall be located entirely outside the building.

(H) The fill connection shall be located at least 8 ft (2.4 m) above ground level.

(I) Containers shall be installed on a level surface.

(J) The container shall be secured to the building structure.

(K) The support of the container shall be designed to the same seismic criteria as the building.

(L) The roof on which the container is located shall be able to support the weight of the container filled with water, with the safety margins required by local codes.

(M) Containers shall be located in areas that have free air circulation, are at least 10 ft (3 m) from building openings (such as windows and doors), and are at least 20 ft (6.1 m) from air intakes of air-conditioning and ventilating systems.

(N) The location of containers shall allow access to all valves and controls and shall have enough surrounding area to allow the required maintenance.

(O) The location of the container shall have fixed stairs or another method to reach it.

(P) If the installation requires the use of more than one container, the distances between containers from Table 6.4.1.1 shall apply.

(Q) If the container location is higher than 23 ft (7 m) from the ground, or if the filling hose cannot be observed by the operators in its entire length, the container shall have a filling line constructed to withstand liquid transfer, and it shall have the following appurtenances:

(1) Filler valve *[see 5.9.4.1(D)]*
(2) Filler valve cap
(3) Two control valves
(4) Hydrostatic relief valve
(5) Venting line

(R) The liquid fill and vapor connections shall be conspicuously marked or labeled.

(S) A fire safety analysis shall be prepared in accordance with 6.29.3.

6.9 Installation of Container Appurtenances.

6.9.1 Reserved.

6.9.2 Installation of Pressure Relief Devices.

6.9.2.1 Pressure relief devices shall be installed so that the relief device is in direct communication with the vapor space of the container.

6.9.2.2 Pressure relief devices on cylinders shall be installed to minimize the possibility of relief device discharge impingement on the cylinder.

△ 6.9.2.3 Pressure relief devices on the following ASME containers shall be installed so that any gas released is vented upward and away from the container to prevent deflection toward the container:

(1) Containers of 125 gal (0.5 m³) or more water capacity installed in stationary service
(2) Portable storage containers
(3) Portable tanks

6.9.2.4 Rain caps or other means shall be provided to minimize the possibility of the entrance of water or other extraneous matter into the relief device or any discharge piping. Provision shall be made for drainage where the accumulation of water is anticipated.

6.9.2.5 The rain cap or other protector shall be designed to remain in place, except during pressure relief device operation, and shall not restrict pressure relief device flow.

6.9.2.6 The design of the pressure relief valve drain opening shall provide the following:

(1) Protection of the container against flame impingement resulting from ignited product escaping from the drain opening
(2) Direction of the pressure relief valve drain opening so that an adjacent container, piping, or equipment is not subjected to flame impingement

6.9.2.7 Shutoff valves shall not be installed between pressure relief devices and the container unless a listed pressure relief valve manifold meeting the requirements of 6.9.2.8 is used.

6.9.2.8 Listed pressure relief valve manifolds shall be exempt from the requirements of 6.9.2.7 when the following conditions are met:

(1) Two or more pressure relief devices are installed in the manifold.
(2) Only one pressure relief device in the manifold is designed to shut off at any one time.
(3) The remaining pressure relief device(s) remains open and provides the rated relieving capacity required for the container.

6.9.2.9 Shutoff valves shall not be installed at the outlet of a pressure relief device or at the outlet of the discharge piping where discharge piping is installed.

6.9.2.10 The pressure relief valve discharge piping from underground containers of 2000 gal (7.6 m³) or less water capacity shall extend beyond the manhole or housing or shall discharge into the manhole or housing, where the manhole or housing is equipped with ventilated louvers or their equivalent, in accordance with 5.9.8.4.

6.9.2.11 Pressure relief valve discharge on underground containers of more than 2000 gal (7.6 m^3) water capacity shall be piped vertically and directly upward to a point at least 7 ft (2.1 m) above the ground. *(See 6.9.2.12.)*

6.9.2.12 Pressure relief devices installed in underground containers serving dispensing systems shall be piped vertically upward to a point at least 10 ft (3 m) above the ground.

6.9.2.13 Where installed, the discharge piping shall comply with 6.9.2.13(A) through 6.9.2.13(F).

(A) Piping shall be supported and protected against physical damage.

(B) Piping from aboveground containers shall be sized to provide the rate of flow specified in Table 5.9.2.6.

(C) Piping from underground containers shall be sized to provide the rate of flow specified in 5.9.2.8.

(D) Piping shall be metallic and have a melting point over 1500°F (816°C).

(E) Discharge piping shall be so designed that excessive force applied to the discharge piping results in breakage on the discharge side of the valve, rather than on the inlet side, without impairing the function of the valve.

(F) Return bends and restrictive pipe or tubing fittings shall not be used.

6.9.3 Reserved.

6.9.4 Reserved.

6.9.5 Reserved.

6.9.6 Reserved.

6.9.7 Reserved.

6.9.8 Reserved.

6.9.9 Reserved.

6.10 Regulators.

6.10.1 Regulator Installation.

6.10.1.1 First-stage, high-pressure, automatic changeover, integral 2 psi service, integral two-stage, and single-stage regulators where allowed shall be installed in accordance with 6.10.1.1(A) through 6.10.1.1(D).

(A) Regulators connected to single container permanent installations shall be installed with one of the following methods:

(1) Attached to the vapor service valve using metallic pipe, tubing, fittings, or adapters that do not exceed 5 ft (1.5 m) in total length
(2) Attached to the vapor service valve with a single flexible metallic connector

(B) Regulators connected to cylinders in other than stationary installations shall be installed with one of the following methods:

(1) Attached to the vapor service valve using metallic pipe, tubing, fittings, or adapters that do not exceed 5 ft (1.5 m) in total length
(2) Attached to the vapor service valve with a single flexible metallic connector

(3) Attached to the vapor service valve with a single flexible hose connector

(C) Regulators connected to manifolded containers shall be installed with the following methods:

(1) Installations shall comply with 6.11.3.8.
(2) The regulator shall be attached with pipe or a single flexible metallic connector to the vapor service manifold piping outlet.
(3) The connection between the container service valve outlet and the inlet side of the manifold piping shall be installed with one of the following methods:

    (a) Attached with a metallic fitting
    (b) Attached with a single flexible metallic connector
    (c) Attached with a flexible hose connector connected to a cylinder in other than stationary installations
    (d) Attached with pipe

(D) Regulators installed on vaporizer outlets shall be installed with one of the following methods:

(1) Attached using metallic pipe, tubing, fittings, or adapters that do not exceed 5 ft (1.5 m) in total length
(2) Attached with a single flexible metallic connector

(E) Regulators connected to underground or mounded containers shall be permitted to be attached to the vapor service valve with a flexible hose connector providing electrical isolation between the container and metallic piping system that complies with UL 569, *Standard for Pigtails and Flexible Hose Connectors for LP-Gas*, and is recommended by the manufacturer for underground service.

6.10.1.2 First-stage regulators installed downstream of high-pressure regulators shall be exempt from the requirement of 6.10.1.1.

6.10.1.3* First-stage and high-pressure regulators shall be installed outside of buildings, except as follows:

(1) Regulators on cylinders installed indoors in accordance with Section 6.22
(2) Regulators on containers of less than 125 gal (0.5 m^3) water capacity for the purpose of being filled or in structures complying with Chapter 10
(3) Regulators on containers on LP-Gas vehicles complying with, and parked or garaged in accordance with, Chapter 11
(4) Regulators on containers used with LP-Gas stationary or portable engine fuel systems complying with Chapter 11
(5) Regulators on containers used with LP-Gas–fueled industrial trucks complying with 11.11.4
(6) Regulators on containers on LP-Gas–fueled vehicles garaged in accordance with Section 11.14
(7) Regulators on cylinders awaiting use, resale, or exchange when stored in accordance with Chapter 8

6.10.1.4 All regulators for outdoor installations shall be designed, installed, or protected so their operation will not be affected by the elements (freezing rain, sleet, snow, ice, mud, or debris).

(A) This protection shall be permitted to be integral with the regulator.

(B) Regulators used for portable industrial applications shall be exempt from the requirements of 6.10.1.4.

6.10.1.5 The point of discharge from the required pressure relief device on regulated equipment installed outside of buildings or occupiable structures in fixed piping systems shall be located not less than 3 ft (1 m) horizontally away from any building or occupiable structure opening below the level of discharge, and not beneath or inside any building or occupiable structure unless this space is not enclosed for more than 50 percent of its perimeter.

6.10.1.6 The point of discharge shall also be located not less than 5 ft (1.5 m) in any direction from any source of ignition, openings into direct-vent (sealed combustion system) appliances, or mechanical ventilation air intakes.

6.10.1.7 The discharge from the required pressure relief device of a second-stage regulator, other than a line pressure regulator, installed inside of buildings in fixed piping systems shall comply with the following:

(1) The discharge shall be directly vented with supported piping to the outside air.
(2) The vent line shall be at least the same nominal pipe size as the regulator vent connection pipe size.
(3) Where there is more than one regulator at a location, either each regulator shall have a separate vent to the outside or the vent lines shall be manifolded in accordance with accepted engineering practices to minimize back pressure in the event of high vent discharge.
(4) The material of the vent line shall comply with 5.10.3.
(5) The discharge outlet shall be located not less than 3 ft (1 m) horizontally away from any building opening below the level of such discharge.
(6) The discharge outlet shall also be located not less than 5 ft (1.5 m) in any direction from any source of ignition, openings into direct-vent appliances, or mechanical ventilation air intakes.
(7) The discharge outlet shall be designed, installed, or protected from blockage so it will not be affected by the elements (freezing rain, sleet, snow, ice, mud, or debris) or insects.

Δ **6.10.1.8** The requirement in 6.10.1.7 shall not apply to appliance regulators otherwise protected, to line pressure regulators listed as complying with ANSI Z21.80/CSA 6.22, *Standard for Line Pressure Regulators*, or to regulators used in connection with containers in buildings as provided for in 6.2.2(1), 6.2.2(2), 6.2.2(4), 6.2.2(5), and 6.2.2(6).

6.10.1.9 The requirement in 6.10.1.7 shall not apply to vaporizers.

6.10.1.10 Single-stage regulators shall be permitted to be used only on portable appliances and outdoor cooking appliances with input ratings of 100,000 Btu/hr (29 kW) maximum.

6.10.1.11 Line pressure regulators shall be installed in accordance with the requirements of NFPA 54.

6.10.2 Selection of Pressure Regulators.

6.10.2.1 A two-stage regulator system, an integral two-stage regulator, or a 2 psi regulator system shall be required on all fixed piping systems that serve ½ psig (3.4 kPag) appliance systems [normally operated at 11 in. water column (2.7 kPag) pressure].

6.10.2.2 The requirement for two-stage regulation shall include fixed piping systems for appliances on recreational vehicles, mobile home installations, manufactured home installations, catering vehicles, and food service vehicle installations.

6.10.2.3 Single-stage regulators shall not be installed in fixed piping systems after June 30, 1997, except for installations covered in 6.10.2.4.

6.10.2.4 Single-stage regulators shall be permitted on small portable appliances and outdoor cooking appliances with input ratings of 100,000 Btu/hr (29 kW) or less.

6.10.2.5 Gas distribution systems utilizing multiple second-stage regulators shall be permitted to use a high-pressure regulator installed at the container, provided that a first-stage regulator is installed downstream of the high-pressure regulator and ahead of the second-stage regulators.

6.10.2.6 High-pressure regulators with an overpressure protection device and a rated capacity of more than 500,000 Btu/hr (147 kW) shall be permitted to be used in two-stage systems where the second-stage regulator incorporates an integral or separate overpressure protection device.

6.10.2.7 The overpressure protection device described in 6.10.2.6 shall limit the outlet pressure of the second-stage regulator to 2.0 psig (14 kPag) when the regulator seat disc is removed and with an inlet pressure equivalent to the maximum outlet pressure setting of the high-pressure regulator.

6.10.2.8 Systems consisting of listed components that provide an equivalent level of overpressure protection shall be exempt from the requirements of 6.10.2.6 and 6.10.2.7.

6.10.2.9 A 2 psi regulator system shall consist of a first-stage regulator and a 2 psi service regulator in compliance with the requirements of 5.10.1.14 in conjunction with a line pressure regulator that is in compliance with ANSI Z21.80/CSA 6.22, *Standard for Line Pressure Regulators.*

6.11 Piping Systems.

6.11.1 Piping System Service Limitations.

6.11.1.1 The physical state (vapor or liquid) and pressure at which LP-Gas is transmitted through piping systems shall be in accordance with 6.11.1.1(A) through 6.11.1.1(E).

(A) Outdoor LP-Gas liquid or vapor metallic piping systems shall have no pressure limitations.

(B) Outdoor underground LP-Gas liquid or vapor polyamide piping systems shall have pressure limitations as defined by the design pressure of the piping being installed.

(C) Polyethylene piping systems shall be limited to the following:

(1) Vapor service not exceeding 30 psig (208 kPag)
(2) Installation outdoors and underground

(D)* LP-Gas vapor at pressures exceeding 20 psig (138 kPag) or LP-Gas liquid shall not be piped into any building unless the installation is in accordance with one of the following:

(1) The buildings or structures are under construction or undergoing major renovation, and the temporary piping systems are in accordance with 6.22.2 and 6.22.12.
(2) The buildings or separate areas of the buildings are constructed in accordance with Chapter 10 and used exclusively to house the following:

(a) Equipment for vaporization, pressure reduction, gas mixing, gas manufacturing, or distribution

(b) Internal combustion engines, industrial processes, research and experimental laboratories, or equipment or processing having a similar hazard

(c) Engine-mounted fuel vaporizers

(3) Industrial occupancies are in accordance with 6.11.1.2.

(E)* Corrugated stainless steel piping systems shall be limited to vapor service not exceeding the listed pressure rating of the product.

6.11.1.2* LP-Gas vapor fixed piping systems at pressures of 20 psig through 50 psig (138 kPag through 345 kPag) in industrial occupancies shall be approved and shall comply with 6.11.1.2(A) through 6.11.1.2(D).

(A) The industrial equipment shall require inlet pressures greater than 20 psig (138 kPag).

(B) Pressure relief valve protection shall be provided for the vapor piping system that will limit any overpressure in the piping system to not more than 10 percent of the design pressure of the system.

(C) Pressure relief valve discharge shall be vented directly to the outdoors.

(D) A low-temperature control system shall positively shut off the flow of LP-Gas into the vapor piping system when the temperature of the LP-Gas vapor is reduced to its condensation point at the maximum design operating pressure of the system.

6.11.1.3 Liquid piping systems in buildings or structures feeding a vaporizer other than those covered by 6.11.1.1(D) shall comply with the material requirements of Chapters 5 and 6.

6.11.2 Sizing of LP-Gas Vapor Piping Systems.

6.11.2.1 LP-Gas vapor piping systems downstream of the first-stage pressure regulator shall be sized so that all appliances operate within their manufacturer's specifications.

6.11.2.2 LP-Gas vapor piping systems shall be sized and installed to provide a supply of gas to meet the maximum demand of all gas utilization equipment using Table 16.1(a) through Table 16.1(p), engineering methods, or sizing tables included in a piping system manufacturer's installation instructions.

6.11.3 Installation of Metallic Pipe, Tubing, and Fittings.

6.11.3.1* All metallic LP-Gas piping shall be installed in accordance with ASME B31.3, *Process Piping,* for normal fluid service, or in accordance with Section 6.11.

6.11.3.2 All welding and brazing of metallic piping shall be in accordance with ASME *Boiler and Pressure Vessel Code,* Section IX.

6.11.3.3 Metallic piping shall comply with 6.11.3.3(A) through 6.11.3.3(D).

(A) Piping used at pressures higher than container pressure, such as on the discharge side of liquid transfer pumps, shall be designed for a pressure rating of at least 350 psig (2.4 MPag).

(B) Vapor LP-Gas piping with operating pressures in excess of 125 psig (0.9 MPag) and liquid piping not covered by 6.11.3.3(A) shall be designed for a working pressure of at least 250 psig (1.7 MPag).

(C) Vapor LP-Gas piping subject to pressures of not more than 125 psig (0.9 MPag) shall be designed for a pressure rating of at least 125 psig (0.9 MPag).

N (D) Schedule 10 steel piping shall be installed above ground and used for vapor service only.

6.11.3.4 Pressure relief valve discharge piping shall be exempt from the requirement of 6.11.3.3(C).

6.11.3.5 Metallic pipe joints shall be permitted to be threaded, flanged, welded, press-connected, or brazed using pipe and fittings that comply with 5.11.3, 5.11.4, and 6.11.3.5(A) through 6.11.3.5(H).

(A) Metallic threaded, welded, press-connected, and brazed pipe joints shall be in accordance with Table 6.11.3.5(A).

(B) Fittings and flanges shall be designed for a pressure rating equal to or greater than the required working pressure of the service for which they are used.

(C) Brazed joints shall be made with a brazing material having a melting point exceeding 1000°F (538°C).

(D) Press-connected joints shall comply with ANSI/CSA 6.32 (LC4a), *Press-Connect Metallic Fittings for Use in Fuel Gas Distribution Systems.*

(E) Gaskets used to retain LP-Gas in flanged connections in piping shall be resistant to the action of LP-Gas.

(F) Gaskets shall be made of metal or material confined in metal having a melting point over 1500°F (816°C) or shall be protected against fire exposure.

(G) When a flange is opened, the gasket shall be replaced.

(H) Aluminum O-rings and spiral-wound metal gaskets shall be permitted to be used.

(I) Nonmetallic gaskets used in insulating fittings shall be permitted to be used.

6.11.3.6 Metallic tubing joints shall be flared or brazed using tubing and fittings in accordance with 5.11.3 and 5.11.4.

△ **Table 6.11.3.5(A) Types of Metallic Pipe Joints in LP-Gas Service**

Service	Schedule 10	Schedule 40	Schedule 80
Liquid	NP	Welded or brazed	Threaded, welded, or brazed
Vapor, ≤125 psig (≤0.9 MPag)	Welded, press-connected, or brazed	Threaded, welded, press-connected, or brazed	Threaded, welded, press-connected, or brazed
Vapor, ≥125 psig (≥0.9 MPag)	NP	Welded or brazed	Threaded, welded, or brazed

6.11.3.7 Piping in systems shall be run as directly as is practical from one point to another, with as few fittings as practical.

6.11.3.8 Where condensation of vapor can occur, piping shall be sloped back to the container or means shall be provided for revaporizing the condensate.

6.11.3.9 Piping systems, including the interconnection of permanently installed containers, shall compensate for expansion, contraction, jarring, vibration, and settling.

(A) Flexible metallic connectors shall be permitted to be used.

(B) The use of nonmetallic pipe, tubing, or hose for permanently interconnecting containers shall be prohibited.

6.11.3.10 Aboveground piping shall be supported to ensure integrity of the piping.

N 6.11.3.11 Aboveground piping shall be protected against physical damage by vehicles.

6.11.3.12 The portion of aboveground piping in contact with a support or a corrosion-causing substance shall be protected against corrosion.

6.11.3.13 Buried metallic pipe and tubing shall be installed underground with a minimum 12 in. (300 mm) of cover.

(A) The minimum cover shall be increased to 18 in. (460 mm) if external damage to the pipe or tubing from external forces is likely to result.

(B) If a minimum 12 in. (300 mm) of cover cannot be maintained, the piping shall be installed in conduit or shall be bridged (shielded).

6.11.3.14 Where underground piping is beneath driveways, roads, or streets, possible damage by vehicles shall be taken into account.

6.11.3.15 Metallic piping shall be protected against corrosion in accordance with 6.11.3.15(A) through 6.11.3.15(C).

(A) Piping and tubing of 1 in. (25 mm) nominal diameter or smaller shall be protected in accordance with 6.19.1 or 6.19.2.

(B) Piping and tubing larger than 1 in. (25 mm) nominal diameter and installed above ground shall be protected in accordance with 6.19.1.

(C) Steel piping installed underground shall have a cathodic protection system in accordance with 6.19.2(C) unless technical justification is approved by the authority having jurisdiction.

6.11.3.16 LP-Gas piping systems shall not be used as a grounding electrode.

6.11.3.17 Underground metallic piping, tubing, or both that convey LP-Gas from a gas storage container shall be provided with dielectric fittings installed above ground and outdoors at the building to electrically isolate it from the aboveground portion of the fixed piping system that enters a building.

6.11.4 Installation of Polyamide and Polyethylene Pipe, Tubing, and Fittings.

6.11.4.1 Polyethylene and polyamide pipe, tubing, and fittings shall be installed outdoors underground only.

6.11.4.2 Polyethylene and polyamide pipe and tubing shall be buried as follows:

(1) With a minimum of 12 in. (300 mm) of cover
(2) With a minimum of 18 in. (460 mm) of cover if external damage to the pipe or tubing is likely to result
(3) With piping installed in conduit or bridged (shielded) if a minimum of 12 in. (300 mm) of cover cannot be provided

6.11.4.3 Assembled anodeless risers shall be used to terminate underground polyamide and polyethylene fixed piping systems above ground.

(A) The horizontal portion of risers shall be buried at least 12 in. (300 mm) below grade, and the casing material used for the risers shall be protected against corrosion in accordance with Section 6.19.

(B) Either the aboveground portion of the riser casing shall be provided with a plastic sleeve inside the riser casing, or the pipe or tubing shall be centered in the riser casing.

(C) Factory-assembled risers shall be sealed and leak tested by the manufacturer.

6.11.4.4 Field-assembled risers shall be supplied only in kit form with all necessary hardware for installation.

(A) Field-assembled risers shall comply with the following:

(1) They shall be design certified.
(2) They shall be sealed and pressure tested by the installer.
(3) They shall be assembled and installed in accordance with the riser manufacturer's instructions.

(B) The casing of the riser shall be constructed of one of the following materials:

(1) ASTM A53/A53M, *Standard Specification for Pipe, Steel, Black and Hot-Dipped, Zinc-Coated, Welded and Seamless,* Schedule 40 steel pipe
(2) ASTM A513/A513M, *Standard Specification for Electric-Resistance-Welded Carbon and Alloy Steel Mechanical Tubing,* mechanical steel tubing with a minimum wall thickness of 0.073 in. (1.9 mm)
(3) Flexible metal tubing with a minimum crush strength of 1000 lb (453.6 kg) and a tensile strength of 300 lb (136 kg), including the transition connection as tested by the manufacturer

6.11.4.5* Polyamide and polyethylene piping shall be designed to sustain and minimize the thrust forces caused by contraction or expansion of the piping or by anticipated external or internal loading.

6.11.4.6 An electrically continuous corrosion-resistant tracer wire (minimum AWG 14) or tape shall be buried with the polyamide or polyethylene pipe to facilitate locating the pipe.

(A) One end of the tracer wire shall be brought above ground at a building wall or riser.

(B) The tracer wire or tape shall not be in direct contact with the polyamide or polyethylene pipe.

6.11.4.7 Polyamide and polyethylene piping that is installed in a vault, the dome of an underground container, or any other belowground enclosure shall be completely encased in one of the following:

(1) Gastight metal pipe and fittings that are protected from corrosion
(2) An anodeless riser

6.11.4.8 Polyamide and polyethylene piping shall be installed in accordance with the manufacturer's installation instructions.

6.11.4.9 Where polyamide or polyethylene pipe or tubing is inserted into an existing steel pipe, it shall comply with 6.11.4.9(A) and 6.11.4.9(B).

(A) The polyamide or polyethylene pipe or tubing shall be protected from being damaged during the insertion process.

(B) The leading end of the polyamide or polyethylene pipe or tubing being inserted shall also be closed prior to insertion.

6.11.4.10 Polyamide and polyethylene pipe that is not encased shall have a minimum wall thickness of 0.090 in. (2.3 mm).

6.11.4.11 Polyamide or polyethylene pipe with an outside diameter of 0.875 in. (22.2 mm) or less shall be permitted to have a minimum wall thickness of 0.062 in. (1.6 mm).

6.11.4.12 Each imperfection or damaged piece of polyamide or polyethylene pipe shall be replaced by fusion or mechanical fittings.

6.11.4.13 Repair clamps shall not be used to cover damaged or leaking sections.

6.11.5 Valves in Polyamide and Polyethylene Piping Systems.

6.11.5.1 Valves in polyamide and polyethylene piping shall comply with following:

(1) Valves shall protect the pipe from excessive torsional or shearing loads when the valve is operated.

(2) Valve boxes shall be installed so as to minimize transmitting external loads to the valve or pipe.

6.11.5.2 Valves shall be recommended for LP-Gas service by the manufacturer.

6.11.5.3 Valves shall be manufactured from thermoplastic materials fabricated from materials listed in ASTM D2513, *Standard Specification for Polyethylene (PE) Gas Pressure Pipe, Tubing, and Fittings*, or ASTM F2945, *Standard Specification for Polyamide 11 Gas Pressure Pipe, Tubing, and Fittings*, that have been shown to be resistant to the action of LP-Gas, or from metals protected to minimize corrosion in accordance with Section 6.19.

6.11.6 Flexible Connectors.

6.11.6.1 Flexible connectors shall be installed in accordance with the manufacturer's instructions.

6.11.6.2 Hose shall be prohibited between the first-stage and second-stage regulators except during temporary use.

6.11.6.3 Flexible metallic connectors shall not exceed 5 ft (1.5 m) in overall length when used with liquid or vapor piping on stationary containers of 2000 gal (7.6 m³) water capacity or less.

6.12 Remote Shutoff Actuation.

6.12.1 Where LP-Gas vapor is used as a pressure source for activating the remote shutoff mechanisms of internal valves and emergency shutoff valves, the following shall apply:

(1) Actuators and pressure supply line components shall be compatible with LP-Gas vapor.

(2) Supply line piping materials shall be limited to a maximum of ⅜ in. (9.0 mm) outside diameter.

(3)* Supply pressure shall be controlled to prevent condensation of the LP-Gas vapor.

(4) The LP-Gas supply maximum flow rate to the system shall not exceed that from a No. 54 drill orifice.

6.12.2 Where compressed air is used as a pressure source for activating internal valves and emergency shutoff valves, the air shall be clean and kept at a moisture level that will not prevent the system from operating.

6.13 Internal Valves.

6.13.1 The requirements of 6.13.2 through 6.13.5 shall be required for internal valves in liquid service that are installed in containers of over 4000 gal (15.2 m³) water capacity by July 1, 2003.

6.13.2 Internal valves shall be installed in accordance with 5.9.4.2 and Table 5.9.4.2 on containers of over 4000 gal (15.2 m³) water capacity.

6.13.3 Thermal Activation.

6.13.3.1 Automatic shutdown of internal valves in liquid service shall be provided using thermal (fire) actuation.

6.13.3.2 The thermal sensing element of the internal valve shall be within 5 ft (1.5 m) of the internal valve.

6.13.3.3 Temperature-sensitive elements installed in accordance with 6.13.3.2 shall not be painted or coated after manufacture.

6.13.4 Remote Shutdown Station.

6.13.4.1 At least one remote shutdown station for internal valves in liquid service shall be installed in accordance with the following:

(1) Not less than 25 ft (7.6 m) or more than 100 ft (30 m) from the liquid transfer point

(2) Not less than 25 ft (7.6 m) from the internal valves that are being controlled

(3) Along a path of egress from the liquid transfer point

6.13.4.2 This requirement shall be retroactive to all internal valves required by the code within 3 years of adoption of this edition.

6.13.5 Emergency remote shutdown stations shall be identified by a sign, visible from the point of transfer, incorporating the words "Propane — Container Liquid Valve Emergency Shutoff" in block letters of not less than 2 in. (51 mm) in height on a background of contrasting color to the letters.

6.14 Emergency Shutoff Valves.

6.14.1 On new installations and on existing installations, stationary container storage systems with an aggregate water capacity of more than 4000 gal (15.2 m³) utilizing a liquid transfer line that is 1½ in. (39 mm) or larger, and a pressure equalizing vapor line that is 1¼ in. (32 mm) or larger, shall be equipped with emergency shutoff valves.

6.14.2 An emergency shutoff valve shall be installed in the transfer lines of the fixed piping transfer system within 20 ft (6 m) of lineal pipe from the nearest end of the hose or swivel-type piping connections.

6.14.3 When the flow is only into the container, a backflow check valve shall be permitted to be used in lieu of an emergency shutoff valve if installed in the piping transfer system downstream of the hose or swivel-type piping connections.

6.14.4 The backflow check valve shall have a metal-to-metal seat or a primary resilient seat with metal backup, not hinged with combustible material, and shall be designed for this specific application.

6.14.5 Where there are two or more liquid or vapor lines with hoses or swivel-type piping connected of the sizes designated, an emergency shutoff valve or a backflow check valve, where allowed, shall be installed in each leg of the piping.

6.14.6 Emergency shutoff valves shall be installed so that the temperature-sensitive element in the valve, or a supplemental temperature-sensitive element that operates at a maximum temperature of 250°F (121°C) that is connected to actuate the valve, is not more than 5 ft (1.5 m) from the nearest end of the hose or swivel-type piping connected to the line in which the valve is installed.

6.14.7 Temperature-sensitive elements of emergency shutoff valves shall not be painted or coated after manufacture.

6.14.8* The emergency shutoff valves or backflow check valves shall be installed in the fixed piping so that any break resulting from a pull will occur on the hose or swivel-type piping side of the connection while retaining intact the valves and piping on the plant side of the connection.

6.14.9 Where emergency shutoff valves are required to be installed in accordance with 6.14.2, a means shall be incorporated to actuate the emergency shutoff valves in the event of a break of the fixed piping resulting from a pull on the hose.

6.14.10 Emergency shutoff valves required by the code shall be tested annually for the functions required by 5.14.2.3(2) and 5.14.2.3(3), and the results of the test shall be documented.

6.14.11 Backflow check valves installed in lieu of emergency shutoff valves shall be checked annually for proper operation, and the results of the test shall be documented.

6.14.12 All new and existing emergency shutoff valves shall comply with 6.14.12.1 through 6.14.12.3.

6.14.12.1 Each emergency shutoff valve shall have at least one clearly identified and easily accessible manually operated remote emergency shutoff device.

6.14.12.2 The shutoff device shall be located not less than 25 ft (7.6 m) or more than 100 ft (30 m) in the path of egress from the emergency shutoff valve.

△ **6.14.12.3** Where an emergency shutoff valve is used in lieu of an internal valve in compliance with 5.9.4.2(D)(2), the remote shutoff device shall be installed in accordance with 6.13.4 and 6.13.5.

6.14.13 Emergency shutoff valves for railroad tank car transfer systems shall be in accordance with 6.21.2.6, 6.30.4, 7.2.3.7, and 7.2.3.8.

6.15 Hydrostatic Relief Valve Installation. A hydrostatic relief valve or a device providing pressure-relieving protection shall be installed in each section of piping and hose in which liquid LP-Gas can be trapped between valves.

6.15.1 Shutoff valves that could isolate the hydrostatic relief valves or devices from the piping or hose shall not be installed.

6.15.2 It shall be permitted to install a three-way isolation valve rated for at least 500 psi working pressure connected to two hydrostatic relief valves.

6.16 Testing New or Modified Piping Systems.

6.16.1 Piping Systems.

6.16.1.1 After installation or modification, piping systems (including hose) shall be proven free of leaks at not less than the normal operating pressure.

6.16.1.2 LP-Gas shall be permitted to be used as the test medium.

6.16.2 Branches.

6.16.2.1 Where new branches are installed, only the newly installed branch(es) shall be required to be tested at not less than the normal operating pressure.

6.16.2.2 Connections between the new piping and the existing piping shall be tested with a noncorrosive leak-detecting fluid or approved leak-detecting methods.

6.16.3 Piping within the scope of NFPA 54 shall be pressure tested in accordance with that code.

6.16.4 Tests shall not be made with a flame.

6.17 Leak Check for Vapor Systems.

6.17.1* All vapor piping systems operating at 20 psig (138 kPag) or less in stationary installations shall be checked for leakage in accordance with 6.17.2 through 6.17.5.

6.17.2* Immediately after the gas is turned on into a new system or into a system that has been initially restored after an interruption of service, the piping system shall be checked for leakage.

6.17.3 Piping within the scope of NFPA 54 shall be checked for leakage in accordance with that code.

6.17.4* Gas systems within the scope of 49 CFR 192 or those outside the scope of NFPA 54 shall be exempt from the requirements of this section.

6.17.5 Where leakage is indicated, the gas supply shall be shut off until the necessary repairs have been made.

6.18 Installation in Areas of Heavy Snowfall.

6.18.1* In areas where the ground snow load is equal to or exceeds 100 psf (488 kgf/m²), piping, regulators, meters, and other equipment installed in the piping system shall be protected from the forces of accumulated snow.

6.19* Corrosion Protection.

6.19.1 All materials and equipment installed above ground shall be of corrosion-resistant material or shall be coated or protected to minimize exterior corrosion.

6.19.2 Except for underground and mounded containers (*see 6.8.6*), all materials and equipment that are buried or mounded shall comply with one of the requirements in 6.19.2(A) through 6.19.2(C).

(A) Materials and equipment shall be made of corrosion-resistant material that are suitable for the environment in which they will be installed.

(B) Materials and equipment shall be manufactured with a corrosion-resistant coating or have a coating applied prior to being placed into service.

(C) Materials and equipment shall have a cathodic protection system installed and maintained in accordance with 6.19.3.

6.19.3 Where installed, cathodic protection systems shall comply with 6.19.3.1 through 6.19.3.3.

6.19.3.1* Cathodic protection systems installed in accordance with this code shall be monitored by testing, the results shall be documented, and confirming tests shall be described by one of the following:

(1) Producing a voltage of −0.85 volt or more negative, with reference to a saturated copper–copper sulfate half cell

(2) Producing a voltage of −0.78 volt or more negative, with reference to a saturated KCl calomel half cell

(3) Producing a voltage of −0.80 volt or more negative, with reference to a silver–silver chloride half cell

(4) Any other method described in Appendix D of 49 CFR 192

Δ **6.19.3.2*** Sacrificial anodes shall be tested in accordance with the following schedule.

(1) Upon installation of the cathodic protection system, unless prohibited by climatic conditions, in which case testing shall be done within 180 days after the installation of the system.

(2) For continued verification of the effectiveness of the system, 12 to 18 months after the initial test.

(3) Upon successful verification testing and in consideration of previous test results, periodic follow-up testing shall be performed at intervals not to exceed 36 months.

(4) Systems failing a test shall be repaired as soon as practical unless climatic conditions prohibit this action, in which case the repair shall be made not more than 180 days thereafter. The testing schedule shall be restarted as required in 6.19.3.2(1) and 6.19.3.2(2), and the results shall comply with 6.19.3.2.

(5) Documentation of the results of the two most recent tests shall be retained.

6.19.3.3* Where an impressed current cathodic protection system is installed, it shall be inspected and tested in accordance with the schedule described in 6.19.3.3(A) and 6.19.3.3(B).

(A) All sources of impressed current shall be inspected and tested at intervals not exceeding 2 months.

(B) All impressed current cathodic protection installations shall be inspected and tested annually.

6.19.4 Corrosion protection of all other materials shall be in accordance with accepted engineering practice.

6.20 Equipment Installation.

6.20.1 Reserved.

6.20.2 Pump Installation.

6.20.2.1 Pumps shall be installed in accordance with the pump manufacturers' installation instructions.

6.20.2.2 Installation shall be made so that the pump casing is not subjected to excessive strains transmitted to it by the suction and discharge piping, which shall be accomplished as follows:

(1) By piping design
(2) By the use of flexible metallic connectors that do not exceed 36 in. (1 m) in overall length
(3) By other means

6.20.2.3 Positive displacement pumps shall incorporate a bypass valve or recirculating device to limit the normal operating discharge pressure.

(A) The bypass valve or recirculating device to limit the normal operating discharge pressure shall discharge either into a storage container or into the pump inlet.

(B) If the bypass valve or recirculating device is equipped with a shutoff valve, a secondary device shall be required and designed to do one of the following:

(1) Operate at not more than 400 psig (2.8 MPag)
(2) Operate at a pressure of 50 psig (345 kPag) above the operating pressure where the design pressure exceeds 350 psig (2.4 MPag)

(C) Engines used to drive portable pumps shall be equipped with exhaust system spark arresters and shielded ignition systems.

(D) The secondary device shall be incorporated, if not integral with the pump, in the pump piping and shall be designed or installed so that it cannot be rendered inoperative and shall discharge either into a storage container or into the pump inlet.

(E) A pump operating control or disconnect switch shall be located near the pump, and remote control points shall be provided for other plant operations such as container filling, loading or unloading of cargo tank vehicles and railroad tank cars, or operation of the dispenser.

6.20.3 Compressor Installation.

6.20.3.1 Compressors shall be installed in accordance with the compressor manufacturers' installation instructions.

6.20.3.2 Installation shall be made so that the compressor housing is not subjected to excessive stresses transmitted to it by the suction and discharge piping. Where used to provide flexibility in the piping system, flexible metallic connectors or metallic-protected flexible hose connectors shall not exceed 36 in. (1 m) in overall total length.

6.20.3.3 Engines used to drive portable compressors shall be equipped with exhaust system spark arresters and shielded ignition systems.

6.20.3.4 Where the compressor is not equipped with an integral means to prevent the LP-Gas liquid from entering the suction, a liquid trap shall be installed in the suction piping as close to the compressor as practical.

6.20.3.5 Portable compressors used with temporary connections shall be excluded from the requirement in 6.20.3.4 unless used to unload railroad tank cars.

6.20.4 Installation of Strainers. Strainers shall be installed so that the strainer element can be removed without removing equipment or piping.

6.20.5 Installation of Meters.

6.20.5.1 Liquid or vapor meters shall be installed in accordance with the manufacturers' installation instructions.

6.20.5.2 Liquid meters shall be installed so that the meter housing is not subject to excessive strains from the connecting piping.

6.20.5.3 If not provided in the piping design, the use of flexible connectors not exceeding 36 in. (1 m) shall be permitted.

6.20.5.4 Vapor meters shall be installed so as to minimize the possibility of physical damage.

6.21 Bulk Plant and Industrial Plant LP-Gas Systems.

6.21.1 Operations and Maintenance. The provisions of Chapter 15 shall apply to new and existing bulk plants and industrial plants.

6.21.2 Installation of Liquid Transfer Facilities.

6.21.2.1 Points of transfer or the nearest part of a structure housing transfer operations shall be located in accordance with 6.7.2.1 and 6.7.2.2.

6.21.2.2 Buildings used exclusively for housing pumps or vapor compressors shall be located in accordance with 6.7.2.2, considering the building as one that houses a point of transfer.

6.21.2.3 Liquid transfer facilities at rail sidings shall comply with 6.21.2.3(A) through 6.21.2.3(C).

(A) The track of the railroad siding or the roadway surface at the transfer points shall be relatively level.

(B) Clearances from buildings, structures, or stationary containers shall be provided for the siding or roadway approaches to the unloading or loading points to prevent the railroad tank car or cargo tank vehicle from contacting buildings, structures, or stationary containers.

(C) Barriers shall be provided at the ends of railroad sidings.

6.21.2.4 Pumps and compressors shall comply with 6.21.2.4(A) through 6.21.2.4(C).

(A) Compressors used for liquid transfer normally shall withdraw vapor from the vapor space of the container being filled and discharge into the vapor space of the container from which the withdrawal is being made.

(B) An operating control or disconnect switch shall be located nearby.

(C) Remote shutoff controls shall be provided as necessary in other liquid transfer systems.

6.21.2.5* Bulk plant and industrial plant liquid inlet piping shall be designed to prevent debris from impeding the action of valves and other components of the piping system. This requirement shall be effective for existing installations on July 1, 2011.

6.21.2.6 Where a hose or swivel-type piping is used for liquid transfer, it shall be protected as follows:

(1) An emergency shutoff valve shall be installed at the railroad tank car end of the hose or swivel-type piping where flow into or out of the railroad tank car is possible.
(2) An emergency shutoff valve or a backflow check valve shall be installed on the railroad tank car end of the hose or swivel-type piping where flow is only into the railroad tank car.
(3)* Where a facility hose is used at a LP-Gas bulk plant or industrial plant to transfer LP-Gas liquid from a cargo tank vehicle in non-metered service to a bulk plant or industrial plant, the facility hose or the facility shall be equipped with an emergency discharge control system that provides a means to shut down the flow of LP-Gas caused by the complete separation of the facility hose within 20 seconds and without the need for human intervention.

6.21.2.7 Transfer hose larger than ½ in. (12 mm) internal diameter shall not be used for making connections to individual containers being filled indoors.

6.21.2.8 If gas is to be discharged from containers inside a building, the provisions of 7.3.3.1 shall apply.

6.21.3 Installation of Electrical Equipment. Installation of electrical equipment shall comply with 6.25.2.

6.21.4 Security and Protection Against Tampering for Section 6.21 and Section 6.27 Systems.

6.21.4.1 The following security measures shall be provided to minimize the possibility of entry by unauthorized persons:

(1) Security awareness training
(2) Limitation of unauthorized access to plant areas that include container appurtenances, pumping equipment, loading and unloading facilities, and container filling facilities

△ **6.21.4.2** Areas that include features required in 6.21.4.1(2) shall be enclosed with a minimum 6 ft (1.8 m) high industrial-type fence, chain-link fence, or equivalent protection.

(A) The enclosure shall have at least two means of emergency egress, unless all the following conditions are met:

(1) The fenced or otherwise enclosed area is not over 100 ft² (9 m²).
(2) The point of transfer is within 3 ft (1 m) of the gate.
(3) Containers are not filled within the enclosure.

(B) The two means of emergency egress, where required, shall be at least 25 ft (7.6 m) apart or as remotely located as is practical.

N (C) Designated means of egress shall be unlocked when the enclosure is occupied or shall be opened without the need for tools, keys, or combination codes.

(D) Clearance of at least 3 ft (1 m) shall be provided to allow emergency access to the required means of egress.

(E) Fencing shall not be required where devices are provided that can be locked in place and prevent unauthorized operation of valves, equipment, and appurtenances.

6.21.4.3 Where guard service is provided, it shall be extended to the LP-Gas installation, and the requirements of Section 4.4 shall apply to guard personnel.

6.21.5 Lighting. If operations are normally conducted during other than daylight hours, lighting shall be provided to illuminate storage containers, containers being loaded, control valves, and other equipment.

6.21.6 Ignition Source Control. Ignition source control shall comply with Section 6.25.

6.22 LP-Gas Systems in Buildings or on Building Roofs or Exterior Balconies.

6.22.1 Application.

6.22.1.1 Section 6.22 shall apply to the installation of the following LP-Gas systems in buildings or structures:

(1) Cylinders inside of buildings or on the roofs or exterior balconies of buildings
(2) Systems in which the liquid is piped from outside containers into buildings or onto the roof

6.22.1.2 The phrase *cylinders in use* shall mean connected for use.

(A) The use of cylinders indoors shall be only for the purposes specified in 6.22.4 through 6.22.10.

(B) The use of cylinders indoors shall be limited to those conditions where operational requirements make the indoor use of cylinders necessary and location outside is impractical.

(C) The use of cylinders on roofs shall be limited to those conditions where operational requirements make the use of cylinders necessary and location other than on roofs of buildings or structures is impractical.

(D) Liquid LP-Gas shall be piped into buildings or structures only for the purposes specified in 6.11.1.1(D).

6.22.1.3 Storage of cylinders awaiting use shall be in accordance with Chapter 8.

6.22.1.4 Transportation of cylinders within a building shall be in accordance with 6.22.3.6.

6.22.1.5 The following provisions shall be required in addition to those specified in Sections 6.2 and 6.4:

(1) Liquid transfer systems shall be in accordance with Chapter 7.
(2) Engine fuel systems used inside buildings shall be in accordance with Chapter 11.
(3) LP-Gas transport or cargo tank vehicles stored, serviced, or repaired in buildings shall be in accordance with Chapter 9.

6.22.2 Additional Equipment Requirements for Cylinders, Equipment, Piping, and Appliances Used in Buildings, Building Roofs, and Exterior Balconies.

6.22.2.1 Cylinders shall be in accordance with the following:

(1) Cylinders shall not exceed 245 lb (111 kg) water capacity [nominal 100 lb (45 kg) propane capacity] each.
(2) Cylinders shall comply with other applicable provisions of Section 5.2, and they shall be equipped as provided in Section 5.9.
(3) Cylinders shall be marked in accordance with 5.2.8.1 and 5.2.8.2.
(4) Cylinders with propane capacities greater than 2 lb (0.9 kg) shall be equipped as provided in Table 5.9.4.1(B), and an excess-flow valve shall be provided for vapor service when used indoors.
(5) Cylinder valves shall be protected in accordance with 5.2.6.1.

(6) Cylinders having water capacities greater than 2.7 lb (1.2 kg) and connected for use shall stand on a firm and substantially level surface.
(7) Cylinders shall be secured in an upright position if necessary.
(8) Cylinders and the valve-protecting devices used with them shall be oriented to minimize the possibility of impingement of the pressure relief device discharge on the cylinder and adjacent cylinders.

6.22.2.2 Manifolds and fittings connecting cylinders to pressure regulator inlets shall be designed for at least 250 psig (1.7 MPag) service pressure.

6.22.2.3 Piping shall comply with Section 5.11 and shall have a pressure rating of 250 psig (1.7 MPag).

6.22.2.4 Liquid piping and vapor piping at pressures above 125 psig (0.9 MPag) shall be installed in accordance with 6.11.3.

6.22.2.5 Hose, hose connections, and flexible connectors shall comply with the following:

(1) Hose used at pressures above 5 psig (34 kPag) shall be designed for a pressure of at least 350 psig (2.4 MPag).
(2) Hose used at a pressure of 5 psig (34 kPag) or less and used in agricultural buildings not normally occupied by the public shall be designed for the operating pressure of the hose.
(3) Hose shall comply with 5.11.6.
(4) Hose shall be installed in accordance with 6.23.4.
(5) Hose shall be as short as practical, without kinking or straining the hose or causing it to be close enough to a burner to be damaged by heat.
(6) Hoses greater than 10 ft (3 m) in length shall be protected from damage.

6.22.2.6* Portable heaters, including salamanders, shall comply with the following:

(1) Portable heaters shall be equipped with an approved automatic device to shut off the flow of gas to the main burner and to the pilot, if used, in the event of flame extinguishment or combustion failure.
(2) Portable heaters shall be self-supporting unless designed for cylinder mounting.
(3) Portable heaters shall not be installed utilizing cylinder valves, connectors, regulators, manifolds, piping, or tubing as structural supports.
(4) Portable heaters having an input of more than 50,000 Btu/hr (53 MJ/hr) shall be equipped with either a pilot that must be lighted and proved before the main burner can be turned on or an approved electric ignition system.

6.22.2.7 The provisions of 6.22.2.6 shall not be applicable to the following:

(1) Tar kettle burners, hand torches, or melting pots
(2) Portable heaters with less than 7500 Btu/hr (8 MJ/hr) input if used with cylinders having a maximum water capacity of 2.7 lb (1.2 kg) and filled with not more than 16.8 oz (0.522 kg) of LP-Gas

6.22.3 Installation Requirements for Cylinders, Equipment, Piping, and Appliances in Buildings, Building Roofs, and Exterior Balconies.

6.22.3.1 Cylinders having water capacities greater than 2.7 lb (1.2 kg) and connected for use shall stand on a firm and substantially level surface, and, if necessary, they shall be secured in an upright position.

6.22.3.2 Cylinders, regulating equipment, manifolds, pipe, tubing, and hose shall be located to minimize exposure to the following:

(1) Abnormally high temperatures (such as might result from exposure to convection and radiation from heating appliances or installation in confined spaces)
(2) Physical damage
(3) Tampering by unauthorized persons

6.22.3.3 Heat-producing appliances shall be installed with clearance to combustibles in accordance with the manufacturer's installation instructions.

6.22.3.4 Heat-producing appliances shall be located and used to minimize the possibility of the ignition of combustibles.

6.22.3.5 Where located on a floor, roof, or balcony, cylinders shall be secured to prevent falling over the edge.

6.22.3.6 Transportation (movement) of cylinders having water capacities greater than 2.7 lb (1.2 kg) within a building shall be restricted to movement directly associated with the uses covered by Section 6.22.

(A) Valve outlets on cylinders having water capacities greater than 2.7 lb (1.2 kg) shall be tightly plugged, capped, or sealed with a listed quick-closing coupling or a listed quick-connect coupling.

(B) Only emergency stairways not normally used by the public shall be used, and precautions shall be taken to prevent the cylinder from falling down the stairs.

(C) Freight or passenger elevators shall be permitted to be used when occupied only by those engaged in moving the cylinder.

6.22.4 Buildings Under Construction or Undergoing Major Renovation.

6.22.4.1 Where cylinders are used and transported in buildings or structures under construction or undergoing major renovation and such buildings are not occupied by the public, the requirements of 6.22.4.2 through 6.22.4.10 shall apply.

6.22.4.2 The use and transportation of cylinders in the unoccupied portions of buildings or structures under construction or undergoing major renovation that are partially occupied by the public shall be approved by the authority having jurisdiction.

6.22.4.3 Cylinders, equipment, piping, and appliances shall comply with 6.22.2.

6.22.4.4 Heaters used for temporary heating shall be located at least 6 ft (1.8 m) from any cylinder. *(See 6.22.4.5 for an exception to this requirement.)*

6.22.4.5 Integral heater-cylinder units specifically designed for the attachment of the heater to the cylinder, or to a supporting standard attached to the cylinder, and designed and installed

to prevent direct or radiant heat application to the cylinder shall be exempt from the spacing requirement of 6.22.4.4.

6.22.4.6 Blower-type and radiant-type units shall not be directed toward any cylinder within 20 ft (6.1 m).

6.22.4.7 If two or more heater-cylinder units of either the integral or nonintegral type are located in an unpartitioned area on the same floor, the cylinder(s) of each such unit shall be separated from the cylinder(s) of any other such unit by at least 20 ft (6.1 m).

6.22.4.8 If heaters are connected to cylinders manifolded together for use in an unpartitioned area on the same floor, the total water capacity of cylinders manifolded together serving any one heater shall not be greater than 735 lb (333 kg) [nominal 300 lb (136 kg) propane capacity]. If there is more than one such manifold, it shall be separated from any other by at least 20 ft (6.1 m).

6.22.4.9 Where cylinders are manifolded together for connection to a heater(s) on another floor, the following shall apply:

(1) Heaters shall not be installed on the same floors with manifolded cylinders.
(2) The total water capacity of the cylinders connected to any one manifold shall not be greater than 2450 lb (1111 kg) [nominal 1000 lb (454 kg) propane capacity].
(3) Manifolds of more than 735 lb (333 kg) water capacity [nominal 300 lb (136 kg) propane capacity], if located in the same unpartitioned area, shall be separated from each other by at least 50 ft (15 m).

6.22.4.10 Where compliance with the provisions of 6.22.4.6 through 6.22.4.9 is impractical, alternate installation provisions shall be allowed with the approval of the authority having jurisdiction.

6.22.5 Buildings Undergoing Minor Renovation When Frequented by the Public.

6.22.5.1 Cylinders used and transported for repair or minor renovation in buildings frequented by the public during the hours the public normally occupies the building shall comply with the following:

(1) The maximum water capacity of individual cylinders shall be 50 lb (23 kg) [nominal 20 lb (9.1 kg) propane capacity], and the number of cylinders in the building shall not exceed the number of workers assigned to the use of the propane.
(2) Cylinders having a water capacity greater than 2.7 lb (1.2 kg) shall not be left unattended.

6.22.5.2 During the hours the building is not open to the public, cylinders used and transported within the building for repair or minor renovation and with a water capacity greater than 2.7 lb (1.2 kg) shall not be left unattended.

6.22.6 Buildings Housing Industrial Occupancies.

6.22.6.1 Cylinders used in buildings housing industrial occupancies for processing, research, or experimental purposes shall comply with 6.22.6.1(A) and 6.22.6.1(B).

(A) If cylinders are manifolded together, the total water capacity of the connected cylinders shall be not more than 735 lb (333 kg) [nominal 300 lb (136 kg) propane capacity]. If there is more than one such manifold in a room, it shall be separated from any other by at least 20 ft (6.1 m).

(B) The amount of LP-Gas in cylinders for research and experimental use in the building shall be limited to the smallest practical quantity.

6.22.6.2 The use of cylinders to supply fuel for temporary heating in buildings housing industrial occupancies with essentially noncombustible contents shall comply with the requirements in 6.22.4 for cylinders in buildings under construction.

6.22.6.3 The use of cylinders to supply fuel for temporary heating shall be permitted only where a portable appliance for space heating is essential and a permanent heating installation is not practical.

6.22.7 Buildings Housing Educational and Institutional Occupancies.

6.22.7.1 The use of cylinders in classrooms shall be prohibited unless they are used temporarily for classroom demonstrations in accordance with 6.22.9.1.

6.22.7.2 Where cylinders are used in buildings housing educational and institutional laboratory occupancies for research and experimental purposes, the following shall apply:

(1) The maximum water capacity of individual cylinders used shall be 50 lb (23 kg) [nominal 20 lb (9.1 kg) propane capacity] if used in educational occupancies and 12 lb (5.4 kg) [nominal 5 lb (2 kg) propane capacity] if used in institutional occupancies.
(2) If more than one such cylinder is located in the same room, the cylinders shall be separated by at least 20 ft (6.1 m).
(3) Cylinders not connected for use shall be stored in accordance with Chapter 8.
(4) Cylinders shall not be stored in a laboratory room.

6.22.8 Temporary Heating and Food Service Appliances in Buildings in Emergencies.

6.22.8.1 Cylinders shall not be used in buildings for temporary emergency heating purposes except when all of the following conditions are met:

(1) The permanent heating system is temporarily out of service.
(2) Heat is necessary to prevent damage to the buildings or contents.
(3) The cylinders and heaters comply with, and are used and transported in accordance with, 6.22.2 through 6.22.4.
(4) The temporary heating appliance is not left unattended.
(5) Air for combustion and ventilation is provided in accordance with NFPA 54.

6.22.8.2 When a public emergency has been declared and gas, fuel, or electrical service has been interrupted, portable listed LP-Gas commercial food service appliances meeting the requirements of 6.22.9.4 shall be permitted to be temporarily used inside affected buildings.

6.22.8.3 The portable appliances used shall be discontinued and removed from the building at the time the permanently installed appliances are placed back in operation.

6.22.9 Use in Buildings for Demonstrations or Training, and Use of Small Cylinders for Self-Contained Torch Assemblies and Food Service Appliances.

6.22.9.1 Cylinders used temporarily inside buildings for public exhibitions or demonstrations, including use in classroom demonstrations, shall be in accordance with the following:

(1) The maximum water capacity of a cylinder shall be 12 lb (5.4 kg) [nominal 5 lb (2 kg) propane capacity].
(2) If more than one such cylinder is located in a room, the cylinders shall be separated by at least 20 ft (6.1 m).

6.22.9.2 Cylinders used temporarily in buildings for training purposes related to the installation and use of LP-Gas systems shall be in accordance with the following:

(1) The maximum water capacity of individual cylinders shall be 245 lb (111 kg) [nominal 100 lb (45 kg) propane capacity], but not more than 20 lb (9.1 kg) of propane shall be placed in a single cylinder.
(2) If more than one such cylinder is located in the same room, the cylinders shall be separated by at least 20 ft (6.1 m).
(3) The training location shall be acceptable to the authority having jurisdiction.
(4) Cylinders shall be promptly removed from the building when the training class has terminated.

6.22.9.3* Cylinders used in buildings as part of approved self-contained torch assemblies or similar appliances shall be in accordance with the following:

(1) Cylinders used in buildings shall comply with UL 147A, *Standard for Nonrefillable (Disposable) Type Fuel Gas Cylinder Assemblies.*
(2) Cylinders shall have a maximum water capacity of 2.7 lb (1.2 kg).

6.22.9.4 Cylinders used with commercial food service appliances shall be used inside restaurants and in attended commercial food catering operations in accordance with the following:

(1) Cylinders and appliances shall be listed.
(2) Commercial food service appliances shall not have more than two 10 oz (296 ml) nonrefillable butane gas cylinders, each having a maximum capacity of 1.08 lb (0.490 kg).
(3) Cylinders shall comply with UL 147B, *Standard for Nonrefillable (Disposable) Type Metal Container Assemblies for Butane.*
(4) Cylinders shall be connected directly to the appliance and shall not be manifolded.
(5) Cylinders shall be an integral part of the listed, approved, commercial food service device and shall be connected without the use of a rubber hose.
(6) Storage of cylinders shall be in accordance with 8.3.1.

6.22.10 Use in Building for Flame Effects Before a Proximate Audience.

6.22.10.1 Where cylinders are used temporarily in buildings for flame effects before an audience, the flame effect shall be in accordance with NFPA 160.

6.22.10.2 The maximum water capacity of individual cylinders shall be 48 lb (22 kg) [nominal 20 lb (9.1 kg) propane capacity].

6.22.10.3* If more than one cylinder is located in the same room, the cylinders shall be separated by at least 20 ft (6.1 m).

6.22.10.4 Where a separation of 20 ft (6.1 m) is not practical, reduction of distances shall be permitted with the approval of the authority having jurisdiction.

6.22.10.5 Cylinders shall not be connected or disconnected during the flame effect or performance.

6.22.11 Cylinders on Roofs or Exterior Balconies.

6.22.11.1 Where cylinders are installed permanently on roofs of buildings, the buildings shall be of fire-resistant construction or noncombustible construction having essentially noncombustible contents, or of other construction or contents that are protected with automatic sprinklers.

(A) The total water capacity of cylinders connected to any one manifold shall be not greater than 980 lb (445 kg) [nominal 400 lb (181 kg) propane capacity]. If more than one manifold is located on the roof, it shall be separated from any other by at least 50 ft (15 m).

(B) Cylinders shall be located in areas where there is free air circulation, at least 10 ft (3 m) from building openings (such as windows and doors), and at least 20 ft (6.1 m) from air intakes of air-conditioning and ventilating systems.

(C) Cylinders shall not be located on roofs that are entirely enclosed by parapets more than 18 in. (460 mm) high unless the parapets are breached with low-level ventilation openings not more than 20 ft (6.1 m) apart, or unless all openings communicating with the interior of the building are at or above the top of the parapets.

(D) Piping shall be in accordance with 6.22.2.3 through 6.22.2.5.

(E) Hose shall not be used for connection to cylinders.

(F) The fire department shall be advised of each installation.

6.22.11.2 Cylinders having water capacities greater than 2.7 lb (1 kg) [nominal 1 lb (0.5 kg) LP-Gas capacity] shall not be located on decks or balconies of dwellings of two or more living units above the first floor unless they are served by exterior stairways.

6.22.12 Liquid LP-Gas Piped into Buildings or Structures.

△ **6.22.12.1** Buildings or separate areas of buildings into which LP-Gas liquid at pressures exceeding 20 psig (138 kPag) is piped shall be constructed in accordance with Chapter 10 and shall be used for the purposes listed in 6.11.1.1(D)(2).

△ **6.22.12.2** Liquid LP-Gas piped into buildings under construction or major renovation in accordance with 6.11.1.1(D)(1) shall comply with 6.22.12.2(A) through 6.22.12.2(J).

(A) Liquid piping shall not exceed ¾ in. (20 mm) and shall comply with 6.11.1 and 6.11.3.

(B) Copper tubing with a maximum outside diameter of ¾ in. (20 mm) shall be used where approved by the authority having jurisdiction.

(C) Liquid piping in buildings shall be kept to a minimum length and shall be protected against construction hazards by fastening it to walls or other surfaces to provide protection against breakage and by locating it so as to avoid exposure to high ambient temperatures.

(D) A readily accessible shutoff valve shall be located at each intermediate branch line where it leaves the main line.

(E) A second shutoff valve shall be located at the appliance end of the branch and upstream of any flexible appliance connector.

(F) Excess-flow valves shall be installed downstream of each branch line shutoff valve.

(G) Excess-flow valves shall be located at any point in the piping system where branch lines are used and the pipe size of the branch line is reduced. The excess flow valve shall be sized for the reduced size of the branch line piping.

(H) Hose shall not be used to carry liquid between the container and building and shall not be used at any point in the liquid line.

(I) Hydrostatic relief valves shall be installed where required.

(J) The release of fuel when any section of piping or appliances is disconnected shall be minimized either by using an approved automatic quick-closing coupling that shuts off the gas on both sides when uncoupled or by closing the shutoff valve closest to the point to be disconnected and allowing the appliances on that line to operate until the fuel in the line is consumed.

6.23 Installation of Appliances.

6.23.1 Application.

6.23.1.1 Section 6.23 shall apply to the installation of LP-Gas appliances.

6.23.1.2 Installation of appliances on commercial vehicles shall be in accordance with 6.26.7.

6.23.2 Installation of Patio Heaters.

6.23.2.1 Patio heaters utilizing an integral LP-Gas container greater than 1.08 lb (0.49 kg) propane capacity shall comply with 6.23.2.2 and 6.23.2.3.

6.23.2.2 Patio heaters shall be listed and used in accordance with their listing and the manufacturer's instructions.

6.23.2.3 Patio heaters shall not be located within 5 ft (1.5 m) of exits from an assembly occupancy.

6.23.3 Cabinet Heaters.

△ **6.23.3.1** Cabinet heaters shall meet the following requirements:

(1) Cabinet heaters shall have a maximum propane input rating of 15,000 Btu/hr and shall be listed in accordance with ANSI Z21.11.3, *Gas-Fired Room Heaters, Volume III, Propane-Fired Portable Emergency Use Heater Systems.*

(2) Cabinet heaters shall be supplied with propane from only listed composite cylinders and shall utilize a cylinder valve that complies with UL 1769, *Standard for Cylinder Valves*, and that incorporates an overfilling prevention device complying with UL 2227, *Standard for Overfilling Prevention Devices.*

(3) Composite cylinders that are used with cabinet heaters shall have a maximum weight capacity of 19 lb (8.7 kg) of propane [nominal 43 lb (19 kg) water capacity].

(4) The composite cylinder shall be located in a separate compartment from the heating element.

(5) Cabinet heaters shall utilize a listed integral two-stage regulator that complies with UL 144, *Standard for LP-Gas Regulators*, and that operates with a maximum outlet pressure setting that does not exceed a nominal gauge pressure of 2 psig (14 kPag).

(6) Cabinet heater integral two-stage regulators shall not be equipped with a pressure relief valve in either stage.

(7) Cabinet heater integral two-stage regulators shall utilize separate vent limiting features on each stage that comply with ANSI Z21.18/CSA 6.3, *Standard for Gas Appliance Pressure Regulators*.

(8) Cabinet heaters shall utilize a CGA 793 appliance side connection that complies with CGA V-1, *Standard for Compressed Gas Cylinder Valve Outlet and Inlet Connections*, and that is listed to the UL 2061, *Standard for Adapters and Cylinder Connection Devices for Portable LP-Gas Cylinder Assemblies*, or ANSI Z21.81/CSA 6.25, *Standard for Cylinder Connection Devices*.

6.23.3.2 Modification of the cabinet heater CGA 793 connection or the use of an adapter that allows an alternate fuel source or allows the use of steel or aluminum cylinders to supply the cabinet heater shall be prohibited.

6.23.4 Hose for Portable Appliances.

6.23.4.1 The requirements of Section 6.23 shall apply to hoses used on the low-pressure side of regulators to connect portable appliances.

6.23.4.2 Where used inside buildings, the following shall apply:

(1) The hose shall be the minimum practical length and shall be in accordance with 6.22.2.5.
(2) The hose shall not extend from one room to another or pass through any partitions, walls, ceilings, or floors except as provided by 6.22.4.9.
(3) The hose shall not be concealed from view or used in concealed locations.

6.23.4.3 Where installed outside of buildings, the hose length shall be permitted to exceed 10 ft (3 m) but shall be as short as practical.

6.23.4.4 Hose shall be securely connected to the appliance.

6.23.4.5 The use of rubber slip ends shall not be permitted.

6.23.4.6 A shutoff valve shall be provided in the piping immediately upstream of the inlet connection of the hose.

6.23.4.7 Where more than one such appliance shutoff is located near another, the valves shall be marked to indicate which appliance is connected to each valve.

6.23.4.8 Hose shall be protected against physical damage.

6.24 Vaporizer Installation.

6.24.1 Nonapplication. Section 6.24 shall not apply to engine fuel vaporizers or to integral vaporizing burners such as those used for weed burners or tar kettles.

6.24.2 Installation of Indirect-Fired Vaporizers.

6.24.2.1 Indirect-fired vaporizers shall be installed outdoors, or in separate buildings or structures that comply with Section 10.2, or in attached structures or rooms that comply with Section 10.3.

6.24.2.2 The separate building or structure shall not have any unprotected drains to sewers or sump pits.

6.24.2.3 Pressure relief valves on vaporizers within buildings in industrial or gas manufacturing plants shall be piped to a point outside the building or structure and shall discharge vertically upward.

6.24.2.4 If the heat source of an indirect-fired vaporizer is gas fired and is located within 15 ft (4.6 m) of the vaporizer, the vaporizer and its heat source shall be installed as a direct-fired vaporizer and shall be subject to the requirements of 6.24.3.

6.24.2.5 The installation of a heat source serving an indirect-fired vaporizer that utilizes a flammable or combustible heat transfer fluid shall comply with one of the following:

(1) It shall be located outdoors.
(2) It shall be located within a structure that complies with Section 10.2.
(3) It shall be located within a structure attached to, or in rooms within, a building or structure that complies with Section 10.3.

6.24.2.6 Gas-fired heating systems supplying heat for vaporization purposes shall be equipped with automatic safety devices to shut off gas to the main burners if ignition fails to occur.

6.24.2.7 The installation of a heat source serving an indirect-fired vaporizer that utilizes a noncombustible heat transfer fluid, such as steam, water, or a water-glycol mixture, shall be installed outdoors or in industrial occupancies.

△ 6.24.2.8 Industrial occupancies in which a source of heat for an indirect-fired vaporizer is installed shall comply with Chapter 40 of NFPA *101* and Section 10.3 of NFPA 54.

6.24.2.9 The following shall apply to indirect-fired vaporizers installed in buildings:

(1) The heat transfer fluid shall be steam or hot water.
(2) The heat transfer fluid shall not be recirculated.
(3) A backflow preventer shall be installed between the vaporizer and the heat source.

6.24.2.10 If the heat transfer fluid is recirculated after leaving the vaporizer, the heat source shall be installed in accordance with 6.24.2.5 and a phase separator shall be installed with the gas vented.

6.24.2.11 Indirect-fired vaporizers employing heat from the atmosphere shall be installed outdoors and shall be located in accordance with Table 6.24.3.6.

6.24.2.12 Where atmospheric vaporizers of less than 1 qt (0.9 L) capacity are installed in industrial occupancies, they shall be installed as close as practical to the point of entry of the supply line in the building.

6.24.2.13 Atmospheric vaporizers of less than 1 qt (0.9 L) capacity shall not be installed in other than industrial occupancies.

6.24.3 Installation of Direct-Fired Vaporizers.

6.24.3.1 Where a direct-fired vaporizer is installed in a separate structure, the separate structure shall be constructed in accordance with Chapter 10.

6.24.3.2 The housing for direct-fired vaporizers shall not have any drains to a sewer or a sump pit that is shared with any other structure.

6.24.3.3 Pressure relief valve discharges on direct-fired vaporizers shall be piped to a point outside the structure or building.

6.24.3.4 Direct-fired vaporizers shall be connected to the liquid space or to the liquid and vapor space of the ASME container.

6.24.3.5 A manually operated shutoff valve shall be installed in each connection of the ASME container supplying the vaporizer.

6.24.3.6 Direct-fired vaporizers of any capacity shall be located in accordance with Table 6.24.3.6.

6.24.4 Installation of Tank Heaters.

6.24.4.1 Direct-type tank heaters shall be installed only on aboveground ASME containers.

6.24.4.2 Direct gas-fired tank heaters shall only be installed on steel containers.

6.24.4.3 Tank heaters containing sources of ignition, together with the container upon which they are installed, shall be located in accordance with Table 6.24.4.3 with respect to the nearest important building, group of buildings, or line of adjoining property that can be built upon.

Table 6.24.3.6 Minimum Separation Distances Between Direct-Fired Vaporizers and Exposures

Exposure	Minimum Distance Required	
	ft	m
Container	10	3.0
Container shutoff valves	15	4.6
Point of transfer	15	4.6
Nearest important building or group of buildings or line of adjoining property that can be built upon	25	7.6
Nearest Chapter 10 building or room housing gas-air mixer	10	3.0
Cabinet housing gas-air mixer outdoors	0	0

Note: Do not apply distances to the building in which a direct-fired vaporizer is installed.

Table 6.24.4.3 Minimum Separation Between Tank Heaters and Exposures

Container Water Capacity		Minimum Distance Required	
gal	m³	ft	m
≤500	≤1.9	10	3.0
501–2,000	>1.9–7.6	25	7.6
2,001–30,000	>7.6–114	50	15.0
30,001–70,000	>114–265	75	23.0
70,001–90,000	>265–341	100	30.5
90,001–120,000	>341–454	125	38.1

6.24.4.4 If the tank heater is similar in operation to an indirect-fired vaporizer, the heat source shall comply with 6.24.2.8 and 6.24.2.11.

6.24.4.5 If a point of transfer is located within 15 ft (4.6 m) of a tank heater having a source of ignition, the source of ignition shall be shut off during product transfer and a caution notice in letters ¾ in. (19 mm) high or larger that reads as follows shall be displayed immediately adjacent to the filling connections:

CAUTION: A device that contains a source of ignition is connected to this container. The source of ignition must be shut off before filling the container.

6.24.4.6* Annual Inspection.

(A) Direct-type tank heaters shall be removed annually and the container surface shall be inspected.

(B) If corrosion or coating damage other than discoloration is found, the container shall be removed from service and tested in accordance with 5.2.1.2(B).

6.24.5 Installation of Vaporizing Burners.

6.24.5.1 Vaporizing burners shall be installed outside of buildings.

6.24.5.2 The minimum distance between any container and a vaporizing burner shall be in accordance with Table 6.24.5.2.

6.24.5.3 Manually operated positive shutoff valves shall be located at the containers to shut off all flow to the vaporizing burners.

6.24.6 Installation of Waterbath Vaporizers.

6.24.6.1 If a waterbath vaporizer is electrically heated and all electrical equipment is designed for Class I, Group D locations, the unit shall be treated as an indirect-fired vaporizer and shall be installed in accordance with 6.24.2.

6.24.6.2 All other waterbath vaporizers shall be treated as direct-fired vaporizers and shall be installed in accordance with 6.24.3.

6.24.7 Installation of Electric Vaporizers. Electric vaporizers, whether direct immersion or indirect immersion, shall be treated as indirect-fired and shall be installed in accordance with 6.24.2.

6.24.8 Installation of Gas-Air Mixers.

6.24.8.1 Piping and equipment installed with a gas-air mixer shall comply with 6.11.1, 6.11.3, and Section 6.16.

6.24.8.2 Where used without a vaporizer, a mixer shall be installed outdoors or in a building complying with Chapter 10.

Table 6.24.5.2 Minimum Separation Distance Between Containers and Vaporizing Burners

Container Water Capacity		Minimum Distance Required	
gal	m³	ft	m
≤500	≤1.9	10	3.0
501–2000	1.9–7.6	25	7.6
>2000	>7.6	50	15.0

6.24.8.3 Where used with an indirect-fired vaporizer, a mixer shall be installed as follows:

(1) In an outdoor location
(2) In the same compartment or room with the vaporizer
(3) In a building complying with Chapter 10
(4) In a location that is both remote from the vaporizer and in accordance with 6.24.2

6.24.8.4 Where used with a direct-fired vaporizer, a mixer shall be installed as follows:

(1) With a listed or approved mixer in a common cabinet with the vaporizer outdoors in accordance with 6.24.3.6
(2) Outdoors on a common skid with the vaporizer in accordance with 6.24.3
(3) Adjacent to the vaporizer to which it is connected in accordance with 6.24.3
(4) In a building complying with Chapter 10 without a direct-fired vaporizer in the same room

6.25 Ignition Source Control.

6.25.1 Scope.

6.25.1.1 This section shall apply to the minimization of ignition of flammable LP-Gas–air mixtures resulting from the normal or accidental release of nominal quantities of liquid or vapor from LP-Gas systems installed and operated in accordance with this code.

6.25.1.2* The installation of lightning protection equipment shall not be required on LP-Gas storage containers.

6.25.1.3* Grounding and bonding shall not be required on LP-Gas systems.

6.25.2 Electrical Equipment.

6.25.2.1 Electrical equipment and wiring installed in unclassified areas shall be in accordance with *NFPA 70*.

6.25.2.2* The extent of electrically classified areas shall be in accordance with Table 6.25.2.2.

6.25.2.3* The provisions of 6.25.2.2 shall apply to vehicular fuel operations.

6.25.2.4 The provisions of 6.25.2.2 shall not apply to fixed electrical equipment at residential or commercial installations of LP-Gas systems or to systems covered by Section 6.26.

6.25.2.5 Fired vaporizers, calorimeters with open flames, and other areas where open flames are present either intermittently or constantly shall not be considered electrically classified areas.

6.25.2.6 Electrical equipment installed on LP-Gas cargo tank vehicles shall comply with Section 9.2.

6.25.3 Other Sources of Ignition.

6.25.3.1 Open flames or other sources of ignition shall not be used or installed in pump houses, cylinder filling rooms, or other similar locations.

6.25.3.2 Direct-fired vaporizers or indirect-fired vaporizers attached or installed adjacent to gas-fired heat sources shall not be installed in pump houses or cylinder filling rooms.

6.25.3.3 Open flames, cutting or welding tools, portable electric tools, and extension lights capable of igniting LP-Gas shall not be installed or used within classified areas specified in Table 6.25.2.2.

6.25.3.4 Open flames or other sources of ignition shall not be prohibited where containers, piping, and other equipment containing LP-Gas have been purged of all liquid and vapor LP-Gas.

6.26 LP-Gas Systems on Vehicles (Other Than Engine Fuel Systems).

6.26.1* Application. Section 6.26 shall apply to the following:

(1) Nonengine fuel systems on all vehicles
(2) Installations served by exchangeable (removable) cylinder systems and by permanently mounted containers

6.26.2 Nonapplication. Section 6.26 shall not apply to the following:

(1) Systems installed on mobile homes
(2) Systems installed on recreational vehicles
(3) Cargo tank vehicles, including trailers and semitrailers, and similar units used to transport LP-Gas as cargo, which are covered by Chapter 9
(4) LP-Gas engine fuel systems on the vehicles, which are covered by Chapter 11

6.26.3 Container Installation Requirements.

6.26.3.1 Containers shall comply with 6.26.3.1(A) through 6.26.3.1(E).

(A) ASME mobile containers shall be in accordance with one of the following:

(1) A MAWP of 312 psig (2.2 MPag) or higher where installed in enclosed spaces of vehicles
(2) A MAWP of 312 psig (2.2 MPag) or higher where installed on passenger vehicles
(3) A MAWP of 250 psig (1.7 MPag) or higher for containers where installed on the exterior of nonpassenger vehicles

(B) LP-Gas fuel containers used on passenger-carrying vehicles shall not exceed 200 gal (0.8 m^3) aggregate water capacity.

(C) The capacity of individual LP-Gas containers on highway nonpassenger vehicles shall be 1000 gal (3.8 m^3) or in accordance with U.S. Department of Transportation regulations.

(D) The capacity of cargo tank motor vehicles shall not be limited by this code.

(E) Containers designed for stationary service only and not in compliance with the container appurtenance protection requirements of 5.2.6 shall not be used.

6.26.3.2 ASME containers and cylinders utilized for the purposes covered by Section 6.26 shall not be installed, transported, or stored (even temporarily) inside any vehicle covered by Section 6.26, except for ASME containers installed in accordance with 6.26.3.4(I), Chapter 9, or DOT regulations.

6.26.3.3 The LP-Gas supply system, including the containers, shall be installed either on the outside of the vehicle or in a recess or cabinet vaportight to the inside of the vehicle but accessible from and vented to the outside, with the vents located near the top and bottom of the enclosure and 3 ft (1 m) horizontally away from any opening into the vehicle below the level of the vents.

△ Table 6.25.2.2 Electrical Area Classification

Part	Location	Extent of Classified Area[a]	Equipment Shall Be Approved for Compliance with *NFPA 70*, Class I[a], Group D[b]
A	Unrefrigerated containers other than cylinders and ASME vertical containers of less than 1000 lb (454 kg) water capacity	Within 15 ft (4.6 m) in all directions from connections, except connections otherwise covered in this table	Division 2
B	Refrigerated storage containers	Within 15 ft (4.6 m) in all directions from connections otherwise covered in this table	Division 2
		Area inside dike to the level of the top of the dike	Division 2
C[c]	Tank vehicle and tank car loading and unloading	Within 5 ft (1.5 m) in all directions from connections regularly made or disconnected for product transfer	Division 1
		Beyond 5 ft (1.5 m) but within 15 ft (4.6 m) in all directions from a point where connections are regularly made or disconnected and within the cylindrical volume between the horizontal equator of the sphere and grade	Division 2
D	Gauge vent openings other than those on cylinders and ASME vertical containers of less than 1000 lb (454 kg) water capacity	Within 5 ft (1.5 m) in all directions from point of discharge	Division 1
		Beyond 5 ft (1.5 m) but within 15 ft (4.6 m) in all directions from point of discharge	Division 2
E	Relief device discharge other than those on cylinders and ASME vertical containers of less than 1000 lb (454 kg) water capacity and vaporizers	Within direct path of discharge	Fixed electrical equipment not permitted to be installed
F[c]	Pumps, vapor compressors, gas-air mixers and vaporizers (other than direct-fired or indirect-fired with an attached or adjacent gas-fired heat source)		
	Indoors without ventilation	Entire room and any adjacent room not separated by a gastight partition	Division 1
		Within 15 ft (4.6 m) of the exterior side of any exterior wall or roof that is not vaportight or within 15 ft (4.6 m) of any exterior opening	Division 2
	Indoors with ventilation	Entire room and any adjacent room not separated by a gastight partition	Division 2
	Outdoors in open air at or above grade	Within 15 ft (4.6 m) in all directions from this equipment and within the cylindrical volume between the horizontal equator of the sphere and grade	Division 2
G	Vehicle fuel dispenser	Entire space within dispenser enclosure, and 18 in. (460 mm) horizontally from enclosure exterior up to an elevation 4 ft (1.2 m) above dispenser base; entire pit or open space beneath dispenser	Division 1

(continues)

Δ Table 6.25.2.2   *Continued*

Part	Location	Extent of Classified Area[a]	Equipment Shall Be Approved for Compliance with *NFPA 70*, Class I[a], Group D[b]
		Up to 18 in. (460 mm) above ground within 20 ft (6.1 m) horizontally from any edge of enclosure (Note: For pits within this area, see part H of this table.)	Division 2
H	Pits or trenches containing or located beneath LP-Gas valves, pumps, vapor compressors, regulators, and similar equipment		
	Without mechanical ventilation	Entire pit or trench	Division 1
		Entire room and any adjacent room not separated by a gastight partition	Division 2
		Within 15 ft (4.6 m) in all directions from pit or trench when located outdoors	Division 2
	With mechanical ventilation	Entire pit or trench	Division 2
		Entire room and any adjacent room not separated by a gastight partition	Division 2
		Within 15 ft (4.6 m) in all directions from pit or trench when located outdoors	Division 2
I	Special buildings or rooms for storage of cylinders	Entire room	Division 2
J	Pipelines and connections containing operational bleeds, drips, vents, or drains	Within 5 ft (1.5 m) in all directions from point of discharge	Division 1
		Beyond 5 ft (1.5 m) from point of discharge, same as part F of this table	
K[c]	Cylinder filling		
	Indoors with ventilation	Within 5 ft (1.5 m) in all directions from a point of transfer	Division 1
		Beyond 5 ft (1.5 m) and entire room	Division 2
	Outdoors in open air	Within 5 ft (1.5 m) in all directions from a point of transfer	Division 1
		Beyond 5 ft (1.5 m) but within 15 ft (4.6 m) in all directions from point of transfer and within the cylindrical volume between the horizontal equator of the sphere and grade	Division 2
L	Piers and wharves	Within 5 ft (1.5 m) in all directions from connections regularly made or disconnected for product transfer	Division 1
		Beyond 5 ft (1.5 m) but within 15 ft (4.6 m) in all directions from a point where connections are regularly made or disconnected and within the cylindrical volume between the horizontal equator of the sphere and the vessel deck	Division 2

[a]The classified area is prohibited from extending beyond an unpierced wall, roof, or solid vaportight partition.
[b]See Article 500, Hazardous (Classified) Locations, in *NFPA 70* for definitions of classes, groups, and divisions.
[c]See A.6.25.2.2.

6.26.3.4 Containers shall be mounted securely on the vehicle or within the enclosing recess or cabinet.

(A) Containers shall be installed with road clearance in accordance with 11.8.3.

(B) Fuel containers shall be mounted to prevent jarring loose and slipping or rotating, and the fastenings shall be designed and constructed to withstand, without permanent visible deformation, static loading in any direction equal to four times the weight of the container filled with fuel.

(C) Where containers are mounted within a vehicle housing, the securing of the housing to the vehicle shall comply with this provision. Any removable portions of the housing or cabinet shall be secured while in transit.

(D) Field welding on containers shall be limited to attachments to nonpressure parts such as saddle plates, wear plates, or brackets applied by the container manufacturer.

(E) All container valves, appurtenances, and connections shall be protected to prevent damage from accidental contact with stationary objects; from loose objects, stones, mud, or ice thrown up from the ground or floor; and from damage due to overturn or similar vehicular accident.

(F) Permanently mounted ASME containers shall be located on the vehicle to provide the protection specified in 6.26.3.4(E).

(G) Cylinders shall have permanent protection for cylinder valves and connections.

(H) Where cylinders are located on the outside of a vehicle, weather protection shall be provided.

(I) Containers mounted on the interior of passenger-carrying vehicles shall be installed in compliance with Section 11.9. Pressure relief valve installations for such containers shall comply with 11.8.5.

6.26.3.5 Cylinders installed on portable tar kettles alongside the kettle, on the vehicle frame, or on road surface heating equipment shall be protected from radiant or convected heat from open flame or other burners by the use of a heat shield or by the location of the cylinder(s) on the vehicle. In addition, the following shall apply:

(1) Cylinder valves shall be closed when burners are not in use.
(2) Cylinders shall not be refilled while burners are in use as provided in 7.2.3.2(B).

6.26.4 Installation of Container Appurtenances.

6.26.4.1 Container appurtenances shall be installed in accordance with the following:

(1) Pressure relief valve installation on ASME containers installed in the interior of vehicles complying with Section 11.9 shall comply with 11.8.5.
(2) Pressure relief valve installations on ASME containers installed on the outside of vehicles shall comply with 11.8.5 and 6.26.3.3.
(3) Main shutoff valves on containers for liquid and vapor shall be readily accessible.
(4) Cylinders shall be designed to be filled in either the vertical or horizontal position, or if they are the universal type, they are permitted to be filled in either position.

(5) All container inlets, outlets, or valves installed in container inlets or outlets, except pressure relief devices and gauging devices, shall be labeled to designate whether they communicate with the vapor or liquid space.
(6) Containers from which only vapor is to be withdrawn shall be installed and equipped with connections to minimize the possibility of the accidental withdrawal of liquid.

6.26.4.2 Regulators shall be installed in accordance with 6.10.2 and 6.26.4.2(A) through 6.26.4.2(E).

(A) Regulators shall be installed with the pressure relief vent opening pointing vertically downward to allow for drainage of moisture collected on the diaphragm of the regulator.

(B) Regulators not installed in compartments shall be equipped with a durable cover designed to protect the regulator vent opening from sleet, snow, freezing rain, ice, mud, and wheel spray.

(C) If vehicle-mounted regulators are installed at or below the floor level, they shall be installed in a compartment that provides protection against the weather and wheel spray.

(D) Regulator compartments shall comply with the following:

(1) The compartment shall be of sufficient size to allow tool operation for connection to and replacement of the regulator(s).
(2) The compartment shall be vaportight to the interior of the vehicle.
(3) The compartment shall have a 1 in.^{2} (650 mm^2) minimum vent opening to the exterior located within 1 in. (25 mm) of the bottom of the compartment.
(4) The compartment shall not contain flame or spark-producing equipment.

(E) A regulator vent outlet shall be at least 2 in. (51 mm) above the compartment vent opening.

6.26.5 Piping.

6.26.5.1 Piping shall be installed in accordance with 6.11.3 and 6.26.5.1(A) through 6.26.5.1(M).

(A) Steel tubing shall have a minimum wall thickness of 0.049 in. (1.2 mm).

(B) A flexible connector shall be installed between the regulator outlet and the fixed piping system to protect against expansion, contraction, jarring, and vibration strains.

(C) Flexibility shall be provided in the piping between a cylinder and the gas piping system or regulator.

(D) Flexible connectors shall be installed in accordance with 6.11.6.

(E) Flexible connectors longer than the length allowed in the code, or fuel lines that incorporate hose, shall be used only where approved.

(F) The fixed piping system shall be designed, installed, supported, and secured to minimize the possibility of damage due to vibration, strains, or wear and to preclude any loosening while in transit.

(G) Piping shall be installed in a protected location.

(H) Where piping is installed outside the vehicle, it shall be installed as follows:

(1) Piping shall be under the vehicle and below any insulation or false bottom.
(2) Fastening or other protection shall be installed to prevent damage due to vibration or abrasion.
(3) At each point where piping passes through sheet metal or a structural member, a rubber grommet or equivalent protection shall be installed to prevent chafing.

(I) Gas piping shall be installed to enter the vehicle through the floor directly beneath or adjacent to the appliance served.

(J) If a branch line is installed, the tee connection shall be located in the main gas line under the floor and outside the vehicle.

(K) Exposed parts of the fixed piping system either shall be of corrosion-resistant material or shall be coated or protected to minimize exterior corrosion.

(L) Hydrostatic relief valves shall be installed in isolated sections of liquid piping as provided in Section 6.15.

(M) Piping systems, including hose, shall be proven free of leaks in accordance with Section 6.16.

6.26.5.2 There shall be no fuel connection between a tractor and trailer or other vehicle units.

6.26.6 Equipment Installation. Equipment shall be installed in accordance with Section 6.20, 6.26.6.1, and 6.26.6.2.

6.26.6.1 Installation shall be made in accordance with the manufacturer's recommendations and, in the case of approved equipment, as provided in the approval.

6.26.6.2 Equipment installed on vehicles shall be protected against vehicular damage as provided for container appurtenances and connections in 6.26.3.4(E).

6.26.7 Appliance Installation on Vehicles.

6.26.7.1 Subsection 6.26.7 shall apply to the installation of all appliances on vehicles. It shall not apply to engines.

6.26.7.2 All appliances covered by 6.26.7 installed on vehicles shall be approved.

6.26.7.3 Where the device or appliance, such as a cargo heater or cooler, is designed to be in operation while the vehicle is in transit, means, such as an excess-flow valve, to stop the flow of gas in the event of a line break shall be installed.

6.26.7.4 Gas-fired heating appliances shall be equipped with shutoffs in accordance with 5.23.7(A), except for portable heaters used with cylinders having a maximum water capacity of 2.7 lb (1.2 kg), portable torches, melting pots, and tar kettles.

6.26.7.5 Gas-fired heating appliances, other than ranges and illuminating appliances installed on vehicles intended for human occupancy, shall be designed or installed to provide for a complete separation of the combustion system from the atmosphere inside the vehicle.

6.26.7.6* Where unvented-type heaters that are designed to protect cargo are used on vehicles not intended for human occupancy, provisions shall be made to provide air from the outside for combustion and dispose of the products of combustion to the outside.

6.26.7.7 Appliances installed in the cargo space of a vehicle shall be readily accessible whether the vehicle is loaded or empty.

6.26.7.8 Appliances shall be constructed or otherwise protected to minimize possible damage or impaired operation due to cargo shifting or handling.

6.26.7.9 Appliances shall be located so that a fire at any appliance will not block egress of persons from the vehicle.

△ **6.26.7.10** A permanent caution plate shall be affixed to either the appliance or the vehicle outside of any enclosure.

N **6.26.7.10.1** The caution plate shall be adjacent to the container(s).

N **6.26.7.10.2** The caution plate shall include the following text:

CAUTION:

(1) Be sure all appliance valves are closed before opening container valve.
(2) Connections at the appliances, regulators, and containers shall be checked periodically for leaks with soapy water or its equivalent.
(3) Never use a match or flame to check for leaks.
(4) Container valves shall be closed when equipment is not in use.

6.26.7.11 Gas-fired heating appliances and water heaters shall be equipped with automatic devices designed to shut off the flow of gas to the main burner and the pilot in the event the pilot flame is extinguished.

6.26.8 Parking, Servicing, and Repair.

6.26.8.1 Where vehicles with LP-Gas fuel systems used for purposes other than propulsion are parked, serviced, or repaired inside buildings, the requirements of 6.26.8.2 through 6.26.8.4 shall apply.

6.26.8.2 The fuel system shall be leak-free, and the container(s) shall not be filled beyond the limits specified in Chapter 7.

6.26.8.3 The container shutoff valve shall be closed, except that the container shutoff valve shall not be required to be closed when fuel is required for test or repair.

6.26.8.4 The vehicle shall not be parked near sources of heat, open flames, or similar sources of ignition, or near unventilated pits.

6.26.8.5 Vehicles having containers with water capacities larger than 300 gal (1.1 m³) shall comply with the requirements of Section 9.7.

6.27 Vehicle Fuel Dispenser and Dispensing Systems.

6.27.1 Application.

6.27.1.1 Section 6.27 includes the location, installation, and operation of vehicle fuel dispensers and dispensing systems.

6.27.1.2 The provisions of Sections 6.2 and 6.4, as modified by Section 6.27, shall apply.

6.27.2 Location.

△ **6.27.2.1** Location of dispensers and dispensing systems shall be in accordance with Table 6.7.2.1.

6.27.2.2 Vehicle fuel dispensers and dispensing systems shall be located away from pits in accordance with Table 6.7.2.1, with no drains or blow-offs from the unit directed toward or within 15 ft (4.6 m) of a sewer system's opening.

6.27.3 General Installation Provisions.

6.27.3.1 Vehicle fuel dispensers and dispensing systems shall be installed in accordance with the manufacturer's installation instructions.

6.27.3.2 Vehicle fuel dispensers and dispensing systems shall not be located within an enclosed building or structure, unless they comply with Chapter 10.

6.27.3.3 No more than 50 percent of the perimeter of an area where a dispenser or dispensing system is located shall be enclosed.

N 6.27.3.4 A weather shelter or canopy shall be permitted to cover the working space for the filling operation.

6.27.3.5 Control for the pump used to transfer LP-Gas through the unit into containers shall be provided at the device in order to minimize the possibility of leakage or accidental discharge.

6.27.3.6* A device that shuts off the flow of gas when flow exceeds the predetermined flow rate shall be installed as close as practical to the point where the dispenser hose connects to the liquid piping.

6.27.3.7 Piping and the dispensing hose shall be provided with hydrostatic relief valves in accordance with Section 6.15.

6.27.3.8 Protection against trespassing and tampering shall be in accordance with 6.21.4.

6.27.3.9 The container liquid withdrawal opening used with vehicle fuel dispensers and dispensing systems shall be equipped with one of the following:

(1) An internal valve fitted for remote closure and automatic shutoff using thermal (fire) actuation
(2) A positive shutoff valve that is located as close to the container as practical and an excess-flow valve installed in the container, plus an emergency shutoff valve that is fitted for remote closure and installed downstream in the line as close as practical to the positive shutoff valve

6.27.3.10 An identified and accessible remote emergency shutoff device for either the internal valve or the emergency shutoff valve required by 6.27.3.9(1) or 6.27.3.9(2) shall be installed not less than 3 ft (1 m) or more than 100 ft (30 m) from the liquid transfer point.

6.27.3.11 Emergency shutoff valves and internal valves that are fitted for remote closure as required in this section shall be tested annually for proper operation.

6.27.3.12 A manual shutoff valve and an excess-flow check valve shall be located in the liquid line between the pump and the dispenser inlet where the dispensing device is installed at a remote location and is not part of a complete storage and dispensing unit mounted on a common base.

6.27.3.13 All dispensers shall be installed on a concrete foundation or shall be part of a complete storage and dispensing unit mounted on a common base and installed in accordance with 6.8.3.1(F).

6.27.3.14 Vehicular barrier protection (VBP) shall be provided for containers serving dispensers where those containers are located within 10 ft (3 m) of a vehicle thoroughfare or parking location in accordance with 6.27.3.14(A) or 6.27.3.14(B).

(A) Concrete filled guard posts shall be constructed of steel not less than 4 in. (100 mm) in diameter with the following characteristics:

(1) Spaced not more than 4 ft (1200 mm) between posts on center
(2) Set not less than 3 ft (900 mm) deep in a concrete footing of not less than 15 in. (380 mm) diameter
(3) Set with the top of the posts not less than 3 ft (900 mm) above ground
(4) Located not less than 3 ft (900 mm) from the protected installation

(B) Equivalent protection in lieu of guard posts shall be a minimum of 3 ft (900 mm) in height and shall resist a force of 6000 lb (26,700 N) applied 3 ft (900 mm) above the adjacent ground surface.

6.27.3.15 Where the dispenser is not mounted on a common base with its storage container and the dispenser is located within 10 ft (3 m) of a vehicle thoroughfare, parking location, or an engine fuel filling station, the dispenser shall be provided with VBP.

6.27.3.16 Dispensers shall be protected from physical damage.

6.27.3.17 A listed quick-acting shutoff valve shall be installed at the discharge end of the transfer hose.

6.27.3.18 An identified and readily accessible switch or circuit breaker shall be installed outside at a location not less than 20 ft (6 m) or more than 100 ft (30 m) from the dispenser to shut off the power in the event of a fire, an accident, or other emergency.

6.27.3.19 The markings for the switches or breakers shall be visible at the point of liquid transfer.

6.27.4 Installation of Vehicle Fuel Dispensers.

6.27.4.1 Hose shall comply with the following:

(1) Hose length shall not exceed 18 ft (5.5 m) unless approved by the authority having jurisdiction.
(2) All hose shall be listed.
(3) When not in use, the hose shall be secured to protect the hose from damage.

6.27.4.2 A listed emergency breakaway device shall be installed and shall comply with UL 567, *Standard for Emergency Breakaway Fittings, Swivel Connectors, and Pipe-Connection Fittings for Petroleum Products and LP-Gas*, and be designed to retain liquid on both sides of the breakaway point, or other devices affording equivalent protection approved by the authority having jurisdiction.

6.27.4.3 Vehicle fuel dispensers shall be located as follows:

(1) Conventional systems shall be at least 10 ft (3.0 m) from any dispensing device for Class I or Class II liquids.
(2) Low-emission transfer systems in accordance with 6.30.5 shall be at least 5 ft (2 m) from any dispensing device for Class I or Class II liquids.

6.27.5 Fugitive Emission Requirements. Vehicle fuel dispensers shall be equipped with low-emission transfer systems in accordance with 6.30.5.

6.28 Containers for Stationary Engines.

6.28.1 LP-Gas containers for stationary installations shall be located outside of buildings unless the buildings comply with the requirements of Chapter 10.

6.28.2 Containers for stationary engines shall be installed to meet the separation requirements of Section 6.4.

6.28.3 Where containers for stationary engines have a fill valve with an integral manual shutoff valve, the minimum separation distances required for fill valves shall be one-half of the distances specified in Section 6.4.

N 6.28.4 Where aboveground containers for stationary engines are located outdoors at telecommunications facilities of noncombustible construction, the minimum separation distances shall be half the distances specified in Section 6.4 when the following conditions are met:

(1) Building area is less than 1500 ft^2 (140 m^2)
(2) Container has a fill valve with an integral manual shutoff valve
(3) Facility is located more than 50 ft (15 m) from other buildings not used for telecommunications

6.29 Fire Protection.

6.29.1 Application. Section 6.29 shall apply to fire protection for industrial plants, bulk plants, and dispensing systems.

6.29.2* Planning.

6.29.2.1 The planning for the response to incidents including the inadvertent release of LP-Gas, fire, or security breach shall be coordinated with local emergency response agencies.

6.29.2.2 Planning shall include consideration of the safety of emergency personnel, workers, and the public.

6.29.3* Protection of ASME Containers.

6.29.3.1* Fire protection shall be provided for installations with an aggregate water capacity of more than 4000 gal (15.2 m^3) and for ASME containers on roofs.

6.29.3.2 The modes of fire protection shall be specified in a written fire safety analysis for new installations, for existing installations that have an aggregate water capacity of more than 4000 gal (15.2 m^3), and for ASME containers on roofs. Existing installation shall comply with this requirement within 2 years of the effective date of this code.

6.29.3.3 The fire safety analysis shall be submitted by the owner, operator, or their designee to the authority having jurisdiction and local emergency responders.

6.29.3.4 The fire safety analysis shall be updated when the storage capacity or transfer system is modified.

6.29.3.5 The fire safety analysis shall be an evaluation of the total product control system, such as the emergency shutoff and internal valves equipped for remote closure and automatic shutoff using thermal (fire) actuation, pullaway protection where installed, and the optional requirements of Section 6.30.

6.29.3.6 If in the preparation for the fire safety analysis it is determined that a hazard to adjacent structures exists that

exceeds the protection provided by the provisions of this code, special protection shall be provided in accordance with 6.29.5.

6.29.4 Other Protection Requirements.

6.29.4.1 Roadways or other means of access for emergency equipment, such as fire department apparatus, shall be provided.

6.29.4.2 Each industrial plant, bulk plant, and distributing point shall be provided with at least one portable fire extinguisher in accordance with Section 4.7 having a minimum capacity of 18 lb (8.2 kg) of dry chemical.

6.29.4.3 Emergency controls shall be conspicuously marked, and the controls shall be located so as to be readily accessible in emergencies.

6.29.5 Special Protection.

6.29.5.1* If insulation is used, it shall be capable of limiting the container temperature to not over 800°F (430°C) for a minimum of 50 minutes as determined by test, with insulation applied to a steel plate and subjected to a test flame applied substantially over the area of the test plate.

6.29.5.2 The insulation system shall be inherently resistant to weathering and the action of hose streams.

6.29.5.3 If mounding is utilized, the provisions of 6.8.6.3 shall be required.

6.29.5.4 If burial is utilized, the provisions of 6.8.6.1 shall be required.

6.29.6 Water Spray Systems.

6.29.6.1 If water spray fixed systems and monitors are used, they shall comply with NFPA 15.

6.29.6.2 Where water spray fixed systems and monitors are used, they shall be automatically actuated by fire-responsive devices and shall also have a capability for manual actuation.

6.29.6.3 Where monitor nozzles are used, they shall be located and arranged so that all container surfaces that can be exposed to fire are wetted.

6.30 Alternative Provisions for Installation of ASME Containers.

6.30.1 Application. Section 6.30 shall apply to alternative provisions for the location and installation of ASME containers that incorporate the use of redundant fail-safe product control measures and the requirements for low-emission transfer, to the filling of DOT cylinders using low-emission transfer for the purpose of enhancing safety, and to mitigate distance and special protection requirements.

6.30.2 Spacing Requirements for Underground and Mounded ASME Containers.

6.30.2.1 Where all the provisions of Section 6.30 are complied with, the minimum distances from important buildings and the line of adjoining property that can be built upon to underground and mounded ASME containers of 2001 gal through 30,000 gal (7.6 m^3 through 114 m^3) water capacity shall be reduced to 10 ft (3 m).

6.30.2.2 Distances for all underground and mounded ASME containers shall be measured from the container surface.

6.30.2.3 No part of an underground or mounded ASME container shall be less than 10 ft (3 m) from a building or line of adjoining property that can be built upon.

6.30.3 ASME Container Appurtenances. The provisions in 6.30.3.1 through 6.30.3.5 shall be required for ASME containers of 2001 gal through 30,000 gal (7.6 m³ through 114 m³) water capacity referenced in Section 6.30.

6.30.3.1 All liquid withdrawal openings and all vapor withdrawal openings that are 1¼ in. (32 mm) or larger shall be equipped with an internal valve.

6.30.3.2 The internal valves shall remain closed except during periods of operation.

6.30.3.3 Internal valves shall be equipped for remote closure and automatic shutoff through thermal (fire) actuation.

6.30.3.4 A positive manual shutoff valve shall be installed as close as practical to each internal valve.

6.30.3.5 All liquid and vapor inlet openings shall be equipped in accordance with 6.30.3.1 through 6.30.3.4 or shall be equipped with a backflow check valve that is designed for the intended application and a positive manual shutoff valve installed as close as practical to the backflow check valve.

6.30.4 Redundant Fail-Safe Product Control.

6.30.4.1 At cargo tank vehicle and railroad tank car transfer points, protection shall be provided in accordance with Section 6.14 using approved emergency shutoff valves or backflow check valves or a combination of the two.

6.30.4.2 Automatic system shutdown of all primary valves (internal valves and emergency shutoff valves) shall be provided through thermal (fire) actuation and in the event of a hose pull-away.

6.30.4.3 Remote shutdown capability, including power supply for the transfer equipment and all primary valves (internal and emergency shutoff), shall be provided.

(A) A remote shutdown station shall be installed within 15 ft (4.6 m) of the point of transfer.

(B) At least one additional remote shutdown station shall be installed not less than 25 ft (7.6 m), or more than 100 ft (30 m), from the transfer point.

Δ (C) Emergency remote shutdown stations shall be identified as such by a sign incorporating the words "Propane" and "Emergency Shutoff" in block letters not less than 2 in. (51 mm) in height on a background of contrasting color to the letters.

N (D) The sign shall be visible from the point of transfer.

6.30.5 Low-Emission Transfer.

6.30.5.1 Where the installation meets all the provisions of 6.30.5, the minimum separation distances shall comply with 6.7.3.4.

6.30.5.2 The transfer site shall be identified as "Low-Emission Transfer Site" by having a sign or other marking posted in the area.

6.30.5.3 Transfer into permanently mounted ASME engine fuel containers on vehicles shall meet the provisions of 6.30.5.3(A) through 6.30.5.3(D).

(A) The delivery valve and nozzle combination shall mate with the filler valve in the receiving container in such a manner that, when they are uncoupled following a transfer of product, not more than 0.24 in.³ (4 cm³) of product (liquid equivalent) is released to the atmosphere.

(B) Fixed maximum liquid level gauges that are installed on engine fuel and mobile containers in accordance with Table 5.9.4.1(B) shall not be used to determine the maximum permitted filling limit at a low-emission transfer site.

(C) The maximum permitted filling limit shall be in accordance with Section 11.5 and shall be determined by an overfilling prevention device or other approved means.

(D) A label shall be placed near the fixed maximum liquid level gauge providing the following instructions: "Do not use this fixed maximum liquid level gauge at low-emission transfer stations."

6.30.5.4 Transfer into a stationary ASME container shall meet the provisions of 6.30.5.4(A) through 6.30.5.4(F).

(A) Where transfer is made through a hose of nominal 1 in. (25 mm) size or smaller, the delivery valve and nozzle combination shall not contain an interstitial volume greater than 0.24 in.³ (4 cm³).

(B) Where transfer is made through hose larger than 1 in. (25 mm) nominal size, no more than 0.91 in.³ (15 cm³) of LP-Gas (liquid equivalent) shall be released to the atmosphere during the transfer operation, including the uncoupling of the transfer hose.

(C) Fixed maximum liquid level gauges on low-emission transfer systems shall be installed and used to verify the (function) accuracy of liquid level gauges or other liquid level gauging devices.

(D) Fixed maximum liquid level gauges shall not be used in the routine filling of low-emission transfer systems.

(E) The use of a float gauge or other approved nonventing device for containers of 2001 gal (7.6 m³) or larger water capacity shall be the only means for determining the maximum filling limit.

(F) The maximum filling limit for containers of less than 2001 gal (7.6 m³) water capacity in low-emission transfer systems shall be controlled through the use of an overfilling prevention device or other device approved for this service.

N 6.30.5.5 Transfer into a portable DOT cylinder shall meet the provisions of 6.30.5.5(A) through 6.30.5.5(F).

N (A) Transfer shall be made only through a hose of nominal 1 in. (25 mm) size or smaller.

N (B) The delivery valve and nozzle combination shall not contain an interstitial volume greater than 0.24 in.³ (4000 mm³).

N (C) Cylinders shall be filled according to weight on a certified scale.

N (D) Fixed maximum liquid level gauges shall not be used in the filling of cylinders.

N (E) An overfilling prevention device shall not be used to determine when a cylinder is filled to the maximum allowable filling limit.

N (F) The cylinder shall have a propane capacity of 100 lb (45.4 kg) or less.

Δ   Chapter 7   LP-Gas Transfer

7.1* Scope.

7.1.1 This chapter applies to the following types of transfers:

(1) Transfer of liquid LP-Gas from one container to another wherever such a transfer involves connections and disconnections in the transfer system or the venting of LP-Gas to the atmosphere

(2) Transfer of LP-Gas vapor between containers and from containers to the atmosphere

7.1.2 This chapter also applies to operational safety and methods for determining the quantity of LP-Gas permitted in containers.

7.2 Operational Safety.

7.2.1 Transfer Personnel.

7.2.1.1 Transfer operations shall be conducted by qualified personnel meeting the provisions of Section 4.4.

7.2.1.2 At least one qualified person shall remain in attendance at the transfer operation from the time connections are made until the transfer is completed, shutoff valves are closed, and lines are disconnected.

7.2.1.3 Transfer personnel shall exercise caution to ensure that the LP-Gases transferred are those for which the transfer system and the containers to be filled are designed.

7.2.1.4* An FAA-certificated balloon pilot or a trained crew member shall be present and ensure the proper filling of the containers under the provisions of 5.2.9.

7.2.2 Filling and Evacuating of Containers.

7.2.2.1 Transfer of LP-Gas to and from a container shall be accomplished only by qualified individuals trained in proper handling and operating procedures meeting the requirements of Section 4.4 and in emergency response procedures.

7.2.2.2 When noncompliance with Section 5.2 or Section 5.9 is found or it is determined in accordance with 7.2.2.7 that the container will not be filled, the container owner and user shall be notified in writing.

7.2.2.3 Injection of compressed air, oxygen, or any oxidizing gas into containers to transfer LP-Gas liquid shall be prohibited.

7.2.2.4 When evacuating a container owned by others, the qualified person(s) performing the transfer shall not inject any material other than LP-Gas into the container.

7.2.2.5* Valve outlets on refillable cylinders of 108 lb (49 kg) water capacity [nominal 45 lb (20 kg) propane capacity] or less shall be equipped with a redundant pressuretight seal or one of the following listed connections: CGA 790, CGA 791, or CGA 810, as described in CGA V-1, *Standard for Compressed Gas Cylinder Valve Outlet and Inlet Connections*.

7.2.2.6 Where redundant pressure seals are used, they shall be in place whenever the cylinder is not connected for use.

N 7.2.2.7* Defects.

N (A) Prior to filling cylinders with CGA 791 and CGA 793 connections, the face seal shall be examined for defects.

N (B) If a defect on the face seal is found, the cylinder shall not be filled.

7.2.2.8 Nonrefillable (disposable) and new unused cylinders shall not be required to be equipped with valve outlet seals.

7.2.2.9 Containers shall be filled only after determination that they comply with the design, fabrication, inspection, marking, and requalification provisions of this code.

7.2.2.10 Prior to refilling a cylinder that has a cylinder sleeve, the cylinder sleeve shall be removed to facilitate the visual inspection of the cylinder.

N 7.2.2.11 Cylinders required to have an overfilling prevention device (OPD) shall not be filled unless they are equipped with this device and a fixed maximum liquid level gauge.

7.2.2.12 The requirements of 7.2.2.10 shall not apply to containers that comply with 5.2.9 and are included in the flight log of a hot air balloon.

7.2.2.13 Hot air balloon containers shall not be required to be removed from the aircraft for filling.

7.2.2.14 "Single trip," "nonrefillable," or "disposable" cylinders shall not be refilled with LP-Gas.

7.2.2.15 Containers shall comply with the following with regard to service or design pressure requirements:

(1) The service pressure marked on the cylinder shall be not less than 80 percent of the vapor pressure of the LP-Gas for which the cylinder is designed at 130°F (54°C).

(2) The maximum allowable working pressure (MAWP) for ASME containers shall be in accordance with Table 5.2.4.3.

7.2.2.16 Universal cylinders shall be permitted to be filled when in the vertical position or in the horizontal position when the positioning slot is in the correct orientation.

7.2.2.17 Transfer of refrigerated product shall be made only into systems that are designed to accept refrigerated product.

7.2.2.18 A container shall not be filled if the container assembly does not meet the requirements for continued service.

7.2.2.19 Transfer hoses larger than ½ in. (12 mm) internal diameter shall not be used for making connections to individual cylinders being filled indoors.

7.2.3 Arrangement and Operation of Transfer Systems.

7.2.3.1 Public access to areas where LP-Gas is stored and transferred shall be prohibited, except where necessary for the conduct of normal business activities.

7.2.3.2 Sources of ignition shall be turned off during transfer operations, while connections or disconnections are made, or while LP-Gas is being vented to the atmosphere.

(A) Internal combustion engines within 15 ft (4.6 m) of a point of transfer shall be shut down while such transfer operations are in progress, with the exception of the following:

(1) Engines of LP-Gas cargo tank vehicles, constructed and operated in compliance with Chapter 9, while such engines are driving transfer pumps or compressors on these vehicles to load containers in accordance with 6.7.2.2

(2) Portable engines with shielded ignition systems and exhaust system spark-arresters located at least 10 ft (3 m) from a point of transfer while such engines are driving transfer pumps or compressors

(3) Engines for industrial (and forklift) trucks powered by LP-Gas used in buildings as provided in Section 11.11

(B) Smoking, open flame, portable electrical tools, and extension lights capable of igniting LP-Gas shall not be permitted within 25 ft (7.6 m) of a point of transfer while filling operations are in progress.

(C) Metal cutting, grinding, oxygen–fuel gas cutting, brazing, soldering, or welding shall not be permitted within 35 ft (10.7 m) of a point of transfer while filling operations are in progress.

(D) Materials that have been heated above the ignition temperature of LP-Gas shall be cooled before LP-Gas transfer is started.

(E) Sources of ignition shall be turned off during the filling of any LP-Gas container on the vehicle.

7.2.3.3 Cargo tank vehicles unloading into storage containers shall be at least 10 ft (3 m) from the container and so positioned that the shutoff valves on both the truck and the container are readily accessible.

7.2.3.4 The cargo tank vehicle shall not transfer LP-Gas into dispensing system storage while parked on a public way.

7.2.3.5 Transfers to containers serving agricultural or industrial equipment requiring refueling in the field shall comply with 7.2.3.5(A) and 7.2.3.5(B).

(A)* Where the intake of air-moving equipment is less than 50 ft (15 m) from a point of transfer, it shall be shut down while containers are being refilled.

(B) Equipment employing open flames or equipment with integral containers shall be shut down while refueling.

7.2.3.6 From the time railroad tank cars are delivered to sidings and disconnected from the motive force for loading or unloading until they are again connected to the motive force for removal, the following shall apply:

(1) A caution sign, with wording such as "STOP. TANK CAR CONNECTED," shall be placed at the active end(s) of the siding while the car is connected for product transfer, as required by DOT regulations.

(2) Wheel chocks shall be placed to prevent movement of the car in either direction.

(3)* Access to the track shall be secured to prevent entry by other rail equipment while the car is connected for product transfer.

(4) The requirements of 7.2.3.6(2) shall not apply to movement on the siding to facilitate loading or unloading.

7.2.3.7 Where a hose or swivel-type piping is used for loading or unloading railroad tank cars, it shall be protected as follows:

(1) An emergency shutoff valve shall be installed at the railroad tank car end of the hose or swivel-type piping where flow into or out of the railroad tank car is possible.

(2) An emergency shutoff valve or a backflow check valve shall be installed on the railroad tank car end of the hose or swivel piping where flow is only into the railroad tank car.

7.2.3.8 Where cargo tank vehicles are filled directly from railroad tank cars on a private track with nonstationary storage tanks involved, the following requirements shall be met:

(1) Transfer protection shall be provided in accordance with Section 6.14.

(2) Ignition source control shall be in accordance with Section 6.25.

(3) Control of ignition sources during transfer shall be provided in accordance with 7.2.3.2.

(4) Fire extinguishers shall be provided in accordance with 9.4.7.

(5) Transfer personnel shall meet the provisions of 7.2.1.

(6) Cargo tank vehicles shall meet the requirements of 7.2.3.

(7) The points of transfer shall be located in accordance with Table 6.7.2.1 with respect to exposures.

(8) Provision for anchorage and breakaway shall be provided on the cargo tank vehicle side for transfer from a railroad tank car directly into a cargo tank vehicle.

(9) The provisions of Chapter 15 shall apply to all LP-Gas transfers performed in accordance with 7.2.3.8.

△ **7.2.3.9** Where cargo tank vehicles are filled from other cargo tank vehicles or cargo tanks, the following requirements shall apply:

(1) Transfer between cargo tanks or cargo tank vehicles where one is used as a bulk plant shall be temporary installations that comply with 4.3.2, 6.21.1, 6.21.2, 6.21.4 through 6.21.6, and 7.2.3.1.

(2) Arrangements and operations of the transfer system shall be in accordance with the following:

(a) The point of transfer shall be in accordance with Table 6.7.2.1.

(b) Sources of ignition within the transfer area shall be controlled during the transfer operation as specified in 7.2.3.2.

(c) Fire extinguishers shall be provided in accordance with 9.4.7.

(3) Cargo tanks shall comply with the requirements of 7.2.2.9.

(4) Provisions designed either to prevent a pull-away during a transfer operation or to stop the flow of products from both cargo tank vehicles or cargo tanks in the event of a pull-away shall be incorporated.

(5) Off-truck remote shutoff devices that meet 49 CFR 173.315(n) requirements and are installed on the cargo tank vehicle unloading the product shall satisfy the requirements of 7.2.3.9(4).

(6) Cargo tank vehicle LP-Gas transfers that are for the sole purpose of testing, maintaining, or repairing the cargo tank vehicle shall be exempt from the requirements of 7.2.3.9(1).

7.2.4 Hose Inspection.

7.2.4.1 Transfer hose assemblies shall be observed for leakage or for damage that could impair their integrity before each use.

Δ **7.2.4.2** Transfer hose assemblies shall be inspected at least annually.

7.2.4.3 Inspection of pressurized hose assemblies shall include inspection for the following:

(1) Damage to outer cover that exposes reinforcement
(2) Kinked or flattened hose
(3) Soft spots or bulges in hose
(4) Couplings that have slipped on the hose, are damaged, have missing parts, or have loose bolts
(5) Leakage other than permeability leakage

7.2.4.4 Hose assemblies shall be replaced, repaired, or continued in service based on the results of the inspection.

7.2.4.5 Leaking or damaged hose shall be immediately repaired or removed from service.

7.3 Venting LP-Gas to Atmosphere.

Δ **7.3.1 Outdoors.**

Δ **7.3.1.1** LP-Gas in liquid or vapor form shall only be vented to the atmosphere under the following conditions:

(1) Where the maximum flow from fixed liquid level, rotary, or slip tube gauges does not exceed that from a No. 54 drill orifice
(2) Between shutoff valves before disconnecting the liquid transfer line from the container
(3) Where necessary, by the use of bleeder valves
(4) Where the rate of discharge does not exceed the discharge from a No. 31 drill size orifice, from listed liquid transfer pumps using such vapor as a source of energy
(5) For purging in accordance with 7.3.3
(6) In emergencies
(7) Where utilized as the pressure source in remote shutdown systems for internal valves and emergency shutoff valves

N **7.3.1.2** Venting of compressor liquid traps shall be attended.

N **7.3.2 Within Structures.** Venting of LP-Gas shall be permitted for the conditions described in 7.3.1.1(1) and 7.3.1.1(2) within structures designed for container filling in accordance with Chapter 10.

7.3.3 Containers and Equipment.

Δ **7.3.3.1** Venting of gas shall be accomplished in accordance with 7.3.3.2 through 7.3.3.4.

Δ **7.3.3.2** Venting of cylinders indoors shall only occur in structures designed and constructed for cylinder filling in accordance with 6.7.1.1, Chapter 10, and 7.3.3.2(A) through 7.3.3.2(C).

(A) Piping shall be installed to convey the vented product outdoors at least 3 ft (1 m) above the highest point of any building within 25 ft (7.6 m).

(B) Only vapors shall be exhausted to the atmosphere.

(C) If a vent manifold is used to allow for the venting of more than one cylinder at a time, each connection to the vent manifold shall be equipped with a backflow check valve.

7.3.3.3 Venting of containers and equipment outdoors shall be performed under conditions that result in rapid dispersion of the product being released.

7.3.3.4 If conditions are such that venting into the atmosphere cannot be accomplished safely, LP-Gas shall be burned at a distance of at least 25 ft (7.6 m) from combustibles.

Δ **7.3.3.5** Venting and burning of LP-Gas from containers and equipment shall be attended.

7.4 Quantity of LP-Gas in Containers.

7.4.1 Application. Section 7.4 applies to the maximum permissible LP-Gas content of containers and the methods of verifying this quantity. *(See Annex F.)*

7.4.2 LP-Gas Capacity of Containers.

7.4.2.1 The capacity of an LP-Gas container shall be determined either by weight in accordance with 7.4.2.2 or by volume in accordance with 7.4.2.3.

7.4.2.2* The maximum filling limit by weight of LP-Gas in a container shall be in accordance with Table 7.4.2.2.

7.4.2.3* The maximum permitted volume of LP-Gas in a container shall be in accordance with Table 7.4.2.3(a), Table 7.4.2.3(b), and Table 7.4.2.3(c).

Table 7.4.2.2 Maximum Filling Limit by Weight of LP-Gas Containers (Percent of Marked Water Capacity in Pounds)

	Aboveground Containers		
Specific Gravity at 60°F (15.6°C)	**0 to 1200 gal (0 to 4.5 m³) Total Water Capacity (%)**	**>1200 gal (>4.5 m³) Total Water Capacity (%)**	**Underground Containers All Water Capacities (%)**
0.496–0.503	41	44	45
0.504–0.510	42	45	46
0.511–0.519	43	46	47
0.520–0.527	44	47	48
0.528–0.536	45	48	49
0.537–0.544	46	49	50
0.545–0.552	47	50	51
0.553–0.560	48	51	52
0.561–0.568	49	52	53
0.569–0.576	50	53	54
0.577–0.584	51	54	55
0.585–0.592	52	55	56
0.593–0.600	53	56	57

△ **7.4.3 General Provisions for Volumetric Method of Filling Containers.**

7.4.3.1 The volumetric method shall be limited to the following containers that are designed and equipped for filling by volume:

(1) Cylinders of less than 200 lb (91 kg) water capacity that are not subject to DOT jurisdiction
(2) Cylinders of 200 lb (91 kg) water capacity or more
(3) Cargo tanks or portable tanks
(4) ASME and API-ASME containers complying with 5.2.1.1 or 5.2.4.3

7.4.3.2 Where used, the volumetric method shall be in accordance with 7.4.3.2(A) through 7.4.3.2(C).

(A) If a fixed maximum liquid level gauge or a variable liquid level gauge without liquid volume temperature correction is used, the liquid level indicated by these gauges shall be computed based on the maximum permitted filling limit when the liquid is at 40°F (4°C) for aboveground containers or at 50°F (10°C) for underground containers.

(B) When a variable liquid level gauge is used and the liquid volume is corrected for temperature, the maximum permitted liquid level shall be in accordance with Table 7.4.2.3(a) through Table 7.4.2.3(c).

(C) ASME containers with a water capacity of 1200 gal (4.5 m^3) or less filled by the volumetric method shall be gauged in accordance with 7.4.3.2(A), utilizing the fixed maximum liquid level gauge, except that containers fabricated on or before December 31, 1965, shall be exempt from this provision.

7.4.3.3 Where containers are to be filled volumetrically by a variable liquid level gauge in accordance with 7.4.3.2(B), provisions shall be made for determining the liquid temperature.

7.4.4* Overfilling.

7.4.4.1 An overfilling prevention device shall not be the primary means to determine when a cylinder is filled to the maximum allowable filling limit.

7.4.4.2 Other means specified in this chapter shall be used to prevent the overfilling of cylinders.

Table 7.4.2.3(a) Maximum Permitted LP-Gas Volume (Percent of Total Container Volume): Aboveground Containers 0 to 1200 gal (0 to 4.5 m³)

Liquid Temperature		Specific Gravity												
°F	°C	0.496 to 0.503	0.504 to 0.510	0.511 to 0.519	0.520 to 0.527	0.528 to 0.536	0.537 to 0.544	0.545 to 0.552	0.553 to 0.560	0.561 to 0.568	0.569 to 0.576	0.577 to 0.584	0.585 to 0.592	0.593 to 0.600
−50	−45.6	70	71	72	73	74	75	75	76	77	78	79	79	80
−45	−42.8	71	72	73	73	74	75	76	77	77	78	79	80	80
−40	−40	71	72	73	74	75	75	76	77	78	79	79	80	81
−35	−37.2	71	72	73	74	75	76	77	77	78	79	80	80	81
−30	−34.4	72	73	74	75	76	76	77	78	78	79	80	81	81
−25	−31.5	72	73	74	75	76	77	77	78	79	80	80	81	82
−20	−28.9	73	74	75	76	76	77	78	79	79	80	81	81	82
−15	−26.1	73	74	75	76	77	77	78	79	80	80	81	82	83
−10	−23.3	74	75	76	76	77	78	79	79	80	81	81	82	83
−5	−20.6	74	75	76	77	78	78	79	80	80	81	82	82	83
0	−17.8	75	76	76	77	78	79	79	80	81	81	82	83	84
5	−15	75	76	77	78	78	79	80	81	81	82	83	83	84
10	−12.2	76	77	77	78	79	80	80	81	82	82	83	84	84
15	−9.4	76	77	78	79	80	80	81	81	82	83	83	84	85
20	−6.7	77	78	78	79	80	80	81	82	83	84	84	84	85
25	−3.9	77	78	79	80	80	81	82	82	83	84	84	85	85
30	−1.1	78	79	79	80	81	81	82	83	83	84	85	85	86
35	1.7	78	79	80	81	81	82	83	83	84	85	85	86	86
40*	4.4	79	80	81	81	82	82	83	84	84	85	86	86	87
45	7.8	80	80	81	82	82	83	84	84	85	85	86	87	87
50	10	80	81	82	82	83	83	84	85	85	86	86	87	88
55	12.8	81	82	82	83	84	84	85	85	86	86	87	87	88
60	15.6	82	82	83	84	84	85	85	86	86	87	87	88	88
65	18.3	82	83	84	84	85	85	86	86	87	87	88	88	89
70	21.1	83	84	84	85	85	86	86	87	87	88	88	89	89
75	23.9	84	85	85	85	86	86	87	87	88	88	89	89	90
80	26.7	85	85	86	86	87	87	87	88	88	89	89	90	90
85	29.4	85	86	87	87	88	88	88	89	89	89	90	90	91
90	32.2	86	87	87	88	88	89	89	90	90	90	90	91	91
95	35	87	88	88	88	89	89	90	90	90	91	91	91	92
100	37.8	88	89	89	89	89	90	90	90	91	91	92	92	92
105	40.4	89	89	90	90	90	90	91	91	91	92	92	92	93
110	43	90	90	91	91	91	91	92	92	92	92	93	93	93
115	46	91	91	92	92	92	92	92	92	93	93	93	94	94
120	49	92	92	93	93	93	93	93	93	93	94	94	94	94
125	51.5	93	94	94	94	94	94	94	94	94	94	94	95	95
130	54	94	95	95	95	95	95	95	95	95	95	95	95	95

*See 7.4.3.2(A).

Shaded text = Revisions.   Δ = Text deletions and figure/table revisions.   • = Section deletions.   *N* = New material.

Table 7.4.2.3(b) Maximum Permitted LP-Gas Volume (Percent of Total Container Volume): Aboveground Containers Over 1200 gal (Over 4.5 m³)

Liquid Temperature		Specific Gravity												
°F	°C	0.496 to 0.503	0.504 to 0.510	0.511 to 0.519	0.520 to 0.527	0.528 to 0.536	0.537 to 0.544	0.545 to 0.552	0.553 to 0.560	0.561 to 0.568	0.569 to 0.576	0.577 to 0.584	0.585 to 0.592	0.593 to 0.600
−50	−45.6	75	76	77	78	79	80	80	81	82	83	83	84	85
−45	−42.8	76	77	78	78	79	80	81	81	82	83	84	84	85
−40	−40	76	77	78	79	80	80	81	82	83	83	84	85	85
−35	−37.2	77	78	78	79	80	81	82	82	83	84	84	85	86
−30	−34.4	77	78	79	80	80	81	82	83	83	84	85	85	86
−25	−31.5	78	79	79	80	81	82	82	83	84	84	85	86	86
−20	−28.9	78	79	80	81	81	82	83	83	84	85	85	86	87
−15	−26.1	79	79	80	81	82	82	83	84	85	85	86	87	87
−10	−23.3	79	80	81	82	82	83	84	84	85	86	86	87	87
−5	−20.6	80	81	81	82	83	83	84	85	85	86	87	87	88
0	−17.8	80	81	82	82	83	84	84	85	86	86	87	88	88
5	−15	81	82	82	83	84	84	85	86	86	87	87	88	89
10	−12.2	81	82	83	83	84	85	85	86	87	87	88	88	89
15	−9.4	82	83	83	84	85	85	86	87	87	88	88	89	90
20	−6.7	82	83	84	85	85	86	86	87	88	88	89	89	90
25	−3.9	83	84	84	85	86	86	87	88	88	89	89	90	90
30	−1.1	83	84	85	86	86	87	87	88	89	89	90	90	91
35	1.7	84	85	86	86	87	87	88	89	89	90	90	91	91
40*	4.4	85	86	86	87	87	88	88	89	90	90	91	91	92
45	7.8	85	86	87	87	88	88	89	89	90	91	91	92	92
50	10	86	87	87	88	88	89	90	90	91	91	92	92	92
55	12.8	87	88	88	89	89	90	90	91	91	92	92	92	93
60	15.6	88	88	89	89	90	90	91	91	92	92	93	93	93
65	18.3	88	89	90	90	91	91	91	92	92	93	93	93	94
70	21.1	89	90	90	91	91	91	92	92	93	93	94	94	94
75	23.9	90	91	91	91	92	92	92	93	93	94	94	94	95
80	26.7	91	91	92	92	92	93	93	93	94	94	95	95	95
85	29.4	92	92	93	93	93	93	94	94	95	95	95	96	96
90	32.2	93	93	93	94	94	94	95	95	95	95	96	96	96
95	35	94	94	94	95	95	95	95	96	96	96	96	97	97
100	37.8	94	95	95	95	95	96	96	96	96	97	97	97	98
105	40.4	96	96	96	96	96	97	97	97	97	97	98	98	98
110	43	97	97	97	97	97	97	97	98	98	98	98	98	99
115	46	98	98	98	98	98	98	98	98	98	99	99	99	99

*See 7.4.3.2(A).

Shaded text = Revisions.   △ = Text deletions and figure/table revisions.   • = Section deletions.   N = New material.

2020 Edition

Table 7.4.2.3(c) Maximum Permitted LP-Gas Volume (Percent of Total Container Volume): All Underground Containers

Liquid Temperature		Specific Gravity												
°F	°C	0.496 to 0.503	0.504 to 0.510	0.511 to 0.519	0.520 to 0.527	0.528 to 0.536	0.537 to 0.544	0.545 to 0.552	0.553 to 0.560	0.561 to 0.568	0.569 to 0.576	0.577 to 0.584	0.585 to 0.592	0.593 to 0.600
−50	−45.6	77	78	79	80	80	81	82	83	83	84	85	85	86
−45	−42.8	77	78	79	80	81	82	82	83	84	84	85	86	87
−40	−40	78	79	80	81	81	82	83	83	84	85	86	86	87
−35	−37.2	78	79	80	81	82	82	83	84	85	85	86	87	87
−30	−34.4	79	80	81	81	82	83	84	84	85	86	86	87	88
−25	−31.5	79	80	81	82	83	83	84	85	85	86	87	87	88
−20	−28.9	80	81	82	82	83	84	84	85	86	86	87	88	88
−15	−26.1	80	81	82	83	84	84	85	86	86	87	87	88	89
−10	−23.3	81	82	83	83	84	85	85	86	87	87	88	88	89
−5	−20.6	81	82	83	84	84	85	86	86	87	88	88	89	89
0	−17.8	82	83	84	84	85	85	86	87	87	88	89	89	90
5	−15	82	83	84	85	85	86	87	87	88	88	89	90	90
10	−12.2	83	84	85	85	86	86	87	88	88	89	90	90	91
15	−9.4	84	84	85	86	86	87	88	88	89	89	90	91	91
20	−6.7	84	85	86	86	87	88	88	89	89	90	90	91	91
25	−3.9	85	86	86	87	87	88	89	89	90	90	91	91	92
30	−1.1	85	86	87	87	88	89	89	90	90	91	91	92	92
35	1.7	86	87	87	88	88	89	90	90	91	91	92	92	93
40	4.4	87	87	88	88	89	90	90	91	91	92	92	93	93
45	7.8	87	88	89	89	90	90	91	91	92	92	93	93	94
50*	10	88	89	89	90	90	91	91	92	92	93	93	94	94
55	12.8	89	89	90	91	91	91	92	92	93	93	94	94	95
60	15.6	90	90	91	91	92	92	92	93	93	94	94	95	95
65	18.3	90	91	91	92	92	93	93	94	94	94	95	95	96
70	21.1	91	91	92	93	93	93	94	94	94	95	95	96	96
75	23.9	92	93	93	93	94	94	94	95	95	95	96	96	97
80	26.7	93	93	94	94	94	95	95	95	96	96	96	97	97
85	29.4	94	94	95	95	95	95	96	96	96	97	97	97	98
90	32.2	95	95	95	95	96	96	96	97	97	97	98	98	98
95	35	96	96	96	96	97	97	97	97	98	98	98	98	99
100	37.8	97	97	97	97	97	98	98	98	98	99	99	99	99
105	40.4	98	98	98	98	98	98	98	99	99	99	99	99	99

*See 7.4.3.2(A).

Chapter 8 Storage of Cylinders Awaiting Use, Resale, or Exchange

8.1 Scope.

8.1.1 The provisions of this chapter apply to the storage of cylinders of 1000 lb (454 kg) water capacity or less, whether filled, partially filled, or empty, as follows:

(1) At consumer sites or dispensing systems, where not connected for use
(2) In storage for resale or exchange by dealer or reseller

8.1.2 This chapter does not apply to new or unused cylinders.

8.1.3 This chapter does not apply to cylinders stored at bulk plants.

8.2 General Provisions.

8.2.1 General Location of Cylinders.

8.2.1.1 Cylinders in storage shall be located to minimize exposure to excessive temperature rises, physical damage, or tampering.

8.2.1.2 Cylinders in storage having individual water capacity greater than 2.7 lb (1.1 kg) [nominal 1 lb (0.45 kg) LP-Gas capacity] shall be positioned so that the pressure relief valve is in direct communication with the vapor space of the cylinder.

8.2.1.3 Cylinders stored in buildings in accordance with Section 8.3 shall not be located near exits, near stairways, or in areas normally used, or intended to be used, for the safe egress of occupants.

8.2.1.4 If empty cylinders that have been in LP-Gas service are stored indoors, they shall be considered as full cylinders for the purposes of determining the maximum quantities of LP-Gas permitted by 8.3.1, 8.3.2.1, and 8.3.3.1.

8.2.1.5 Cylinders shall not be stored on roofs.

8.2.2 Protection of Valves on Cylinders in Storage.

8.2.2.1 Cylinder valves shall be protected as required by 5.2.6.1 and 7.2.2.5.

8.2.2.2 Screw-on-type caps or collars shall be in place on all cylinders stored, regardless of whether they are full, partially full, or empty, and cylinder outlet valves shall be closed.

8.2.2.3 Valve outlets on cylinders less than 108 lb (49 kg) water capacity [nominal 45 lb (20 kg) propane capacity] shall be plugged, capped, or sealed in accordance with 7.2.2.5.

8.3 Storage Within Buildings.

8.3.1 General. Storage of cylinders in buildings shall be in accordance with Table 8.3.1(a), Table 8.3.1(b), or the requirements of Section 8.3.

8.3.2 Storage Within Buildings Frequented by Public.

8.3.2.1 The quantity of LP-Gas in cylinders stored or displayed shall not exceed 200 lb (91 kg) in one location, with additional storage separated by 50 ft (15 m). The maximum quantity to be stored in one building shall not exceed 1000 lb (454 kg).

(A) Where the total quantity stored in a building exceeds 200 lb (91 kg), an approved sprinkler system that, at a minimum, meets the requirement of NFPA 13 for Ordinary Hazard (Group 2) shall be installed.

(B) The sprinkler density shall be 0.300 gpm/ft^2 (12.2 mm/min) over the most remote 2000 ft^2 (18.6 m^2) area, and the hose stream allowance shall be 250 gpm (946 L/min).

8.3.2.2 The cylinders shall not exceed a water capacity of 2.7 lb (1.1 kg) [nominal 1 lb (0.45 kg) LP-Gas].

8.3.2.3 In restaurants and at food service locations, storage of 10 oz (283 g) butane nonrefillable containers shall be limited to not more than 24 containers and 24 additional 10 oz (283 g) butane nonrefillable containers stored in another location within the building where constructed with at least 2-hour fire wall protection.

8.3.3 Storage Within Buildings Not Frequented by Public.

8.3.3.1 The maximum quantity of LP-Gas allowed in one storage location shall not exceed 735 lb (334 kg) water capacity [nominal 300 lb (136 kg) propane capacity].

8.3.3.2 Where additional storage locations are required on the same floor within the same building, they shall be separated by a minimum of 300 ft (91.4 m).

8.3.3.3 Storage beyond the limitations described in 8.3.3.2 shall comply with 8.3.4.

8.3.3.4 Cylinders carried as part of the service equipment on highway mobile vehicles shall not be part of the total storage capacity requirements of 8.3.3.1, where such vehicles are stored in private garages and carry no more than three cylinders with a total aggregate capacity per vehicle not exceeding 100 lb (45.4 kg) of propane.

8.3.3.5 Cylinder valves shall be closed when not in use.

8.3.4 Storage Within Special Buildings or Rooms.

8.3.4.1 The maximum quantity of LP-Gas stored in special buildings or rooms shall be 10,000 lb (4540 kg).

8.3.4.2 Special buildings or rooms for storing LP-Gas cylinders shall not be located where the buildings or rooms adjoin the line of property occupied by schools, churches, hospitals, athletic fields, or other points of public gathering.

8.3.4.3 The construction of all special buildings and rooms specified in 8.3.4.2 shall comply with Chapter 10 and the following:

(1) Vents to the outside only shall be provided at both the top and bottom of the building and shall be located at least 5 ft (1.5 m) from any building opening.
(2) The entire area shall be classified for purposes of ignition source control in accordance with Section 6.25.

8.3.5 Storage Within Residential Buildings. Storage of cylinders within a residential building, including the basement or any storage area in a common basement of a multiple-family building and attached or detached garages, shall be limited to cylinders each with a maximum water capacity of 2.7 lb (1.2 kg) and shall not exceed 5.4 lb (2.4 kg) aggregate water capacity per each living space unit.

Δ **Table 8.3.1(a) Maximum Allowable Storage Quantities of LP-Gas in Other Than Industrial, Storage, and Mercantile Occupancies**

Occupancy	Assembly	Educational	Day Care	Health Care	Ambulatory Health Care	Detention and Correctional	One- and Two-Family Dwellings	Lodging or Rooming House	Hotel and Dormitory	Apartment	Residential Board and Care	Business
Maximum Allowable Quantity (MAQ):												
Storage	2 lb	2 lb	2 lb	2 lb	2 lb	2 lb	2 lb	2 lb	2 lb	2 lb	2 lb	2 lb
Total MAQ for cylinders stored in cabinets	2 lb	2 lb	2 lb	2 lb	2 lb	2 lb	2 lb*	2 lb*	2 lb	2 lb*	2 lb	2 lb
Total MAQ for cylinders protected by suppression	2 lb	2 lb	2 lb	2 lb	2 lb	2 lb	2 lb*	2 lb*	2 lb	2 lb*	2 lb	2 lb
Total for cylinders both stored in cabinets and protected by suppression	2 lb	2 lb	2 lb	2 lb	2 lb	2 lb	2 lb*	2 lb*	2 lb	2 lb*	2 lb	2 lb
Total for attended catered food service per NFPA 58 in 10 oz maximum cylinders	15 lb	15 lb	15 lb	15 lb	15 lb	15 lb	15 lb	15 lb	15 lb	15 lb	15 lb	15 lb
Total for 10 oz cylinders in storage protected by a 2-hr fire wall	15 lb	15 lb	15 lb	15 lb	15 lb	15 lb	15 lb	15 lb	15 lb	15 lb	15 lb	15 lb
Total MAQ after any exemptions	20 lb	20 lb	0	5 lb								
	Flame effects per NFPA 160; additional 20 lb units with 20 ft (6 m) separation	In labs, not in classrooms; additional 20 lb units with 20 ft (6 m) separation		In labs only; additional 5 lb units with 20 ft separation								

For SI units, 1 lb = 0.45 kg; 1 oz = 0.028 kg; 1 ft = 0.3 m.
*1 lb maximum cylinder

8.4 Storage Outside of Buildings.

8.4.1* Location of Storage Outside of Buildings.

8.4.1.1 Storage outside of buildings for cylinders awaiting use or resale or that are part of a cylinder exchange point shall be located as follows:

(1) At least 5 ft (1.5 m) from any doorway or opening in a building frequented by the public where occupants have at least two means of egress as defined by NFPA *101*

(2) At least 10 ft (3 m) from any doorway or opening in a building or sections of a building that has only one means of egress

(3) At least 20 ft (6.1 m) from any automotive service station fuel dispenser

8.4.1.2 Distances from cylinders in storage outside of buildings shall be in accordance with Table 8.4.1.2 with respect to the following:

(1) Nearest important building or group of buildings
(2) Line of adjoining property that can be built upon
(3) Busy thoroughfares or sidewalks on other than private property
(4) Line of adjoining property occupied by schools, churches, hospitals, athletic fields, or other points of public gathering
(5) Dispenser

8.4.1.3 Fire-Resistive Protective Structure.

(A) The distances in Table 8.4.1.2 shall be reduced to 0 where a 2-hour fire-resistive protective structure made of noncombustible materials is provided that breaks the line of sight of the storage and the building.

△ **Table 8.3.1(b) Maximum Allowable Storage Quantities of LP-Gas in Mercantile, Industrial, and Storage Occupancies**

Occupancy	Mercantile	Industrial	Storage
Maximum Allowable Quantity (MAQ):			
Storage	200 lb (1 lb maximum/ cylinder)	300 lb	300 lb
Total MAQ for cylinders protected by suppression	200 lb	300 lb	300 lb
Total MAQ for cylinders both stored in cabinets and protected by suppression	200 lb	300 lb	300 lb
Total MAQ after any exemptions above	1000 lb Separation of groups of 200 lb by 50 ft and a sprinkler density of 0.300 gpm/ft² (12.2 mm/min) over the most remote 2000 ft² (18.6 m²) area and 250 gpm (946 L/min) hose stream allowance	Additional 300 lb 300 ft separation	10,000 lb In special rooms or buildings per Chapter 10

For SI units, 1 lb = 0.45 kg; 1 gpm = 3.8 L/min; 1 ft = 0.3 m; 1 ft² = 0.09 m².

Table 8.4.1.2 Distances from Cylinders in Storage and Exposures

Quantity of LP-Gas Stored		Horizontal Distance to ...					
		(1) and (2)		(3) and (4)		(5)*	
lb	kg	ft	m	ft	m	ft	m
≤720	≤227	0	0	0	0	5	1.5
721–2,500	>227–1,134	0	0	10	3	10	3
2,501–6,000	>1,134–2,721	10	3	10	3	10	3
6,001–10,000	>2,721–4,540	20	6.1	20	6.1	20	6.1
>10,000	>4,540	25	7.6	25	7.6	25	7.6

*The minimum distance from a point of transfer associated with a dispensing system must comply with Table 6.7.2.1.

(B) For buildings with exterior walls rated 2-hour fire resistance and constructed of noncombustible materials not provided with eaves over the storage, the exterior wall shall be allowed in lieu of a protective structure to reduce the distance to 0.

8.4.1.4 Cylinders in the filling process shall not be considered to be in storage.

8.4.2 Protection of Cylinders.

N 8.4.2.1* Cylinders at a location open to the public shall be placed on shelves constructed of materials with a flame spread index of less than 25, in accordance with ASTM E84, *Standard Test Method for Surface Burning Characteristics of Building Materials*, or ANSI/UL 723, *Standard for Test for Surface Burning Characteristics of Building Materials*, and shall be of sufficient strength to support the cylinders.

8.4.2.2 Cylinders at a location open to the public shall be protected by either of the following:

(1) An enclosure in accordance with 6.21.4.2
(2) A lockable ventilated enclosure of metal exterior construction

8.4.2.3* Vehicular barrier protection (VBP) shall be provided where vehicle traffic is expected at the location, except where cylinders are protected in accordance with 8.4.2.2(2).

8.4.3 Alternative Location and Protection of Storage. Where the provisions of 8.4.1 and 8.4.2.2 are impractical at construction sites or at buildings or structures undergoing major renovation or repairs, alternative storage of cylinders shall be acceptable to the authority having jurisdiction.

8.5 Fire Protection and Electrical Area Classification.

△ **8.5.1*** Retail cylinder exchange locations having aggregate quantities of 720 lb (327 kg) or more of propane shall be provided with at least one portable fire extinguisher having a minimum dry chemical agent capacity of 10 lb (4.5 kg) per Section 4.7.

△ **8.5.2** Other than those complying with 8.5.1, propane storage locations having aggregate quantities of propane exceeding 720 lb (327 kg) shall be provided with at least one portable fire extinguisher having a minimum dry chemical agent capacity of 18 lb (8.2 kg) per Section 4.7.

8.5.3 The required fire extinguisher shall be located within 50 ft (15 m) travel distance of the propane storage location.

8.5.4 The storage of cylinders awaiting resale shall be exempt from the electrical classification requirements of this code.

8.6 Automated Cylinder Exchange Stations.

8.6.1 Cylinder exchange cabinets that include an automated vending system for exchanging cylinders shall comply with the requirements in 8.6.2 through 8.6.6.

8.6.2 Electrical equipment installed in cylinder storage compartments shall comply with the requirements for Class I, Division 2 equipment in accordance with *NFPA 70*.

8.6.3 Cabinets shall be designed such that cylinders can be placed inside only in the upright position.

8.6.4 Door releases for access to stored cylinders shall be permitted to be pneumatic, mechanical, or electrically powered.

8.6.5 A manual override control shall be permitted for use by authorized personnel.

8.6.6 The vending system shall not be capable of returning to automatic operation after a manual override until the system has been inspected and reset by authorized personnel.

Chapter 9   Vehicular Transportation of LP-Gas

9.1 Scope.

9.1.1 This chapter applies to containers, container appurtenances, piping, valves, equipment, and vehicles used in the transportation of LP-Gas, as follows:

(1) Transportation of cylinders
(2) Transportation in cargo tank vehicles, whether fabricated by mounting cargo tanks on conventional truck or trailer chassis or constructed as integral cargo units in which the container constitutes in whole, or in part, the stress member of the vehicle frame
(3)* Transfer equipment and piping and the protection of such equipment and the container appurtenances against overturn, collision, or other vehicular accidents

9.1.2 This chapter does not apply to the following:

(1) Cylinders and related equipment incident to their use on vehicles as covered in Section 6.26 and Chapter 11
(2) Transportation of LP-Gas containers on vehicles where the containers are used to fuel the vehicle or appliances located on the vehicle as covered in Sections 6.26, 11.13, and 11.14
(3)* LP-Gas systems used for engine fuel

9.2 Electrical Requirements.

9.2.1 Only electrical lighting shall be used with the vehicles covered by this chapter.

9.2.2 Wiring shall be insulated and protected from physical damage.

9.3 Transportation in Portable Containers.

9.3.1 Application. Section 9.3 shall apply to the vehicular transportation of portable containers filled with LP-Gas delivered as "packages," including containers built to DOT cylinder specifications and other portable containers.

9.3.2 Transportation of Cylinders.

9.3.2.1 Cylinders having an individual water capacity not exceeding 1000 lb (454 kg) [nominal 420 lb (191 kg) propane capacity], when filled with LP-Gas, shall be transported in accordance with the requirements of Section 9.3.

9.3.2.2 Cylinders shall be constructed as provided in Section 5.2 and equipped in accordance with Section 5.9 for transportation as cylinders.

9.3.2.3 The quantity of LP-Gas in cylinders shall be in accordance with Chapter 7.

9.3.2.4 Cylinder valves shall comply with the following:

(1) Valves of cylinders shall be protected in accordance with 5.2.6.1.
(2) Screw-on-type protecting caps or collars shall be secured in place.
(3) The provisions of 7.2.2.5 shall apply.

9.3.2.5 The cargo space of the vehicle shall be isolated from the driver's compartment, the engine, and the engine's exhaust system.

(A) Open-bodied vehicles shall be considered to be in compliance with this provision.

(B) Closed-bodied vehicles having separate cargo, driver, and engine compartments shall be considered to be in compliance with this provision.

(C) Closed-bodied vehicles, such as passenger cars, vans, and station wagons, shall not be used for transporting more than 215 lb (98 kg) water capacity [nominal 90 lb (41 kg) propane capacity], but not more than 108 lb (49 kg) water capacity [nominal 45 lb (20 kg) propane capacity] per cylinder, unless the driver and engine compartments are separated from the cargo space by a vaportight partition that contains no means of access to the cargo space.

9.3.2.6 Cylinders and their appurtenances shall be determined to be leak-free before being loaded into vehicles.

9.3.2.7 Cylinders shall be loaded into vehicles with flat floors or equipped with racks for holding cylinders.

9.3.2.8 Cylinders shall be fastened in position to minimize the possibility of movement, tipping, and physical damage.

9.3.2.9 Cylinders being transported by vehicles shall be positioned in accordance with Table 9.3.2.9.

9.3.2.10 Vehicles transporting cylinders where the total weight is more than 1000 lb (454 kg), including the weight of the LP-Gas and the cylinders, shall be placarded as required by DOT regulations or state law.

9.3.3 Transportation of Portable Containers of More Than 1000 lb (454 kg) Water Capacity.

9.3.3.1 Portable tanks having an individual water capacity exceeding 1000 lb (454 kg) [nominal 420 lb (190 kg) propane capacity] when filled with LP-Gas shall be transported in compliance with the requirements of 9.3.3.

9.3.3.2 Portable tanks shall be constructed in accordance with Section 5.2 and shall comply with DOT portable tank specifications for LP-Gas service.

9.3.3.3 The quantity of LP-Gas put into portable tanks shall be in accordance with Chapter 7.

9.3.3.4 Valves and other portable tanks appurtenances shall be protected in accordance with 5.2.6.2.

Table 9.3.2.9 Orientation of Cylinders on Vehicles

Propane Capacity of Cylinder		Open Vehicles	Enclosed Spaces of Vehicles
lb	kg		
≤45	≤20	Any position	
>45	>20	Relief valve in communication with the vapor space	
≤4.2	≤1.9		Any position
>4.2	>1.9		Relief valve in communication with the vapor space

9.3.3.5 Transportation of portable tanks and their appurtenances shall be in accordance with the following:

(1) Portable tanks and their appurtenances shall be leak-free before being loaded into vehicles.

(2) Portable tanks shall be transported in a rack or frame or on a flat surface.

(3) Portable tanks shall be fastened in a position to minimize the possibility of movement, tipping, or physical damage, relative to each other or to the supporting structure, while in transit.

9.3.3.6 Portable tanks shall be transported with pressure relief devices in communication with the vapor space.

9.3.3.7 Vehicles carrying more than 1000 lb (454 kg), including the weight of the propane and the portable tanks, shall be placarded as required by DOT regulations or state law.

9.3.3.8 Where portable containers complying with the requirements of 9.3.3 are installed permanently or semipermanently on vehicles to serve as cargo tanks, so that the assembled vehicular unit can be used for making liquid deliveries to other containers at points of use, the provisions of Section 9.4 shall apply.

9.3.4 Transportation of Portable Storage Containers. ASME containers to be used as portable storage containers, including movable fuel storage tenders and farm carts for temporary stationary service (normally not more than 12 months duration at any location), when moved shall contain a liquid volume of 5 percent or less of the water capacity of the container, except for agricultural purposes where allowed in a DOT exemption.

9.3.5 Fire Extinguishers.

9.3.5.1 Each truck or trailer transporting portable containers in accordance with 9.3.2 or 9.3.3 shall be equipped with at least one portable fire extinguisher in accordance with Section 4.7 having a minimum capacity of 18 lb (8.2 kg) dry chemical.

9.4 Transportation in Cargo Tank Vehicles.

9.4.1 Application.

9.4.1.1 Section 9.4 applies to cargo tank vehicles used for the transportation of LP-Gas as liquid cargo.

9.4.1.2 Transfer shall be made by a pump or compressor mounted on the vehicle or by a transfer means at the delivery point.

9.4.1.3 All LP-Gas cargo tank vehicles, whether used in interstate or intrastate service, shall comply with the applicable portion of the U.S. Department of Transportation Hazardous Materials Regulations of the DOT Federal Motor Carrier Safety Regulations (49 CFR, Parts 171–180, 393, 396, and 397) and shall also comply with any added requirements of this code.

9.4.2 Cargo Tanks Mounted on, or a Part of, Cargo Tank Vehicles.

9.4.2.1 Cargo tanks mounted on, or comprising in whole or in part, the stress member used in lieu of a frame for cargo tank vehicles shall comply with DOT cargo tank vehicle specifications for LP-Gas service.

9.4.2.2 The cargo tanks specified in 9.4.2.1 shall also comply with Section 5.2 and be equipped with appurtenances for cargo service as provided in Section 5.9.

9.4.2.3 Liquid hose of 1½ in. (38 mm) (nominal size) and larger and vapor hose of 1¼ in. (32 mm) (nominal size) and larger shall be protected with an internal valve that is fitted for remote closure and automatic shutoff using thermal (fire) actuation.

9.4.2.4 Where flow is only into the cargo tank, a backflow check valve or an internal valve shall be installed in the cargo tank.

9.4.3 Piping (Including Hose), Fittings, and Valves.

9.4.3.1 Pipe, tubing, pipe and tubing fittings, valves, hose, and flexible connectors shall comply with the following:

(1) Section 5.11
(2) The provisions of DOT cargo tank vehicle specifications for LP-Gas
(3) The service pressure rating specified in 5.20.1.2

△ **9.4.3.2** The following shall also apply to pipe, tubing, pipe and tubing fittings, valves, hose, and flexible connectors:

(1) Pipe shall be wrought iron, steel, brass, copper, or austenitic stainless steel in accordance with 5.11.3.1.
(2) Tubing shall be steel, brass, or copper in accordance with 5.11.3.2.
(3) Pipe and tubing fittings shall be steel, brass, copper, malleable iron, or ductile (nodular) iron suitable for use with the pipe or tubing used as specified in 9.4.3.2(1) or 9.4.3.2(2).
(4) Pipe joints shall be threaded, flanged, welded, or brazed, and fittings, where used, shall comply with 9.4.3.2(3).
(5) Where joints are threaded, or threaded and back welded, pipe and nipples shall be Schedule 80 or heavier.
(6) Copper or brass pipe and nipples shall be of equivalent strength as Schedule 80 steel pipe or heavier.
(7) Where joints are welded or brazed, the pipe and nipples shall be Schedule 40 or heavier.
(8) The pressure ratings of fittings or flanges shall comply with Table 5.20.1.2.
(9) Brazed joints shall be made with a brazing material having a melting point exceeding 1000°F (538°C).
(10) Tubing joints shall be brazed using a brazing material having a melting point of at least 1000°F (538°C).

9.4.3.3 Pipe, tubing, pipe and tubing fittings, valves, hose, and flexible connectors, and complete cargo tank vehicle piping systems including connections to equipment, after assembly, shall comply with 5.20.1.2.

9.4.3.4 Valves, including shutoff valves, excess-flow valves, backflow check valves, and remotely controlled valves, used in piping shall comply with the following:

(1) DOT cargo tank vehicle specifications for LP-Gas service
(2) Section 5.14
(3) Pressure rating requirements of 5.20.1.2

9.4.3.5 Hose, hose connections, and flexible connectors shall comply with 5.11.6 and 9.4.3.1.

9.4.3.6 Flexible connectors used in the piping system to compensate for stresses and vibration shall be limited to 3 ft (1 m) in overall length and, when replaced, shall comply with 5.11.6.

Shaded text = Revisions. △ = Text deletions and figure/table revisions. • = Section deletions. N = New material.

2020 Edition

9.4.3.7 Flexible hose connectors shall comply with the following:

(1) Flexible hose connectors shall be permanently marked to indicate the date of installation of the flexible hose connector.

(2) The flexible hose portion of the connector shall be replaced with an unused connector within 10 years of the indicated date of installation of the connector and visually inspected before the first delivery of each day.

(3) The flexible hose portion of flexible connectors shall be replaced whenever a cargo tank unit is remounted on a different chassis, or whenever the cargo tank unit is repiped if such repiping encompasses that portion of piping in which the connector is located.

(4) Replacement of the flexible hose portion of the flexible connector shall not be required if the reinstallation or repiping is performed within 1 year of the date of assembly of the connector.

9.4.3.8 All threaded primary valves and fittings used in liquid filling or vapor equalization directly on the cargo tank of transportation equipment shall be of steel, malleable iron, or ductile iron construction.

9.4.3.9 All existing equipment shall be so equipped as described in 9.4.3.8 not later than the scheduled requalification date of the container.

9.4.4 Equipment.

9.4.4.1 LP-Gas equipment, such as pumps, compressors, meters, dispensers, regulators, and strainers, shall comply with Section 5.20 for design and construction and shall be installed in accordance with the applicable provisions of Section 6.20.

9.4.4.2 Equipment on cargo tank vehicles shall be mounted in place and connected to the fixed piping system in accordance with the manufacturer's instructions.

9.4.4.3 Cargo tank openings whose only function is for pump bypass return shall be provided with one of the following:

(1) A positive shutoff valve capable of being secured in the open position and located as close to the tank as practical and a steel backflow check valve installed in the tank

(2) An internal valve with excess-flow protection

(3) A valve that is specifically recommended and listed by the manufacturer for bypass return service and that meets the requirements of 6.20.2.3

9.4.4.4 Where an electric drive is used to power pumps or compressors mounted on vehicles and the energy is obtained from the electrical installation at the delivery point, the installation on the vehicle shall comply with 6.25.2.1.

9.4.4.5 Where wet hose is carried while connected to the truck's liquid pump discharge piping, an automatic device such as a differential back pressure valve shall be installed between the pump discharge and the hose connection to prevent liquid discharge while the pump is not operating.

(A) Where a meter or dispenser is used, the automatic device specified in 9.4.4.5 shall be installed between the meter outlet and the hose connection.

(B) If an excess-flow valve is used, it shall not be the exclusive means of complying with the provision of 9.4.4.5.

9.4.5 Protection of Cargo Tank Appurtenances, Piping System, and Equipment. Cargo tank appurtenances, piping, and equipment comprising the complete LP-Gas system on the cargo tank vehicle shall be mounted in position *(see 9.4.2.1 for container mounting)*, shall be protected against damage, and shall be in accordance with DOT regulations.

9.4.6 Painting and Marking Cargo Tank Vehicles.

9.4.6.1 Painting of cargo tank vehicles shall comply with 49 CFR.

9.4.6.2 Placarding and marking shall comply with 49 CFR.

9.4.7 Fire Extinguishers.

9.4.7.1 Each cargo tank vehicle or tractor shall be provided with at least one portable fire extinguisher in accordance with Section 4.7 having a minimum capacity of 18 lb (8.2 kg) dry chemical.

△ **9.4.8* Wheel Stops for Cargo Tank Vehicles.** Each cargo tank vehicle or trailer shall utilize wheel stops, in addition to the parking or hand brake, to prevent movement in either direction whenever the cargo tank vehicle is loading, unloading, or parked.

9.4.9 Exhaust Systems. The truck engine exhaust system shall comply with Federal Motor Carrier Safety regulations.

9.4.10 Smoking Prohibition. No person shall smoke or carry lighted smoking material as follows:

(1) On or within 25 ft (7.6 m) of a vehicle that contains LP-Gas liquid or vapor

(2) At points of liquid transfer

(3) When delivering or connecting to containers

9.5 Trailers, Semitrailers, and Movable Fuel Storage Tenders, Including Farm Carts.

9.5.1 Application. Section 9.5 applies to all cargo tank vehicles, other than trucks, that are parked at locations other than bulk plants.

9.5.2 Fuel Storage Tenders Including Farm Carts.

9.5.2.1 Movable fuel storage tenders including farm carts *(see 3.3.61.1, Movable Fuel Storage Tender)* shall comply with Section 9.5.

9.5.2.2 Where used over public ways, movable fuel storage tenders shall comply with applicable state regulations.

9.5.2.3 Movable fuel storage tenders shall be constructed in accordance with Section 5.2 and equipped with appurtenances as provided in Section 5.9.

9.5.2.4 Threaded piping shall be not less than Schedule 80, and fittings shall be designed for not less than 250 psig (1.7 MPag).

9.5.2.5 Piping, hose, and equipment, including valves, fittings, pressure relief valves, and container accessories, shall be protected against collision or upset.

9.5.2.6 Movable fuel storage tenders shall comply with the following:

(1) Movable fuel storage tenders shall be so positioned that container pressure relief valves communicate with the vapor space.

(2) Movable fuel storage tenders shall not be filled on a public way.

(3) Movable fuel storage tenders shall contain no more than 5 percent of their water capacity in liquid form during transportation to or from the bulk plant.

(4) Movable fuel storage tenders shall be moved on the shortest practical route when transporting tenders between points of utilization.

9.6 Transportation of Stationary Containers to and from Point of Installation.

9.6.1 Application.

9.6.1.1 Section 9.6 applies to the transportation of containers designed for stationary service at the point of use and secured to the vehicle only for transportation.

9.6.1.2 Containers described in 9.6.1.1 shall be transported in accordance with 9.6.2.

9.6.2 Transportation of Containers.

9.6.2.1 ASME containers of 125 gal (0.5 m^3) water capacity or more shall contain no more than 5 percent of their water capacity in liquid form during transportation.

9.6.2.2 Where a container is transported with more LP-Gas than 5 percent of its water capacity in a liquid form, all of the following conditions shall apply:

(1) The container shall not be filled beyond the filling limit of Section 7.4.

(2) Transportation shall be permitted only to move containers from a stationary or temporary installation to a bulk plant.

(3) Valves and fittings shall be protected by a method approved by the authority having jurisdiction to minimize the possibility of damage.

(4) Lifting lugs shall not be used to move these containers.

9.6.2.3 Containers shall be installed to minimize movement relative to each other or to the carrying vehicle while in transit, giving consideration to vehicular operation.

9.6.2.4 Valves, regulators, and other container appurtenances shall be protected against physical damage during transportation.

9.6.2.5 Pressure relief valves shall be in direct communication with the vapor space of the container.

9.7 Parking and Garaging Vehicles Used to Carry LP-Gas Cargo.

9.7.1 Application. Section 9.7 applies to the parking and garaging of vehicles used for the transportation of LP-Gas.

9.7.2 Parking Outdoors.

9.7.2.1 Vehicles shall not be left unattended on any street, highway, avenue, or alley, except for necessary absences from the vehicle associated with drivers' normal duties, including stops for meals and rest stops during the day or night, except as follows:

(1) This requirement shall not apply in an emergency.

(2) This requirement shall not apply to vehicles parked in accordance with 9.7.2.3 and 9.7.2.4.

9.7.2.2* Vehicles shall not be parked in congested areas.

9.7.2.3 Where vehicles are parked off the street in uncongested areas, they shall be at least 50 ft (15 m) from any building used for assembly, institutional, or multiple residential occupancy.

9.7.2.4 Where vehicles carrying portable containers or cargo tank vehicles of 3500 gal (13 m^3) water capacity or less are parked on streets adjacent to the driver's residence in uncongested residential areas, the parking locations shall be at least 50 ft (15 m) from a building used for assembly, institutional, or multiple residential occupancy.

9.7.3 Parking Indoors.

9.7.3.1 Cargo tank vehicles parked in any public garage or building shall have LP-Gas liquid removed from the following:

(1) Cargo tank
(2) Piping
(3) Pump
(4) Meter
(5) Hose
(6) Related equipment

9.7.3.2 Vehicles used to carry portable containers shall not be moved into any public garage or building for parking until all portable containers have removed from the vehicle.

9.7.3.3 The pressure in the delivery hose and related equipment shall be reduced to approximately atmospheric.

9.7.3.4 All valves shall be closed before the vehicle is moved indoors.

9.7.3.5 Delivery hose or valve outlets shall be plugged or capped before the vehicle is moved indoors.

9.7.3.6 Vehicles carrying or containing LP-Gas shall only be parked in buildings complying with Chapter 10 and located on premises owned or under the control of the operator of such vehicles where the following provisions are met:

(1) The public shall be excluded from such buildings.

(2) Floor level ventilation shall be provided in all parts of the building where such vehicles are parked.

(3) Leaks in the vehicle LP-Gas systems shall be repaired before the vehicle is moved indoors.

(4) Primary shutoff valves on cargo tanks and other LP-Gas containers on the vehicle (except propulsion engine fuel containers) shall be closed and delivery hose outlets shall be plugged or capped to contain system pressure before the vehicle is moved indoors.

(5) Primary shutoff valves on LP-Gas propulsion engine fuel containers shall be closed while the vehicle is parked.

(6) No LP-Gas container shall be located near a source of heat or within the direct path of hot air being blown from a blower-type heater.

(7) LP-Gas containers shall be gauged or weighed to determine that they are not filled beyond the maximum filling limit according to Section 7.4.

9.7.3.7 Where vehicles are serviced or repaired indoors, the following shall apply:

(1) When it is necessary to move a vehicle into any building located on premises owned or operated by the operator of such vehicle for service on engine or chassis, the provisions of 9.7.3.6 shall apply.

(2) When it is necessary to move a vehicle carrying or containing LP-Gas into any public garage or repair facility for service on the engine or chassis, the provisions of 9.7.3.1 shall apply, or the driver or a qualified representative of an LP-Gas operator shall be in attendance at all times while the vehicle is indoors, and the following shall apply:

(a) Leaks in the vehicle LP-Gas systems shall be repaired before the vehicle is moved indoors.

(b) Primary shutoff valves on cargo tanks, portable containers, and other LP-Gas containers installed on the vehicle (other than propulsion engine fuel containers) shall be closed.

(c) LP-Gas liquid shall be removed from the piping, pump, meter, delivery hose, and related equipment and the pressure therein reduced to approximately atmospheric before the vehicle is moved inside.

(d) Delivery hose or valve outlets shall be plugged or capped before the vehicle is moved indoors.

(e) No container shall be located near a source of heat or within the direct path of hot air blown from a blower or from a blower-type heater.

(f) LP-Gas containers shall be gauged or weighed to determine that they are not filled beyond the maximum filling capacity in accordance with Section 7.4.

9.7.3.8 If repair work or servicing is to be performed on a cargo tank vehicle system, all LP-Gas shall be removed from the cargo tank and piping, and the system shall be thoroughly purged before the vehicle is moved indoors.

Chapter 10 Buildings or Structures Housing LP-Gas Distribution Facilities

10.1 Scope.

10.1.1 Application. This chapter applies to the construction, ventilation, and heating of structures, parts of structures, and rooms housing LP-Gas systems where specified by other parts of the code.

10.1.2 Nonapplication. This chapter does not apply to buildings constructed or converted before December 31, 1972.

10.2 Separate Structures or Buildings.

10.2.1 Construction of Structures or Buildings.

10.2.1.1 Separate buildings or structures shall be one story in height and shall have walls, floors, ceilings, and roofs constructed of noncombustible materials.

10.2.1.2* Either of the following shall apply to the construction of exterior walls, ceilings, and roofs:

(1) Exterior walls and ceilings shall be of lightweight material designed for explosion venting.

(2) Walls or roofs of heavy construction, such as solid brick masonry, concrete block, or reinforced concrete construction, shall be provided with explosion venting windows that have an explosion venting area of at least 1 ft^2 (0.1 m^2) for each 50 ft^3 (1.4 m^3) of the enclosed volume.

10.2.1.3 The floor of separate structures shall not be below ground level.

10.2.1.4 Any space beneath the floor shall be of solid fill, or the perimeter of the space shall be left entirely unenclosed.

10.2.2 Structure or Building Ventilation. The structure shall be ventilated using air inlets and outlets, the bottom of which shall be not more than 6 in. (150 mm) above the floor, and ventilation shall be provided in accordance with the following:

(1) Where mechanical ventilation is used, the rate of air circulation shall be at least 1 ft^3/min·ft^2 (0.3 m^3/min·m^2) of floor area.

(2) Outlets shall discharge at least 5 ft (1.5 m) from any opening into the structure or any other structure.

(3) Where natural ventilation is used, each exterior wall shall be provided with one opening for each 20 ft (6.1 m) of length.

(4) Each opening shall have a minimum size of 50 in.^{2} (32,250 mm^2), and the total of all openings shall be at least 1 in.^{2}/ft^2 (6900 mm^2/m^2) of floor area.

10.2.3 Structure or Building Heating. Heating shall be by steam or hot water radiation or other heating transfer medium, with the heat source located outside of the building or structure *(see Section 6.25)*, or by electrical appliances listed for Class I, Group D, Division 2 locations in accordance with *NFPA 70.*

10.3 Attached Structures or Rooms Within Structures.

10.3.1 Construction of Attached Structures.

10.3.1.1 Attached structures shall be spaces where 50 percent or less of the perimeter of the enclosed space is comprised of common walls.

10.3.1.2 Attached structures shall comply with 10.2.1.

10.3.1.3 Common walls of structures shall have the following features:

(1) A fire resistance rating of at least 1 hour

(2) Where openings are required in common walls for rooms used only for storage of LP-Gas, 1½-hour (Class B) fire doors

(3) A design that withstands a static pressure of at least 100 lb/ft^2 (4.8 kPa)

10.3.1.4 Where the building to which the structure is attached is occupied by operations or processes having a similar hazard, the provisions of 10.3.1.3 shall not apply.

10.3.1.5 Ventilation and heating shall comply with 10.2.2 and 10.2.3.

10.3.2 Construction of Rooms Within Structures.

10.3.2.1 Rooms within structures shall be spaces where more than 50 percent of the perimeter of the space enclosed is comprised of common walls.

10.3.2.2 Rooms within structures shall be located in the first story and shall have at least one exterior wall with unobstructed free vents for freely relieving explosion pressures.

10.3.2.3 Walls, floors, ceilings, or roofs of the rooms shall be constructed of noncombustible materials.

10.3.2.4 Exterior walls and ceilings shall be of lightweight material designed for explosion venting.

10.3.2.5* Walls and roofs of heavy construction (such as solid brick masonry, concrete block, or reinforced concrete construction) shall be provided with explosion venting windows or panels that have an explosion venting area of at least 1 ft^2 (0.1 m^2) for each 50 ft^3 (1.4 m^3) of the enclosed volume.

10.3.2.6* Walls and ceilings common to the room and to the building within which it is located shall have the following features:

(1) Fire resistance rating of at least 1 hour
(2) Where openings are required in common walls for rooms used only for storage of LP-Gas, 1½-hour (Class B) fire doors
(3) Design that withstands a static pressure of at least 100 lb/ft^2 (4.8 kPa)

10.3.2.7 Where the building to which the structure is attached is occupied by operations or processes having a similar hazard, the provisions of 10.3.1.3 shall not apply.

10.3.2.8 Ventilation and heating shall comply with 10.2.2 and 10.2.3.

Chapter 11   Engine Fuel Systems

11.1 Scope.

△ 11.1.1* This chapter applies to engine fuel systems installed on mobile and nonstationary engines and off-road vehicles using LP-Gas in internal combustion engines, including containers, container appurtenances, carburetion equipment, piping, hose, and fittings, and their installation.

N 11.1.2 This chapter does not apply to over-the-road LP-Gas fueled vehicles. *(See Chapter 12.)*

11.1.3* Chapter 11 applies to the installation of fuel systems supplying engines used to propel motorized vehicles as defined in 11.1.1.

11.1.4 This chapter applies to garaging of vehicles where such systems are installed.

11.2 Training. Each person engaged in installing, repairing, filling, or otherwise servicing an LP-Gas engine fuel system shall be trained in accordance with Section 4.4.

11.3 Containers.

11.3.1*   General.

11.3.1.1 Containers shall be designed, fabricated, tested, and marked (or stamped) in accordance with the regulations of the U.S. Department of Transportation (DOT); the ASME *Boiler and Pressure Vessel Code*, Section VIII, "Rules for the Construction of Unfired Pressure Vessels"; or the API-ASME *Code for Unfired Pressure Vessels for Petroleum Liquids and Gases*, except for UG-125 through UG-136.

11.3.1.2 Adherence to applicable ASME Code case interpretations and addenda that have been adopted and published by ASME 180 calendar days prior to the effective date of this code shall be considered as compliant with the ASME Code.

11.3.1.3 Where containers fabricated to earlier editions of regulations, rules, or codes listed in 5.2.1.1 and of the Interstate Commerce Commission (ICC) *Rules for Construction of Unfired Pressure Vessels*, prior to April 1, 1967, are used, the requirements of Section 1.4 shall apply.

11.3.1.4 Containers that have been involved in a fire and show no distortion shall comply with the following:

N (A) Cylinders shall be requalified in accordance with CGA C-6, *Standard for Visual Inspection of Steel Compressed Gas Cylinders*, for continued service before being used or reinstalled.

(B) Cylinders shall be requalified by a manufacturer of the type of cylinder or by a repair facility approved by DOT.

(C) ASME or API-ASME containers shall be inspected and requalified in compliance with the requirements of NBBI NB23, *National Board Inspection Code*.

(D) All container appurtenances shall be replaced.

(E) DOT 4E specification (aluminum) cylinders or composite cylinders involved in a fire shall be permanently removed from service.

11.3.1.5 A cylinder with an expired requalification date shall not be refilled until it is requalified by the methods prescribed in DOT regulations.

11.3.1.6 Cylinders shall be designed and constructed for at least a 240 psig (1.6 MPag) service pressure.

11.3.1.7 Cylinders shall be continued in service and transported in accordance with DOT regulations.

• 11.3.2 Container   Maximum   Allowable   Working   Pressure (MAWP).

11.3.2.1 ASME engine fuel containers shall have an MAWP of at least 312 psig (2.2 MPag) or shall comply with 11.3.2.2.

△ 11.3.2.2 ASME engine fuel containers installed outside of enclosed spaces of nonpassenger vehicles shall have a minimum MAWP of 250 psig (1.7 MPag).

11.3.3   Container Repairs and Alterations.

11.3.3.1* Containers that show excessive denting, bulging, gouging, or corrosion shall be removed from service.

11.3.3.2 Repairs or alteration of a container shall comply with either 11.3.3.3 or the regulations, rules, or code under which the container was fabricated.

11.3.3.3 Repairs or alterations to ASME containers shall be in accordance with the NBBI NB23, *National Board Inspection Code*.

11.3.3.4 Field welding shall be permitted only on saddle plates, lugs, pads, or brackets that are attached to the container by the container manufacturer.

11.3.4 ASME Container Nameplates. The markings specified for ASME containers shall be on a stainless steel metal nameplate attached to the container, located to remain visible after the container is installed.

(A) The nameplate shall be attached in such a way as to minimize corrosion of the nameplate or its fastening means and not contribute to corrosion of the container.

(B) ASME containers shall be marked with the following information:

(1) Service for which the container is designed (e.g., underground, aboveground, or both)

(2) Name and address of container supplier or trade name of container

(3) Water capacity of container in pounds or U.S. gallons (kg or m³)

(4) MAWP in pounds per square inch (psig) (MPag)

(5) Wording that reads "This container shall not contain a product that has a vapor pressure in excess of 215 psig (1.5 MPag) at 100°F (38°C)" *(see Table 5.2.4.3)*

(6) Outside surface area in square feet (m²)

(7) Year of manufacture

(8) Shell thickness and head thickness

(9) OL (overall length), OD (outside diameter), and HD (head design)

(10) Manufacturer's unique serial number

(11) ASME Code symbol

(12) Minimum design metal temperature: "___°F at MAWP ___ psig (___ °C at MAWP ___ MPag)"

(13) Type of construction: "W"

(14) Degree of radiography: "RT-___"

11.3.5 Container Filling. Containers larger than 30 gal (0.1 m³) water capacity shall be equipped for filling into the vapor space.

11.3.6 Container Connections.

11.3.6.1 The connections for pressure relief valves shall communicate directly with the vapor space of the container and shall not reduce the relieving capacity of the relief device.

11.3.6.2 The connection for the pressure relief valve shall be internally piped to the uppermost point practical in the vapor space of the container if the connection is located at any position other than the uppermost point practical in the vapor space of the container.

11.3.6.3 The container openings shall be labeled on the container or valves connected to the container opening to designate whether they communicate with the vapor or with the liquid space.

11.3.6.4 Labels shall not be required on openings for pressure relief valves and gauging devices.

11.3.7* Container Corrosion Protection.

(A) Engine fuel containers constructed of steel shall be painted or powder coated to minimize corrosion.

(B) Stainless steel, composite, or aluminum containers shall not be required to be painted or powder coated.

11.4 Container Appurtenances.

11.4.1 General Requirements for Appurtenances.

11.4.1.1 Container appurtenances (such as valves and fittings) shall comply with Section 5.9 and 11.4.1.2 through 11.4.1.16(A).

11.4.1.2 Container appurtenances shall have a pressure rating equal to or greater than the design pressure of the container.

11.4.1.3 Manual shutoff valves shall be designed to provide positive closure under service conditions and shall be equipped with an internal excess-flow check valve designed to close automatically at the rated flows of vapor or liquid specified by the manufacturers.

Δ **11.4.1.4** A filler valve shall comply with 5.9.4.1(C)(7) and shall be installed in the fill opening of the container.

(A) A filler valve used for remote filling shall be permitted to incorporate a single backflow check valve and shall be connected to the filler valve on the container by metal tubing or flexible hose connector.

(B) Where a flexible hose connector is used, it shall comply with 11.7.3.1.

11.4.1.5 Containers shall be fabricated so they can be equipped with a fixed maximum liquid level gauge as follows:

(1) The fixed maximum liquid level gauge shall be capable of indicating the maximum permitted filling level in accordance with 7.4.3.2(A).

(2) Fixed maximum liquid level gauges in the container shall be designed so the bleeder valve maximum opening to the atmosphere is not larger than a No. 54 drill size.

(3) The container fixed maximum liquid level gauge opening and the remote bleeder valve opening shall not be larger than a No. 54 drill size where the bleeder valve is installed at a location remote from the container.

11.4.1.6 ASME containers shall be equipped with full internal or flush-type full internal pressure relief valves conforming with applicable requirements of UL 132, *Standard for Safety Relief Valves for Anhydrous Ammonia and LP-Gas,* or other equivalent pressure relief valve standards.

(A) Fusible plugs shall not be used.

(B) The start-to-leak setting of the pressure relief valves specified in 11.4.1.6, with relation to the MAWP of the container, shall be in accordance with Table 5.9.2.5(A).

11.4.1.7 Permanently mounted ASME containers shall be equipped with a valve or combination of valves in the liquid outlet connection that has manual shutoff, excess-flow, and automatic closure features.

(A) The valve assembly shall prevent the flow of fuel when the engine is not in an operating mode even if the ignition switch is in the "on" position.

(B) This requirement shall not apply to industrial and forklift trucks.

11.4.1.8 Pressure relief valves shall be marked as follows:

(1) In accordance with CGA S-1.3, *Pressure Relief Device Standards, Part 3 — Stationary Storage Containers for Compressed Gases,* and ASME Code, Section VIII, UG-125 through UG-136

(2) With the rated relieving capacity in cubic feet per minute of air at 60°F (16°C) and 14.7 psia (101 kPa)

(3) With the manufacturer's name and catalog number

11.4.1.9 Cylinders used in engine fuel service for industrial trucks shall be equipped with full internal or flush-type full internal pressure relief valves.

Δ **11.4.1.10** Single-opening cylinders in industrial truck service shall be equipped with a listed multiple function valve in accordance with 5.9.4.1(C)(11) and 5.9.4.1(C)(12).

11.4.1.11 A float gauge, if used, shall be designed and approved for use with LP-Gas.

11.4.1.12 A solid steel plug shall be installed in unused threaded openings.

11.4.1.13 A bolted blind flange with gasket shall be installed in all unused flanged openings.

11.4.1.14 ASME containers fabricated after January 1, 1984, for use as engine fuel containers on vehicles shall be equipped or fitted with an overfilling prevention device.

△ **11.4.1.15** Where an overfilling prevention device is installed on the ASME container or exterior of the compartment and remote filling is used, a filler valve complying with 5.9.4.1(C)(7)(a) or 5.9.4.1(C)(7)(b) shall be installed in the exterior fill opening, and a filler valve complying with 5.9.4.1(C)(7)(c) shall be installed in the container filler valve opening.

11.4.1.16* Where an overfilling prevention device is installed on an ASME engine fuel container, venting of gas through the fixed maximum liquid level gauge during filling shall not be required.

(A) Where the fixed maximum liquid level gauge is not used during filling in accordance with 11.4.1.16, the fixed maximum liquid level gauge or other approved means shall be used annually to verify the operation of the overfilling prevention device.

(B) If the container is found to be overfilled during the test, corrective action shall be taken.

(C) The result shall be documented.

(D) A label shall be affixed to the container near the fill point indicating the expiration date of the successful test.

11.5 Quantity of LP-Gas in Engine Fuel Containers. The maximum permitted filling limit for engine fuel containers shall be as follows:

(1) For permanently mounted ASME engine fuel containers, the maximum permitted filling limit shall not exceed the amount shown in Table 7.4.2.3(a) when the liquid is at 40°F (4°C).
(2) For removable engine fuel containers, the maximum permitted filling limit shall be in accordance with 7.4.2 and 7.4.3.

11.6 Carburetion Equipment.

11.6.1 Pressure. Carburetion equipment subject to a pressure of 125 psig (0.9 MPag) or greater shall be designed for a pressure rating of 250 psig (1.7 MPag) or for the MAWP of the container where the MAWP of the container is greater than 250 psig (1.7 MPag).

11.6.2 Vaporizers.

11.6.2.1 Vaporizers shall be fabricated of materials resistant to corrosion by LP-Gas under service conditions.

11.6.2.2 Vaporizers shall be designed for engine fuel service.

11.6.2.3 Vaporizers subjected to pressures up to the MAWP of the supply container shall have a pressure rating of 250 psig (1.7 MPag) or the MAWP of the container where the MAWP of the container is greater than 250 psig (1.7 MPag).

11.6.2.4 Vaporizers shall be marked with the design pressure of the fuel-containing portion in psig (MPag), and the marking shall be visible when the vaporizer is installed.

11.6.2.5 The vaporizer shall not be equipped with a fusible plug.

11.6.2.6 Each vaporizer shall be capable of having the water or heating fluid drained from the engine cooling system drain or water hose or shall have a valve or plug located at or near the lowest portion of the section occupied by the water or other heating fluid to allow drainage of the water or heating fluid.

11.6.2.7 Where engine exhaust gases are used as a direct source of heat to vaporize the fuel, the materials of construction of those parts of the vaporizer in contact with the exhaust gases shall be resistant to corrosion by these gases, and the vaporizer system shall be designed to prevent a pressure in excess of 200 psig (1.4 MPag).

11.6.2.8 Devices that supply heat directly to the fuel container shall be equipped with an automatic device to cut off the supply of heat before the pressure in the container reaches 200 psig (1.4 MPag).

N 11.6.2.9 Fuel injection systems shall comply with the applicable requirements of Chapter 12.

11.6.3 Fuel Shutoff Valve.

11.6.3.1 An automatic shutoff valve shall be provided in the fuel system as close as practical to the inlet of the gas regulator.

11.6.3.2 The valve shall prevent flow of fuel to the carburetor when the engine is not running even if the ignition switch is in the "on" position.

11.6.3.3 Atmospheric-type regulators (zero governors) shall not be considered as automatic shutoff valves for the purpose of the requirements of 11.6.3.

11.7 Piping, Hose, and Fittings.

11.7.1 Pipe and Tubing.

11.7.1.1 Pipe shall be wrought-iron or steel (black or galvanized), brass, or copper and shall comply with the following:

(1) Wrought-iron: ASME B36.10M, *Welded and Seamless Wrought Steel Pipe*
(2) Steel pipe: ASTM A53/A53M, *Standard Specification for Pipe, Steel, Black and Hot-Dipped, Zinc-Coated, Welded and Seamless*
(3) Steel pipe: ASTM A106/A106M, *Standard Specification for Seamless Carbon Steel Pipe for High-Temperature Service*
(4) Brass pipe: ASTM B43, *Standard Specification for Seamless Red Brass Pipe, Standard Sizes*
(5) Copper pipe: ASTM B42, *Standard Specification for Seamless Copper Pipe, Standard Sizes*

△ **11.7.1.2** Tubing shall be steel, stainless steel, brass, or copper and shall comply with the following:

(1) Brass tubing: ASTM B135/B135M, *Standard Specification for Seamless Brass Tube*
(2) Copper tubing:

    (a) ASTM B75/B75M, *Standard Specification for Seamless Copper Tube*
    (b) Type K or L: ASTM B88, *Standard Specification for Seamless Copper Water Tube*
    (c) ASTM B280, *Standard Specification for Seamless Copper Tube for Air Conditioning and Refrigeration Field Service*

(3) Stainless Steel shall be one of the 300 series as follows:

    (a) ASTM A213/A213M, *Standard Specification for Seamless Ferritic and Austenitic Alloy-Steel Boiler, Superheater, and Heat-Exchanger Tubes*

(b) ASTM A249/A249M, *Standard Specification for Welded Austenitic Steel Boiler, Superheater, Heat-Exchanger, and Condenser Tubes*

(c) ASTM A269/A269M, *Standard Specification for Seamless and Welded Austenitic Stainless Steel Tubing for General Service*

(4) Steel Tubing: SAE J356, *Welded Flash-Controlled Low-Carbon Steel Tubing Normalized for Bending, Double Flaring, and Beading*

11.7.2 Fittings for Metallic Pipe and Tubing.

11.7.2.1 Fittings shall be steel, brass, copper, malleable iron, or ductile (nodular) iron.

11.7.2.2 Pipe fittings shall have a minimum pressure rating as specified in Table 11.7.2.2 and shall comply with the following:

(1) Cast-iron pipe fittings shall not be used.
(2) Brazing filler material shall have a melting point that exceeds 1000°F (538°C).

11.7.2.3 Metal tube fittings shall have a minimum pressure rating as specified in Table 11.7.2.2.

11.7.3 Hose, Hose Connections, and Flexible Connectors.

11.7.3.1 Hose, hose connections, and flexible hose connectors *(see 3.3.28)* used for conveying LP-Gas liquid or vapor at pressures in excess of 5 psig (34.5 kPag) shall be fabricated of materials resistant to the action of LP-Gas both as liquid and vapor, and the hose and flexible hose connector shall be reinforced with stainless steel wire braid.

11.7.3.2 Hose that can be exposed to container pressure shall be designed for a pressure rating of 350 psig (2.4 MPag) with a safety factor of 5 to 1, and the reinforcement shall be stainless steel wire braid.

11.7.3.3 Hose Marking.

(A) Hose shall be marked "LP-GAS, PROPANE, 350 PSI WORKING PRESSURE" and the manufacturer's name or trademark. Marking shall comply with one of the following:

(1) Permanent markings at intervals not exceeding 6 in. (152 mm)
(2) Permanent labels applied not less than once per foot (305 mm) of length

(B) Each installed piece of hose shall contain at least one such marking.

Table 11.7.2.2 Service Pressure Rating of Pipe, Tube Fittings, and Valves

Service	Minimum Pressure
Higher than container pressure	350 psig (2.4 MPag) or the MAWP, whichever is higher, or 400 psig (2.8 MPag) WOG rating
LP-Gas liquid or vapor at operating pressure over 125 psig (0.9 MPag) and at or below container pressure	250 psig (1.7 MPag)
LP-Gas vapor at operating pressure or 125 psig (0.9 MPag) or less	125 psig (0.9 MPag)

11.7.3.4 Pressure Capacity.

(A) After the application of couplings, hose assemblies shall be capable of withstanding a pressure of not less than 700 psig (4.8 MPag).

(B) If a pressure test is performed, such assemblies shall be pressure tested at 120 percent of the pressure rating [350 psig (2.4 MPag) minimum] of the hose.

11.7.3.5 Hose used for vapor service at 5 psig (34.5 kPag) or less shall be constructed of material resistant to the action of LP-Gas.

11.7.3.6 Hose in excess of 5 psig (34.5 kPag) service pressure and quick connectors shall be approved.

11.7.3.7 Hose that is utilized at lower than container pressure shall be designed and marked for its maximum anticipated operating pressure.

11.8 Installation of Containers and Container Appurtenances.

11.8.1 Location of Containers.

11.8.1.1 Containers shall be located to minimize the possibility of damage to the container and its fittings.

11.8.1.2 Where containers are located in the rear of the vehicle, they shall be protected.

11.8.1.3 Containers located less than 18 in. (460 mm) from the exhaust system, the transmission, or a heat-producing component of the internal combustion engine shall be shielded by a vehicle frame member or by a noncombustible baffle with an air space on both sides of the frame member or baffle.

11.8.1.4 After a container is permanently installed on a vehicle, container markings shall be readable either directly or with a portable lamp and mirror.

11.8.2 Protection of Containers and Appurtenances.

11.8.2.1 Container valves, appurtenances, and connections shall be protected to prevent damage due to accidental contact with stationary objects, or from stones, mud, or ice, and from damage due to an overturn or similar vehicular accident.

11.8.2.2 Protection of container valves, appurtenances, and connections shall be provided by one of the following:

(1) By locating the container so that parts of the vehicle furnish the necessary protection
(2) By the use of a fitting guard furnished by the manufacturer of the container
(3) By other means to provide equivalent protection

11.8.3 Container Clearances.

11.8.3.1 Containers shall not be mounted directly on roofs or ahead of the front axle or beyond the rear bumper of the vehicles.

11.8.3.2 No part of a container or its appurtenances shall protrude beyond the sides or top of the vehicle.

11.8.3.3 Containers shall be installed with as much ground clearance as practicable.

Δ **11.8.3.4** Clearance shall be measured to the bottom of the container or the lowest fitting, support, or attachment on the container or its housing, if any, whichever is lowest.

△ **11.8.3.5** Containers installed between axles shall comply with 11.8.3.6 or shall not be lower than the lowest point forward of the container with the vehicle suspension under full-rated load compression on the following points:

(1) Lowest structural component of the body
(2) Lowest structural component of the frame or subframe
(3) Lowest point on the engine
(4) Lowest point of the transmission (including the clutch housing or torque converter housing, as applicable)

△ **11.8.3.6** Containers installed behind the rear axle and extending below the frame shall comply with 11.8.3.7 or shall not be lower than the lowest of the following points and surfaces with the vehicle suspension under full-rated load compression:

(1) Containers shall not be lower than the lowest point of a structural component of the body, engine, and transmission (including clutch housing or torque converter housing, as applicable) forward of the container.
(2) Containers shall not be lower than lines extending rearward from each wheel at the point where the wheels contact the ground directly below the center of the axle to the lowest and most rearward structural interference.

11.8.3.7 Where an LP-Gas container is substituted for the fuel container installed by the original manufacturer of the vehicle, the LP-Gas container either shall fit within the space in which the original fuel container was installed or shall comply with 11.8.3.5 or 11.8.3.6.

11.8.4 Container Installation.

△ **11.8.4.1** Fuel containers shall be installed to prevent their jarring loose and slipping or rotating, and the fastenings shall be designed and constructed to withstand static loading in any direction equal to four times the weight of the container filled with fuel.

11.8.4.2 Welding for the repair or alterations of containers shall comply with 11.3.3.4.

11.8.4.3* Main shutoff valves on a container for liquid and vapor shall be readily accessible without the use of tools, or other equipment shall be provided to shut off the container valves.

11.8.5 Pressure Relief Valve Discharge System.

11.8.5.1 The pressure relief valve discharge from fuel containers on vehicles other than industrial (and forklift) trucks shall be in accordance with the following:

(1) It shall be directed upward or downward within 45 degrees of vertical.
(2) It shall not directly impinge on the vehicle fuel container(s), the exhaust system, or any other part of the vehicle.
(3) It shall not be directed into the interior of the vehicle.

11.8.5.2 Where the pressure relief valve discharge must be piped away, the pipeaway system shall have a breakaway adapter.

(A) The breakaway adapter shall have a melting point of not less than 1500°F (816°C).

(B) The adapter either shall be an integral part of the pressure relief valve or shall be a separate adapter attached directly to the pressure relief valve.

(C) The pipeaway system shall be designed and installed to prevent failure due to thermal or mechanical stress.

(D) Where used, nonmetallic hose shall be as short as practicable and shall be able to withstand the downstream pressure from the relief valve in the full open position, and the hose shall be fabricated of materials resistant to the action of LP-Gas.

(E) Where hose is used to pipe away the relief valve discharge on containers installed on the outside of the vehicle, the breakaway adapter and any attached fitting shall deflect the relief valve discharge upward or downward within 45 degrees of vertical and shall meet the other requirements of 11.8.5.1 without the hose attached. If an additional fitting is necessary to meet this requirement, it shall have a melting point not less than 1500°F (816°C).

(F) The pipeaway system shall have a protective cover to minimize the possibility of the entrance of water or dirt into either the relief valve or its discharge system.

(G) No portion of the system shall have an internal diameter less than the internal diameter of the recommended breakaway adapter.

(H) The breakaway adapter either shall be threaded for direct connection to the relief valve and shall not interfere with the operation of the relief valve or shall be an integral part of the pressure relief valve. It shall break away without impairing the function of the relief valve.

(I) The pipeaway system connections shall be mechanically secured and shall not depend on adhesives or sealing compounds and shall not be routed between a bumper system and the vehicle body.

(J) Where a pipeaway system is not required, the pressure relief valve shall have a protective cover.

11.9 Installation in Interior of Vehicles.

11.9.1 Installation of Containers and Appurtenances.

11.9.1.1 Installation of containers in the interior of vehicles or in enclosed compartments shall comply with either 11.9.1.2 or 11.9.1.3.

11.9.1.2* The container and its appurtenances shall be installed in an enclosure that is securely mounted to the vehicle.

(A) The enclosure shall be gastight with respect to driver or passenger compartments and to any space containing radio transmitters or other spark-producing equipment.

(B) The enclosure shall be vented to the outside of the vehicle.

11.9.1.3 The container appurtenances and their connections shall be installed in an enclosure that is securely mounted on the container.

(A) The appurtenances and their connections shall be installed in an enclosure that is gastight with respect to the driver or passenger compartments or with any space carrying radio transmitters or other sources of ignition.

(B) The enclosure shall be vented to the outside of the vehicle.

△ 11.9.1.4 Fuel containers and piping shall be installed so that no gas from fueling and gauging operations can be released inside of the passenger or enclosed compartments of the vehicle.

11.9.1.5 Enclosures, structures, seals, and conduits used to vent enclosures shall be designed and fabricated of durable materials and shall be designed to resist damage, blockage, or dislodgement through movement of articles carried in the vehicle or by the closing of luggage compartment enclosures or vehicle doors and shall require the use of tools for removal.

11.10 Pipe and Hose Installation.

11.10.1 General Requirements.

11.10.1.1 The piping system shall be designed, installed, supported, and secured in such a manner as to minimize damage due to expansion, contraction, vibration, strains, abrasion, UV deterioration, and wear.

11.10.1.2* Pipe, tubing, and hoses shall be installed in a manner that protects them from damage due to accidental contact with stationary objects, impact from stones, mud, or ice, or a vehicular accident.

11.10.1.3 Piping and hose shall be installed in a manner that permits visual inspection.

11.10.1.4 Fastening or other protection shall be installed to prevent damage due to vibration or abrasion.

11.10.1.5 At each point where piping passes through sheet metal or a structural member, a rubber grommet or equivalent protection shall be installed to prevent chafing.

11.10.1.6 Fuel line piping that must pass through the floor of a vehicle shall be installed to enter the vehicle through the floor directly beneath or adjacent to the container.

11.10.1.7 If a branch fuel line is required, the tee connection shall be in the main fuel line outside the passenger compartment of the vehicle.

11.10.1.8 Where liquid service lines of two or more individual containers are connected together, a spring-loaded backflow check valve or equivalent shall be installed in each of the liquid lines prior to the point where the liquid lines tee together to prevent the transfer of LP-Gas from one container to another.

11.10.1.9 Exposed parts of the piping system shall be of corrosion-resistant material or shall be protected to minimize exterior corrosion.

11.10.1.10 Piping systems, including hose, shall be tested and proven free of leaks at not less than normal operating pressure.

11.10.1.11 There shall be no fuel connection between a tractor and trailer or other vehicle units.

11.10.2 Hydrostatic Relief Valves.

11.10.2.1 A hydrostatic relief valve or device providing pressure-relieving protection shall be installed in each section of piping (including hose) in which liquid LP-Gas can be isolated between shutoff valves, so as to relieve to the atmosphere.

11.10.2.2 Hydrostatic relief valves shall have a pressure setting of not less than 400 psig (2.8 MPag) or more than 500 psig (3.5 MPag).

11.11 Industrial (and Forklift) Trucks Powered by LP-Gas.

11.11.1 Scope. Section 11.11 applies to LP-Gas installation on industrial trucks (including forklift trucks), both to propel them and to provide the energy for their materials-handling attachments.

11.11.2 Industrial Truck Cylinders.

11.11.2.1 Cylinders shall be designed, constructed, or fitted for installation and filling in either the vertical or horizontal position or, if the cylinder is a universal cylinder, in either position.

11.11.2.2 Universal cylinders shall be permitted to be filled in the vertical position or in the horizontal position, provided the positioning hole or slot is in the proper orientation.

11.11.2.3 The fixed maximum liquid level gauge shall indicate the maximum permitted filling level in either position.

11.11.2.4 The pressure relief valves shall be in direct communication with the vapor space of the cylinder in either position.

11.11.2.5 The cylinder vapor or liquid withdrawal valves shall function in either position.

11.11.2.6 The cylinder pressure relief valve discharge shall be directed upward within 45 degrees of vertical and otherwise shall not impinge on the cylinder, the exhaust system, or any other part of the industrial truck.

11.11.2.7 The discharge opening shall be provided with a protective cover to minimize the possibility of the entry of water or any extraneous matter.

△ 11.11.2.8 Industrial truck cylinders shall have pressure relief valves that conform with 5.9.4.1(C)(11) or 5.9.4.1(C)(12).

△ 11.11.3 Hose.

N 11.11.3.1 Hose used in vapor service and greater than 5 ft (1.5 m) in length shall be of stainless steel wire braid construction.

N 11.11.3.2 Hose used in liquid service shall be of stainless steel wire braid construction.

11.11.4 Operations. The operation of industrial trucks (including forklift trucks) powered by LP-Gas engine fuel systems shall comply with 11.11.4.1 through 11.11.4.4.

11.11.4.1 Industrial trucks shall be refueled outdoors.

11.11.4.2 Where cylinders are exchanged indoors, the fuel piping system shall be equipped to minimize the release of fuel when cylinders are exchanged, in accordance with either of the following:

(1) Using an approved quick-closing coupling in the fuel line
(2) Closing the shutoff valve at the fuel cylinder and allowing the engine to run until the fuel in the line is exhausted

11.11.4.3 Where LP-Gas–fueled industrial trucks are used in buildings or structures, the following shall apply:

(1) The number of fuel cylinders on such a truck shall not exceed two.
(2) The use of industrial trucks in buildings frequented by the public, including those times when such buildings are occupied by the public, shall require the approval of the authority having jurisdiction.

(3) The total water capacity of the fuel cylinders on an individual truck shall not exceed 105 lb (48 kg) [nominal 45 lb (20 kg) propane capacity].

(4) Trucks shall not be parked and left unattended in areas occupied by or frequented by the public without the approval of the authority having jurisdiction. If left unattended with approval, the cylinder shutoff valve shall be closed.

(5) In no case shall trucks be parked and left unattended in areas of excessive heat or near sources of ignition.

11.11.4.4 All cylinders used in industrial truck service (including forklift truck cylinders) shall have the cylinder pressure relief valve replaced in accordance with 5.9.2.14.

11.12 General Provisions for Vehicles Having Engines Mounted on Them (Including Floor Maintenance Machines).

11.12.1 Scope.

11.12.1.1 Section 11.12 applies to the installation of equipment on vehicles that supply LP-Gas as a fuel for engines installed on these vehicles.

11.12.1.2 Vehicles include floor maintenance and any other portable mobile unit, whether the engine is used to propel the vehicle or is mounted on it for other purposes.

11.12.2 General Requirements.

11.12.2.1 Industrial trucks (including forklift trucks) and other engines on vehicles operating in buildings other than those used exclusively to house engines shall have an approved automatic shutoff valve installed in the fuel system.

11.12.2.2 The source of air for combustion shall be isolated from the driver and passenger compartment, ventilating system, or air-conditioning system on the vehicle.

11.12.2.3 Non–self-propelled floor maintenance machinery (floor polishers, scrubbers, buffers) and other similar portable equipment shall be listed.

(A) A label shall be affixed to the machinery or equipment, with the label facing the operator, with the text denoting that the cylinder or portion of the machinery or equipment containing the cylinder shall be stored in accordance with Chapter 8.

(B) The use of floor maintenance machines in buildings frequented by the public, including the times when such buildings are occupied by the public, shall require the approval of the authority having jurisdiction.

11.13 Engine Installation Other Than on Vehicles.

11.13.1 Portable Engines.

11.13.1.1 The use of portable engines in buildings shall be limited to emergencies.

11.13.1.2 Portable engines shall be used only where sufficient air for combustion and cooling is available.

11.13.1.3 Exhaust gases shall be discharged to a point outside the building or to an area in which they will not constitute a hazard.

11.13.1.4 Where atmospheric-type regulators (zero governors) are used on engines operated only outdoors, a separate automatic shutoff valve shall not be required.

11.13.1.5 Engines used to drive pumps and compressors shall be equipped in accordance with 5.20.7.

11.14 Garaging of Vehicles. Where vehicles with LP-Gas engine fuel systems mounted on them, and general-purpose vehicles propelled by LP-Gas engines, are stored or serviced inside garages, the following conditions shall apply:

(1) The fuel system shall be leak-free.

(2) The container shall not be filled beyond the limits specified in Chapter 7.

(3) The container shutoff valve shall be closed when the vehicle or the engine is being repaired, except when the engine is required to operate. Containers equipped with an automatic shutoff valve as specified in 11.4.1.7 satisfy this requirement.

(4) The vehicle shall not be parked near sources of heat, open flames, or similar sources of ignition or near inadequately ventilated pits.

Δ **Chapter 12 Motor Vehicles Intended for Over-the-Road Use or Designed to Transport Passengers and Are Fueled by LP-Gas**

12.1 Scope.

12.1.1* This chapter applies to the design, installation, operation, and maintenance of LP-Gas fuel system components and ASME containers installed on motor vehicles intended for onroad use, where LP-Gas is used for the engine propulsion of the vehicle.

12.1.2 This chapter shall not apply to vehicles qualified under the U.S. Federal Motor Vehicle Safety Standards (FMVSS).

12.1.3 This chapter shall not apply to LP-Gas systems used on boats.

12.1.4 Where the term *LP-Gas* is used, the requirements of this chapter include and apply equally to any material that is composed predominantly of any of the following hydrocarbons or a mixture of them: propane, propylene, butane (normal butane or isobutane), and butylenes.

Δ **12.1.5** With the permission of the Canadian Standards Association (operating as CSA Group), certain material contained within Chapter 12 hereof is reproduced from CSA Group standard, B149.5 entitled *Installation Code for Propane Fuel Systems and Containers on Motor Vehicles*, which is copyrighted by CSA Group, 178 Rexdale Blvd., Toronto, ON, M9W 1R3. This material is not the complete and official position of CSA Group on the referenced subject, which is represented solely by the standard in its entirety. While use of the material has been authorized, CSA Group is not responsible for the manner in which the data is presented, nor for any interpretations thereof. For more information or to purchase standards from CSA Group, please visit http://shop.csa.ca/ or call 1-800-463-6727.

N **12.2 Installation of Components and Systems.** Components and systems shall be installed in accordance with the manufacturer's instructions.

12.3 ASME Containers, Materials, and Equipment.

12.3.1 General.

12.3.1.1 Materials in contact with LP-Gas shall be compatible with LP-Gas and recommended by the manufacturer for their intended service.

12.3.1.2* A cylinder *(see 3.3.18)* shall not be utilized as a permanent container to supply fuel to an LP-Gas vehicle engine.

12.3.1.3* Where the materials and equipment referred to in this chapter are not addressed by any standards referenced in this code, the requirements of ECE R67.01, *Agreement Concerning the Adoption of Uniform Technical Prescriptions for Wheeled Vehicles, Equipment and Parts Which Can Be Fitted and/or Be Used on Wheeled Vehicles and the Conditions for Reciprocal Recognition of Approvals Granted on the Basis of these Prescriptions,* shall be used to evaluate those materials and equipment.

(A)* Evaluations and testing shall be performed by an approved testing laboratory.

(B) Cold weather testing shall be performed at a temperature no warmer than -40°F (-40°C).

12.3.2 ASME Containers.

12.3.2.1 ASME containers used for any LP-Gas application shall comply with the applicable requirements in 11.3.1, 11.3.3, and 11.3.4.

12.3.2.2 ASME containers manufactured after April 1, 2001, and for use on vehicles within the scope of this chapter, shall have a design pressure of not less than 312 psig (2150 kPag).

12.3.2.3 The capacity of individual containers shall comply with 6.26.3.1(C).

△ 12.3.2.4 The maximum aggregate capacity of containers supplying fuel to a LP-Gas–powered vehicle shall be 300 gal (1.1 m³) water capacity.

12.3.2.5* A new or reconditioned ASME container, or an ASME container that has had its interior exposed to the atmosphere, shall be purged and have contaminants removed prior to being filled with LP-Gas.

12.3.2.6 ASME containers having internal electrical components within them shall not be prepared for service by purging with LP-Gas unless the components are de-energized and the entire vehicle, including the LP-Gas system, is grounded to earth.

12.3.2.7 An ASME container intended for vapor service only shall be installed or equipped in a manner to minimize the possibility of withdrawing liquid LP-Gas.

12.3.2.8 Openings in an LP-Gas ASME container other than those for the pressure relief valve and liquid level gauge shall bear a stamped or durable adhesive label.

N 12.3.2.8.1 The label shall be made of metal or of a material that is resistant to the effects of water, UV radiation exposure, and temperature extremes.

N 12.3.2.8.2 The label or stamp shall be adjacent to the inlet and outlet openings and designate the vapor or liquid service of the opening.

N 12.3.2.8.3 The label shall be marked with lettering a minimum of 0.25 in. (6.4 mm) in height.

12.3.2.9 Multiple-function valves with integrated functions in a single body or flange shall be permanently marked to indicate whether the openings in the valves communicate with the liquid or vapor space in the ASME container.

12.3.3 ASME Container Appurtenances and Pressure Relief Valves.

12.3.3.1 Container appurtenances shall comply with the applicable requirements of Section 11.4.

12.3.3.2 ASME container appurtenances, other than pressure relief valves, shall be rated for at least the maximum allowable working pressure (MAWP) of the ASME container, as indicated on the ASME data plate.

12.3.3.3 An ASME container shall be provided with one or more internal spring-type pressure relief valves in accordance with 5.9.2.

N 12.3.3.4 Manifold ASME containers shall consist of two or more containers fabricated by the original manufacturer interconnected to each other by rigid, integral, nonremovable liquid and vapor passages and braced to form a single rigid unit that is certified under the ASME *Boiler and Pressure Vessel Code* as a single pressure vessel.

12.3.3.5 Manifold ASME containers with interconnecting piping providing adequate relief capacity and one or more pressure relief valves shall not require a pressure relief valve on each container.

12.3.4 Fixed Maximum Liquid Level Gauges.

12.3.4.1 Systems installed with fixed liquid level gauges shall have a water- and weather-resistant label placed near the bleeder valve with the following text: "Do not use fixed maximum liquid level gauge at low-emissions fueling stations. OPD verification shall be done elsewhere."

12.3.4.2 The use of a fixed maximum liquid level gauge during refilling shall not be required where the ASME container is equipped with an overfilling prevention device (OPD) in accordance with 12.3.7.

12.3.5 Filler Valves and Excess-Flow Valves.

12.3.5.1 Filler valves and excess-flow check valves shall be listed in accordance with UL 125, *Standard for Flow Control Valves for Anhydrous Ammonia and LP-Gas (Other than Safety Relief).*

12.3.5.2 Filler valves shall comply with 5.9.4.1(C)(7) and shall be installed in the fill opening of the container.

12.3.5.3 A filler valve used for remote filling shall be permitted to incorporate a single backflow check valve and shall be connected to the filler valve on the container by metal tubing or hose.

12.3.5.4 Engine fuel systems installed after January 1, 2020, shall incorporate the fill connection of quick-connect/release Type K15 in accordance with ISO/DIS 19825, *Road vehicles — Liquefied petroleum gas (LPG) refuelling connector.*

12.3.6 Fuel Supply Control Valves.

12.3.6.1 An LP-Gas fuel supply line on an ASME container shall be equipped with a manual shutoff valve that incorporates an internal excess-flow valve.

12.3.6.2 The excess-flow valve shall meet the following requirements:

(1) Either be part of the valve (where installed in a dedicated opening), internal to the container, or be located in the opening portion of a multipurpose valve body or manifold, in the container opening
(2) Be of the fully internal type
(3) Have a rated flow not exceeding the flow capacity of the piping, tubing, or hose it is protecting

12.3.6.3 The fuel delivery system shall be designed to prevent the flow of fuel to the engine unless the engine is operating or the system is preparing to begin engine operation.

12.3.6.4 Flow control and purge valves shall maintain the operating pressure of the fuel delivery system within the design MAWP.

N 12.3.6.5 Where installed, a purge valve shall remove vapor from liquid fuel lines prior to engine operation.

12.3.6.6 Electric solenoid valves shall be listed in accordance with UL 125, *Standard for Flow Control Valves for Anhydrous Ammonia and LP-Gas (Other than Safety Relief).*

12.3.7 Overfilling Prevention Devices.

Δ 12.3.7.1 All LP-Gas ASME containers manufactured after January 1, 1984, shall be equipped with a listed overfilling prevention device (OPD).

12.3.7.2 Overfilling prevention devices shall be listed in accordance with UL 2227, *Standard for Overfilling Prevention Devices.*

12.3.7.3 ASME containers shall be filled in compliance with Section 11.5.

12.3.7.4 Where the overfilling prevention device is used as the primary means to fill the ASME container, the fixed maximum liquid level gauge or other approved means shall be used at least once annually to verify the operation of the overfilling prevention device.

12.3.7.4.1 If the container is found to be overfilled during the test, corrective action shall be taken.

12.3.7.4.2 The result of the verification attempt shall be documented.

12.3.7.4.3 A label shall be affixed to the container near the fill point indicating the date of the next required verification test.

12.3.8 Fuel Pumps.

Δ 12.3.8.1 Fuel pumps shall comply with Annex 4 of ECE R67.01.

12.3.8.2 The fuel delivery system shall be designed so that the pressure inside the ASME container does not exceed its MAWP.

12.3.8.3 Modifications to fuel pumps used on high-pressure direct injection systems shall only be performed in accordance with the LP-Gas fuel system manufacturer's requirements.

12.3.8.4 Modifications to fuel pumps used on high-pressure direct injection systems shall comply with the following:

(1) Modifications shall only be performed by the LP-Gas fuel system manufacturer.

(2) Modified or remanufactured fuel pumps shall have been tested to verify compatibility with the MAWP of the fuel system prior to installation.
(3) Where modified or remanufactured fuel pumps are used, the pump or the vehicle shall be marked with the pump modifier's name, the date of the modification or remanufacturing, and the maximum allowable working pressure (MAWP) prior to installation.

12.3.9 Fuel Injectors, Fuel Rails, and Distribution Blocks.

Δ 12.3.9.1 Fuel injectors, fuel rails, distribution blocks, and fuel-switching devices shall comply with the requirements of Annex 11 of ECE R67.01.

N 12.3.9.2 Where installed, a distribution block shall establish a connection point to convey fuel from the container to other components in the fuel system.

12.3.9.3* Electrical connections for fuel injectors shall comply with SAE J1292, *Automobile and Motor Coach Wiring,* and shall plug into the harness with either a direct connection using the same connector or an adapter.

N 12.3.9.4 Where installed, a fuel rail shall deliver regulated quantities of fuel to the injectors.

12.3.9.5* Fuel rails and distribution blocks shall be fabricated from corrosion-resistant materials compatible with LP-Gas and other fluids in the engine compartment and shall be rated for the maximum design pressure within the system.

12.3.9.6 Fuel rails and distribution blocks shall be marked with the model number, MAWP, and manufacturer's name.

12.3.9.7 Distribution blocks and other components on systems operating at pressures greater than 350 psig (2.4 MPag) shall be designed and rated for their intended pressures and shall incorporate into their design a means for protecting downstream fuel lines and components that are designed for a lower operating pressure, from exposure to pressures in excess of their ratings.

12.3.9.8* Distribution blocks and other components that are capable of retaining liquid between two positive shutoff valves shall have a means to protect the system from pressures exceeding its rated maximum operating pressure.

N 12.3.9.9 Where installed, a fuel-switching device shall provide a means for delivering dissimilar fuels to common fuel system components.

12.3.9.10 Fuel-switching devices used on bifuel vehicles shall be designed to prevent the unintended migration of either fuel into the container or piping system of the other fuel.

Δ 12.3.9.11 Fuel-switching devices shall be marked with a MAWP that is equal to or greater than that of the systems in which they are installed.

12.3.10 Piping and Tubing.

12.3.10.1 Pipe shall comply with 11.7.1.

12.3.10.2 Fittings shall comply with 11.7.2.

12.3.10.3 LP-Gas vapor-phase piping with design pressures not exceeding 125 psig (860 kPag) shall be at least Schedule 40.

12.3.10.4 Vapor phase piping with design pressures over 125 psig (860 kPag) and all liquid piping shall be at least Schedule 80.

Δ **12.3.10.5** Tubing shall be stainless steel, brass, or copper and shall comply with 11.7.1.2.

12.3.11 Joints, Fittings, and Connections.

12.3.11.1 Pipe joints shall be threaded, welded, or brazed.

12.3.11.2 A pipe or pipe fitting thread shall be tapered and shall comply with ANSI/ASME B1.20.1, *Pipe Threads, General Purpose, Inch.*

Δ **12.3.11.3** Tube fittings operating at a pressure below 125 psig (860 kPag) shall be made of steel, stainless steel, brass, or anodized aluminum with a design pressure of not less than 125 psig (860 kPag).

Δ **12.3.11.4** Tubing and fittings operating above 125 psig (860 kPag) shall be rated for a minimum of 250 psig (1725 kPag) or the design pressure of the system, whichever is greater.

12.3.11.5 Joints in the tubing shall be made by means of a flare joint, compression fitting, or other approved fitting that is compatible with the tubing.

12.3.11.6 A bulkhead fitting used to secure a LP-Gas fuel line passing through a partition, firewall, frame, or other such vehicle part shall meet the following requirements:

(1) Be made of either steel, brass, or anodized aluminum, and rated for the service pressure of the fuel line

(2) Use a flare, tapered pipe, compression fitting, or other approved fitting to connect the LP-Gas fuel line fitting to the bulkhead fitting

12.3.11.7 The separation and disconnection of quick-connect fittings shall require either two separate actions, a special removal tool, or another means to prevent unintended separation.

N **12.3.11.8** Quick-connect fittings shall be rated by the manufacturer for the specific application and use.

12.3.11.9 Bulkhead fittings for protecting penetrations of piping or tubing shall be steel or brass.

12.3.11.10 Nesting of bushings shall be prohibited.

12.3.11.11 A pipe fitting containing both left-hand and right-hand threads shall not be used.

12.3.11.12 A bend in piping or tubing shall be as follows:

(1) The minimum bend radius shall be equal to or greater than that recommended by the fuel line manufacturer.

(2) All bends shall be made with tooling recommended by the fuel line manufacturer.

12.3.12 Hose.

12.3.12.1 Hose and hose fittings used for vapor service shall be constructed of a material resistant to the action of LP-Gas.

12.3.12.2 Hose and hose fittings shall be rated by the manufacturer of the hose for the service, with a minimum pressure rating of the greater between 350 psig (2.4 MPag) or the rated pressure of the system.

12.3.12.3 Hose and hose fittings in liquid service shall comply with UL 21, *Standard for LP-Gas Hose,* or CSA CAN/CGA-8.1-M86, *Elastomeric Composite Hose and Hose Couplings for Conducting Propane and Natural Gas,* Type III.

12.3.12.4 Hose and hose fittings in liquid service shall be of either stainless -steel or synthetically reinforced and recommended for the intended use.

12.3.12.5 Hose shall be marked with the following information:

(1) LP-GAS HOSE or LPG HOSE
(2) Maximum working pressure
(3) Manufacturers' name or coded designation
(4) Month or quarter and year of manufacture
(5) Product identification

12.3.12.6 Hose assemblies shall be assembled and tested in accordance with the hose manufacturer's recommendations.

12.3.12.7 Minimum test pressures for assemblies shall be 120 percent of the rated working pressure.

12.3.12.8 Bends in installed sections of hose shall be equal to or greater than the minimum bend radius recommended by the manufacturer.

12.3.12.9 Hose sections shall be secured to minimize chaffing, rubbing, or abrasion.

12.3.12.10* The temperature of hose shall not exceed its maximum rated temperature.

12.3.12.11 Sections of hose that have been kinked or bent beyond their minimum bend radius or otherwise weakened shall be replaced prior to placing the vehicle into service.

12.3.13 Vaporizers, Pressure Regulators, and Carburetors.

12.3.13.1 Every vaporizer and pressure regulator shall be of sufficient size to provide the required flow and system-required regulated outlet pressure of LP-Gas, at the rated extremes of inlet pressures.

12.3.13.2 Carburetors, carburetor mixers, and carburetor adapters shall be recommended for the application by the manufacturer of the equipment.

12.3.13.3 Vaporizers, pressure regulators, carburetors, carburetor mixers, and carburetor adapters shall not be fabricated or modified by an installer.

12.3.13.4 Vaporizers, pressure regulators, and carburetors shall be listed to UL 1337, *Outline of Investigation for LP-Gas, Natural Gas, and Manufactured Gas Devices for Engine Fuel Systems.*

12.3.14 Wiring.

12.3.14.1* Electrical wiring and connectors used on vehicles shall be recommended by the manufacturer for automotive applications.

12.3.14.2 All wiring shall be of the stranded type.

12.3.14.3 All wiring shall have insulation recommended by the manufacturer for automotive use equal to or greater than the wire type used in the wiring of the vehicle and shall be of a gauge size sufficient for the rated current of the circuit in maximum amperes of normal operational power levels.

N 12.3.14.4 Soldered connections shall be sealed with shrink tubing.

N 12.3.14.5 Where installed, a power supply bushing shall be used to seal the electrical conductors passing from the inside to the outside of the ASME container.

Δ 12.3.14.6 Electrical power supply bushings installed within the container and used for conducting electricity into the container for any purpose shall be made from a material compatible with LP-Gas, in accordance with the following:

(1) The power supply bushing shall be rated to operate at a pressure of not less than 1.5 times the MAWP of the container.

(2) The power supply bushing shall be designed in such a way that it is installed from the inside of the container or the appurtenance and shall not be capable of blowing out in the event of a failure of the retaining fixtures.

(3) The power supply bushing shall have mating electrical connectors complying with SAE J2223-1, *Connections for On-Board Road Vehicle Electrical Wiring Harnesses — Part 1: Single-Pole Connectors — Flat Blade Terminals — Dimensional Characteristics and Specific Requirements*, and SAE J2223-3, *Connections for On-Board Road Vehicle Electrical Wiring Harnesses — Part 3: Multipole Connectors — Flat Blade Terminals — Dimensional Characteristics and Specific Requirements*, and such connections shall permit disconnection for service and inspection without removing the fitting or damaging the wiring harness.

(4) The power supply bushing conductors shall be compatible with LP-Gas and resistant to chemical or electrolysis corrosion.

(5) The power supply bushing shall be approved in accordance with Annex 3 of ECE R67.01.

N 12.3.15 Evaporative Emissions Control.

N 12.3.15.1 LP-Gas system evaporative emissions control devices shall be managed by the LP-Gas system controller.

N 12.3.15.2 LP-Gas system evaporative emissions control devices shall be designed so that all captured vapors are retained and controlled.

12.4 LP-Gas Fuel Systems.

12.4.1 General.

12.4.1.1 Accessories, components, and equipment shall be installed in accordance with the manufacturer's installation instructions and this Code.

12.4.1.2 Where an ASME container is being repaired, removed, or scrapped, its liquid contents shall be removed by flaring or by transfer to another ASME container, or the gas shall be vented in accordance with Section 7.3.

Δ 12.4.1.3 Replacement parts shall be at least the equivalent of the original part with respect to its performance and safety attributes and shall be compatible with the original equipment.

12.4.1.4 Smoking, welding, torch cutting, grinding, or any other source of ignition shall not be permitted in the area where work is being done on piping, tubing, or equipment that contains or has contained LP-Gas unless the piping, tubing, or equipment has been purged of LP-Gas.

12.4.1.5 Before returning an ASME container purged of LP-Gas back into service, the ASME container and all connecting components and fuel lines shall be tested by pressurizing the ASME container and connecting components to 140 psig (965 KPag) using LP-Gas, air, or an inert gas, and the system shall not experience a loss of pressure for a minimum time of 10 minutes.

Δ 12.4.1.6 Fuel shall not be released from a system in an enclosed area or within 35 ft (11 m) of any sources of ignition.

12.4.1.7 Where a vehicle is configured to operate on LP-Gas only, existing gasoline or diesel tank fill connections shall have their fill connections removed or plugged after purging of any residual fuel or vapors.

12.4.1.8 An ASME container providing engine fuel for the vehicle shall not be mounted on a trailer or an articulated portion of a vehicle separate from the portion where the engine is mounted.

12.4.1.9 The use of a cargo tank for supplying fuel to an engine powering a cargo tank LP-Gas motor vehicle shall be permitted when the cargo tank is mounted on the same frame as the engine and the installation is compatible with the specific engine system installed.

12.4.1.10 The source of combustion air for an LP-Gas fueled engine shall be isolated from the ventilating or air-conditioning system of the vehicle.

12.4.1.11 Any part of the LP-Gas fuel system equipment that utilizes a drain valve or plug shall have the drain valve or plug located in the lowest possible position unless the equipment is removable for maintenance purposes.

12.4.1.12 Equipment service drains or pressure taps shall be capable of attaching a hose or tube for the remote discharge.

Δ 12.4.1.13 ASME container fittings shall be leak checked with a liquid leak detector solution or listed combustible gas detector after the equipment is connected, activated, and pressurized.

N 12.4.1.14 If leakage is detected, leaks shall be repaired before the container is put into service.

12.4.1.15 When a vehicle is involved in an accident or fire, the system shall be inspected and tested prior to being put back into service.

12.4.2 Training Requirements.

Δ 12.4.2.1* Each person engaged in installing or maintaining a LP-Gas engine fuel system shall be trained as follows:

(1) In accordance with the requirements of Section 4.4
(2) With general training on the nature of LP-Gas engine fuel systems and their components
(3) With training on the specific LP-Gas fuel system to be installed or maintained

N 12.4.2.2 All training in accordance with 12.4.2.1 shall be documented.

12.4.3 Welding. Welding shall be performed as follows:

(1) Welding shall be performed in accordance with the ASME *Boiler and Pressure Vessel Code.*
(2) Welding shall be performed by a certified ASME pressure vessel welder with an ASME "U" or "R" certification.

---

(3) Welding by a qualified welder for brackets or other attachments shall be permitted on weld pads or other non-pressure containing portions of the ASME container.

(4) Welding of attachments or supports to ASME containers shall not reduce the structural integrity of the ASME container.

12.4.4 Structural Requirements for Mounting ASME Containers. ASME containers shall be mounted and fastened in accordance with the following:

(1)* ASME containers shall be installed to prevent them from jarring loose and slipping or rotating.

(2) The fastenings shall be designed and constructed to withstand static loading in any direction equal to four times the weight of the container filled with fuel.

(3)* Prior to being returned to service, an ASME container shall be inspected to determine its suitability for continued service.

(4) Structural members that have been drilled shall be protected from corrosion.

(5)* ASME container mounting brackets shall be provided by or recommended by the ASME container manufacturer and shall be provided with a resilient material to be installed between the supports or clamping bands and the ASME container such that there is no direct metal-to-metal contact.

(6) Welding shall not be used as a means of attaching ASME container brackets to a vehicle.

(7) ASME containers shall not be used as structural members.

(8) Filling connections for ASME containers shall be located such that the attendant is not required to lay on the ground.

(9) Filling connections and related fittings shall not be installed in a manner that will necessitate access for filling from the passenger compartment or any contiguous portion of the vehicle where the potential for vapors to migrate into the passenger compartment is possible.

(10) ASME containers and their means of attachment shall be protected from corrosion and abrasion.

12.4.5 ASME Containers Located within Vehicles. ASME containers located within an enclosed space of a vehicle shall be installed in accordance with either 12.4.5.1 or 12.4.5.2.

12.4.5.1* The ASME container and its appurtenances shall be installed in an enclosure that is securely mounted to the vehicle.

(A) The enclosure shall be gastight with respect to driver or passenger compartments and to any space containing radio transmitters or other sources of ignition.

(B) The enclosure shall be vented to the outside of the vehicle.

△ **12.4.5.2** The ASME container appurtenances and their connections shall be installed in an enclosure on the ASME container.

(A) The appurtenances and their connections shall be installed in an enclosure that is gastight with respect to the driver or passenger compartments or with any space.

(B) The enclosure shall be vented to the outside of the vehicle.

△ **12.4.5.3** ASME containers and piping shall be installed so that no gas from fueling and gauging operations can be released inside of the passenger or enclosed compartments of the vehicle.

12.4.5.4 Enclosures, structures, seals, and conduits used to vent enclosures shall be designed and fabricated to resist damage, blockage, or dislodgement through movement of articles carried in the vehicle or by the closing of luggage compartment enclosures or vehicle doors and shall require the use of tools for removal.

12.4.5.5 The remote fill outside fittings shall be located so as to provide access for refueling without requiring a person to lie on the ground.

12.4.6 Multiple ASME Containers. Multiple ASME container installations shall be installed in accordance with 12.4.4, 12.4.5, and the following:

(1) Multiple ASME containers shall either have separate fill connections, or the system shall be designed to prevent the overfilling or over-pressurization of any of the containers.

(2) Where individual ASME containers are interconnected by piping, tubing, or hoses, each liquid withdrawal line shall be equipped with a backflow check valve or an equivalent means of preventing unintended transfer between containers.

(3) Multiple ASME containers installed with separate fill connections located on separate sides of the vehicle, or that are separated by a distance greater than 3 ft (1 m), shall each have all applicable safety markings and labels on the containers and at each fill connection.

12.4.7 ASME Container Road Clearances. Where an LP-Gas container is substituted for the fuel container installed by the original manufacturer of the vehicle, the LP-Gas container either shall fit within the space in which the original fuel container was installed or shall comply with either of the following:

(1) Containers installed between axles shall not be lower than the lowest point forward of the container on the following points:

   (a) Lowest structural component of the body as illustrated in Figure 12.4.7

   (b) Lowest structural component of the frame or subframe

   (c) Lowest point on the engine

   (d) Lowest point of the transmission (including the clutch housing or torque converter housing, as applicable)

(2) Containers installed behind the rear axle and extending below the frame shall not be lower than the lowest of the following points and surfaces:

   (a) Containers shall not be lower than the lowest point of a structural component of the body, engine, and transmission (including clutch housing or torque converter housing, as applicable) forward of the container.

(b) Containers shall not be lower than lines extending rearward from each wheel at the point where the wheels contact the ground directly below the center of the axle to the lowest and most rearward structural interference, as illustrated in Part 2 of Figure 12.4.7. This determination shall be made when the vehicle is loaded to its gross vehicle weighted rating (GVWR) of the vehicle.

△ **12.4.8 ASME Container Protection.** ASME containers shall comply with the following:

(1) An ASME container shall be located to minimize the possibility of damage due to external forces.

(2) If mounted within 10 in. (254 mm) of the engine or the exhaust system, not including the catalytic converter, an ASME container shall be protected with a radiation heat shield located not less than 1 in. (25 mm) from the ASME container.

(3) Adhesive heat shielding/radiant barriers that are recommended by the manufacturer for automotive application shall be permitted to be affixed to the ASME container.

(4) Modifications of a spare tire well to accommodate the installation of an ASME container shall be permitted, provided the space between the opening created in the tire well and the surface of the ASME container is sealed to prevent the infiltration of water and road debris.

(5) An ASME container shall not be mounted within 8 in. (203 mm) of a catalytic converter unless thermal protection is provided to maintain the pressure in the container below the MAWP.

(6) An ASME container shall not project beyond the side of the vehicle.

(7) No part of an ASME container shall be located above the highest point of the vehicle as received from the manufacturer or ahead of the front axle of a self-propelled vehicle.

(8) An ASME container located behind the rear axle of a passenger bus with a frame and body that are constructed as a single assembly without a separate frame on which the body is installed shall comply with all of the following:

(a) The vehicle bumper shall be reinforced by the addition of two 2 in. × 2 in. × 0.25 in. (50 mm × 50 mm × 6.4 mm) hollow square steel members (or equivalent) attached to the existing bumper mounting points.

(b) The ASME container shall be located as follows:

i. A minimum of 4 in. (100 mm) from the differential housing

ii. Not less than 12 in. (305 mm) from the rearmost point of the bumper to the ASME container, ASME container valve(s), or any ASME container appurtenance — unless the bumper is reinforced

iii. As high as practical without modifying the vehicle structure (*see Figure 12.4.8*) and in accordance with 12.4.7

12.4.9 Protection for Appurtenances and Remote Fill Connections and Fittings. All valves, connections, and gauging devices on an ASME container shall be protected from external damage in accordance with the following:

(1) All openings greater than a No. 54 orifice shall be protected by an excess flow valve or a double back check valve or shall be protected from shearing forces by recess or guarding.

(2) Parts of the vehicle shall be permitted to provide protection to valves and fittings.

(3) Filling and gauging fittings in a location remote from the ASME container shall be protected from physical damage by one of the following means:

(a) In a metal enclosure, or using another material that provides an equivalent level of protection to that provided for the fuel receptacle, which is permanently mounted to the vehicle and does not protrude outside the vehicle's body

(b) Located in such a way that the rear bumper or another part of the vehicle will provide protection

(c) By attachment of the protective devices that are designed and installed to fail prior to the failure of the container

(d) By not mounting remote valves and fittings in or on the bumpers of a vehicle or beyond the portion of the body from which the bumper protrudes

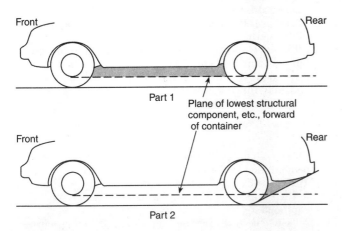

FIGURE 12.4.7 Plane of Lowest Structural Component for Container Placement with Vehicle Loading.

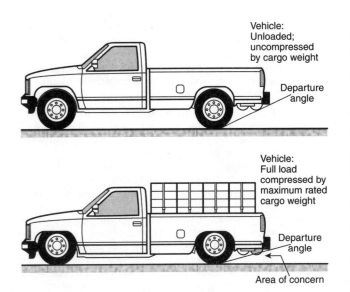

△ **FIGURE 12.4.8 ASME Container Mounted Behind the Rear Axle.**

(4) Valves and appurtenances shall either be constructed of corrosion-resistant material or be coated or protected to minimize exterior corrosion.

△ 12.4.10 Pressure Relief and Hydrostatic Pressure Control. Pressure relief valves and hydrostatic relief valves shall be installed in accordance with the following:

(1) Pressure relief valves shall be installed to communicate with the vapor space of the ASME container.

(2) The system shall be designed to ensure that during normal operation or refueling the pressure relief valve will not open.

(3) Shutoff valves or other equipment shall not be installed between the pressure relief valves and the opening in the ASME container.

(4) Where liquefied LP-Gas is isolated in piping or between shutoff valves, hydrostatic pressure shall be controlled by one of the following methods:

   (a) A backflow check valve or internal relief valve that is installed in such a manner as to relieve any increase in pressure in the isolated portion of the fuel lines, either into the container or into another portion of the system that is protected by a hydrostatic relief valve

   (b) A hydrostatic relief valve complying with Section 5.15

   (c) Any method recommended by the manufacturer

(5) The discharge of the hydrostatic relief valve shall be located outside the engine compartment and in accordance with 12.4.10.

(6) The discharge of an installed hydrostatic pressure relief valve underneath the vehicle shall be directed downward and away from any potential sources of ignition, the catalytic converter, or any portion of the exhaust system.

△ 12.4.11 Pressure Relief Valve Discharge System. The pressure relief valve discharge from an ASME container shall be in accordance with the following:

(1) It shall be sized for the minimum required flow rate for all relief valves it serves.

(2) It shall be directed upward or downward within 45 degrees of vertical.

(3) It shall not directly impinge on the ASME container(s), the exhaust system, or any other part of the vehicle.

(4) It shall not be directed into the interior of the vehicle.

(5) Where the pressure relief valve discharge is piped away, the pipe-away system shall have a breakaway adapter in accordance with the following:

   (a) The breakaway adapter shall have a melting point greater than the melting point of the hose or conduit connected to it for the purpose of redirecting discharged pressure.

   (b) The breakaway adapter either shall be an integral part of the pressure relief valve or shall be a separate adapter attached directly to the pressure relief valve.

   (c) The pipe-away system shall be permitted to utilize a length of nonmetallic hose or conduit with a melting point less than the pipe-away adapter connected to the pressure relief valve. The hose or conduit shall be permitted to have metallic reinforcement.

   (d) The nonmetallic hose shall be as short as practical and shall be able to withstand the downstream

pressure from the pressure relief valve in the full open position, and the hose shall be fabricated of materials resistant to the action of LP-Gas.

   (e) Where hose is used to pipe away the pressure relief valve discharge on ASME containers installed on the outside of the vehicle, the breakaway adapter and any attached fitting shall deflect the pressure relief valve discharge upward or downward within 45 degrees of vertical and shall meet the other requirements of 11.8.5.1 without the hose attached, and any additional fitting necessary to meet this requirement shall have a melting point not less than that of the pipe-away adapter connected to the pressure relief valve or the discharge hose/conduit.

   (f) The pipe-away system shall have a protective cover to minimize the possibility of the entrance of water or dirt into either the pressure relief valve or its discharge system, and the cover shall not restrict the flow.

   (g) No portion of the system shall have an internal diameter less than the minimum internal diameter of the recommended breakaway adapter.

   (h) The breakaway adapter either shall be threaded for direct connection to the pressure relief valve and shall not interfere with the operation of the pressure relief valve, or it shall be an integral part of the pressure relief valve and shall break away without impairing the function of the pressure relief valve.

   (i) The pipe-away system connections shall be mechanically secured, shall not depend on adhesives or sealing compounds, and shall not be routed between a bumper system and the vehicle body.

   (j) Where a pipe-away system is not required, the pressure relief valve shall have a protective cap or cover to protect it from water or debris.

12.4.12 Shutoff Valves. ASME container shutoff valves shall be installed in accordance with the following:

(1) A manual shutoff valve on an ASME container shall be accessible.

(2) Where the manual shutoff valve is not visible from the outside of the vehicle, a label visible with an arrow pointing to the area of the valve, and marked "Shutoff Valve" shall be affixed.

(3) An electrically operated solenoid valve shall be installed in the ASME container.

(4) All safety controls for the original fuel pump, including but not limited to crash sensors, inertia switches, run dry protection, or other safety functions, shall be retained and fully functional when operating the LP-Gas shutoff valve for bifuel systems.

△ 12.4.13* Fuel Pumps. Fuel pumps shall comply with the following:

(1) ASME containers with the fuel pump installed inside shall be identified by the words "Fuel Pump Inside."

(2) The electrical power to a fuel pump shall be switched off in the event of a crash that actuates a crash sensor, if so equipped.

(3) All safety controls for the fuel pump, including, but not limited to, crash sensors, inertia switches, run dry protection, or other safety functions, shall be retained and fully

functional when operating the fuel pump for either bifuel or monofuel systems.

(4) All fuel pump power circuits shall be fuse protected.

(5) To prevent overpressurization, fuel pump discharge piping shall have a means of relieving pressure inside the ASME container in the event of a restriction or blockage in the discharge piping.

(6) Internal fuel pump wiring shall have an insulation material that is compatible with LP-Gas.

(7) Internal fuel pump wiring connectors shall comply with SAE J2223-1, *Connections for On-Board Road Vehicle Electrical Wiring Harnesses — Part 1: Single-Pole Connectors — Flat Blade Terminals — Dimensional Characteristics and Specific Requirements*, and SAE J2223-3, *Connections for On-Board Road Vehicle Electrical Wiring Harnesses — Part 3: Multipole Connectors — Flat Blade Terminals — Dimensional Characteristics and Specific Requirements*.

(8) Internal fuel pump wiring shall be secured in a manner that prevents damage from vibration, chaffing, or abrasion.

12.5 Electrical Installation.

12.5.1 The electrical components of the LP-Gas fuel system shall be protected against overloads, with at least one separate fuse that is sized for the rated load of the system provided, and its location shall be marked in the operator's manual.

12.5.2 Electrical cables shall be protected from damage due to flexing, abrasion, and other stresses, and they shall be secured to the vehicle chassis or other vehicle structure.

12.5.3 Installed sections of wire(s) shall be enclosed in a protected sheath of materials recommended by the manufacturer for that application.

12.5.4 The use of electrical tape to insulate bare wire connections shall not be permitted.

12.5.5 Installed sections of wiring shall be protected from abrasion, chaffing, snags, or external forces.

12.5.6 Electrical connections shall be sized for the rated load and shall be made with sealed connections having positive locking mechanisms.

12.5.7 All wiring connections shall either use connectors recommended by the manufacturer or be soldered, and the connections shall be protected by heavy wall shrink insulation or other approved insulation.

12.5.8* Electrical connections made inside of an ASME container, or in any portion of the system that contains fuel, shall use positive locking connectors that comply with SAE J2223-1, *Connections for On-Board Road Vehicle Electrical Wiring Harnesses — Part 1: Single-Pole Connectors — Flat Blade Terminals — Dimensional Characteristics and Specific Requirements*, and SAE J2223-3, *Connections for On-Board Road Vehicle Electrical Wiring Harnesses — Part 3: Multipole Connectors — Flat Blade Terminals — Dimensional Characteristics and Specific Requirements*.

12.5.9* All wiring bundles shall be protected with loom or another protective cover that complies with recognized testing methods.

12.5.10 Where wiring bundles will be exposed to radiant heat from the engine or exhaust components, protection from overheating shall be provided.

12.6 Installation of Pipe, Tubing, and Hose.

12.6.1* Where applicable, all threaded connections shall be tightened to the torque specification of the fitting or fuel system manufacturer's specifications.

12.6.2 LP-Gas piping, tubing, and hose shall be secured to the vehicle at intervals not greater than 24 in. (61 cm) by corrosion-resistant hose/tubing mounting fixtures that are constructed of a material recommended for the application.

12.6.3 Any pipe, tubing, or hose connection not in use shall be capped or plugged.

12.6.4 All pipe and tubing joints and hose connections shall be accessible for service and inspection after installation.

12.6.5 All piping and tubing fittings shall be inspected or tested to assure that they are correctly installed.

12.6.6 Defects in LP-Gas piping or tubing that can affect its performance shall not be repaired, and the piping or tubing shall be removed from service.

12.7 Protection of Pipe, Tube, and Hose.

12.7.1 Exposed metallic piping or tubing shall be protected against exterior corrosion by the application of a corrosion-resistant coating or material.

△ 12.7.2 Piping, tubing, and hose shall be protected against damage or breakage due to vibration, abrasion, strain, or wear.

12.7.3 Tubing and hose within a luggage compartment or other area contiguous to the passenger area of the vehicle shall be protected from damage and installed so that in the event of a leak or permeation of the hose, vapor cannot migrate into the passenger space of the vehicle.

△ 12.7.4 Hose shall be protected from the engine exhaust system by either of the following requirements:

(1) A clearance of not less than 8 in. (203 mm) shall be maintained between a hose or sheathed copper and an engine exhaust system.

(2) The hose or sheathed copper shall be shielded against heat radiation, with the shield located not less than 1 in. (25 mm) from the hose or sheathed copper and a minimum of 1 in. (25 mm) from the exhaust system, and shall meet the following requirements:

   (a) The heat shield shall be noncombustible material and shall extend for a minimum distance of 10 in. (250 mm) beyond either edge of the heat source that it is shielding.

   (b) The heat shield shall not be attached to or in contact with any portion of the exhaust system.

   (c) As an alternative to 12.7.4(1), the use of an insulated or radiant barrier sleeve shall be permitted to be extended to a point no less than 8 in. (203 mm) in each direction from the area of the hose/tubing exposed to the heat source.

12.8 Testing of Piping, Tubing, Hose, and Fittings.

12.8.1 Prior to installation on the vehicle, all piping, tubing, and hose assemblies in the fuel system shall be pressure tested to a minimum 120 percent of the design operating pressure of the system using air or an inert gas.

12.8.2 After installation or prior to returning to service, the fuel system shall be proven to be free of leaks at the operating pressure of the system.

△ 12.9 LP-Gas Liquid and Vapor Injectors.

12.9.1 Injectors shall be securely mounted.

12.9.2 Injectors shall be installed so that vibration, rubbing, and abrasion shall not damage or affect the operation of the injectors.

12.9.3 The use of tie straps or other nonrigid mounting of injectors shall not be permitted.

12.9.4 Injectors shall not be mounted to any portion of the exhaust system.

△ 12.9.5 Injectors shall be recommended by the system manufacturer.

N 12.10 Fuel Rails and Distribution Blocks.

N 12.10.1 Fuel rails and distribution blocks shall be installed so that vibration, rubbing, and abrasion will not damage or affect their operation.

N 12.10.2 Fuel rails and distribution blocks shall be installed in accordance with the manufacturer's recommendations.

N 12.10.3 The mounting position of fuel rails and distribution blocks shall be accessible to connections for service and inspection.

N 12.10.4 Fuel rails shall be mounted so there is no relative movement between the fuel rails and the engine.

N 12.10.5 The use of tie straps or other nonrigid mounting of fuel rails shall not be permitted.

N 12.10.6 Fuel rails shall not be mounted to any portion of the exhaust system.

N 12.10.7 Fuel rails shall be mounted to brackets with fasteners that are stainless steel, plated, or otherwise protect the rail body from corrosion.

12.11 Vaporizer/Regulator Systems.

12.11.1 A vaporizer/pressure regulator system shall be securely fastened in a manner that will prevent damage to the component or the vehicle due to vibration, operating temperature, or corrosion.

12.11.2 Exhaust gas shall not pass through any vaporizer/pressure regulator unless the vaporizer/pressure regulator is designed for exhaust gas utilization.

12.11.3 A vaporizer/pressure regulator system shall not be equipped with a fusible plug.

12.11.4 Any pressure relief valve installed in the unit shall discharge at a point outside of the vehicle and the vehicle engine compartment.

12.11.5 A LP-Gas supply line to the vaporizer/pressure regulator shall be equipped with a fuel lock-off valve that prevents the flow of LP-Gas to the carburetor or fuel injector when the ignition switch is turned off or when the engine is not running.

12.11.6 The fuel lockoff valve shall be installed at the container opening or in accordance with the following:

(1) On carbureted systems, the lockoff valve shall be located upstream of the primary pressure regulator or vaporizer.
(2) On LP-Gas fuel injection systems, the lockoff valve shall be located upstream of the LP-Gas injection device provided as part of the LP-Gas fuel system.
(3) The lockoff valve shall be controlled by one or more of the following:

    (a) Vacuum from the engine
    (b) Oil pressure from the engine
    (c) An electrical circuit that closes the valve whenever the engine is not running, unless it is in a prestart purge mode initiated prior to engine operation to remove all vapor from the fuel system

12.11.7 An atmospheric-type regulator (zero governor) shall not be permitted to be used as a safety lockoff valve.

12.12 Fuel Lockoffs.

12.12.1 A bifuel system shall prevent the unintended flow of either fuel.

12.12.2 Where a lockoff valve is added between the fuel pump for the alternate fuel and the engine, the connection between the fuel pump and the lockoff valve shall be made with tubing or with hose and fittings equivalent to those used on the outlet of the fuel pump by the original manufacturer of the vehicle.

12.12.3 Fuel lockoffs shall be installed in accordance with the manufacturer's recommendations and shall be installed to prevent movement or damage from vibration.

12.12.4 The LP-Gas fuel lockoff shall be installed so that it prevents the uncontrolled flow of fuel to the engine in the event of an accident, or at any time the key is in the "run" position but the engine is not running or is in a "start-purge" mode.

12.13 Servicing, Parking, and Display of Vehicles Indoors.

12.13.1 Garaging Vehicles. Where vehicles with LP-Gas engine fuel systems mounted on them, and general-purpose vehicles propelled by LP-Gas engines, are stored or serviced inside garages, the following conditions shall apply:

(1) The fuel system shall be leak-free.
(2) The ASME container shall not be filled beyond the limits specified in Section 7.4.
(3) The ASME container shutoff valve shall be closed when the vehicle or the engine is being repaired, except when the engine is required to operate and the ASME containers equipped with an automatic shutoff valve as specified in 11.4.1.7 satisfy this requirement.
(4) The vehicle shall not be parked near sources of heat, open flames, or similar sources of ignition or near inadequately ventilated pits.

12.13.2 Displaying Vehicles Indoors.

△ 12.13.2.1 Vehicles parked indoors for display or nonrunning demonstration shall have the following:

(1) No more than 50 percent of fuel capacity or 10 gal (37.9 dm³), whichever is less
(2) All manual shutoff valves in the closed position
(3) The battery is disconnected

Shaded text = Revisions. △ = Text deletions and figure/table revisions. • = Section deletions. N = New material.

12.14 Commissioning Vehicles.

12.14.1 The vehicle owner or operator shall be instructed in the basic operations of the LP-Gas fuel system in order to safely operate an LP-Gas vehicle.

12.14.2 The basic operating and maintenance instructions for the vehicle shall be provided to the user.

12.14.3 Each vehicle shall have an owner's manual that provides the following minimal information:

(1) A description of the specific fuel system installed, with component locations indicated
(2) A description of the safety and emergency valves, and how to operate them
(3) Basic maintenance intervals in either months or miles
(4) Any specification special maintenance items (e.g., oils, lubricants, and filters) unique to the LP-Gas fuel system that are different from those defined in the basic vehicle maintenance manual

12.14.4 All LP-Gas–fueled motor vehicles shall be identified by a weather-resistant diamond-shaped label affixed to its exterior vertical, or near vertical, lower right rear surface, but not attached to its bumper.

12.14.4.1 The label shall be approximately 4¾ in. (120 mm) wide by 3¼ in. (83 mm) high.

12.14.4.2 The label marking shall consist of a border and the word PROPANE in letters not less than 1 in. (25 mm) in height, centered in the diamond, of silver or white reflective luminous material on a black background.

Chapter 13 Refrigerated Containers

13.1 Construction and Design of Refrigerated Containers.

13.1.1 Container Material and Construction Requirements.

13.1.1.1 Containers designed to operate at greater than 15 psig (103 kPag) shall be designed and constructed in accordance with the ASME *Boiler and Pressure Vessel Code*, Section VIII, except that construction using joint efficiencies listed in Table UW 12, Column C, shall not be permitted.

13.1.1.2 Materials used in refrigerated containers shall be selected from those included in the following:

(1) ASME *Boiler and Pressure Vessel Code*, Section VIII (materials that maintain their integrity at the boiling temperature of the liquid stored)
(2) API 620, *Design and Construction of Large, Welded, Low-Pressure Storage Tanks*, Appendix R or Appendix Q

13.1.1.3 Containers designed to operate below 15 psig (103 kPag) shall be in accordance with API 620, *Design and Construction of Large, Welded, Low-Pressure Storage Tanks*, including Appendix R.

13.1.1.4 Where austenitic stainless steels or nonferrous materials are used, API 620, *Design and Construction of Large, Welded, Low-Pressure Storage Tanks*, Appendix Q, shall be used in the selection of materials.

13.1.1.5 Emergency Shutoff Valve.

(A) All new construction shall incorporate on any bottom or side penetrations that communicate with the liquid space of the container either an internal emergency shutoff valve or a backflow check valve.

(B) Any emergency shutoff valve shall be incorporated into a facility emergency shutdown system and be capable of being operated remotely.

13.1.2 Container Design Temperature and Pressure.

13.1.2.1 Design Pressure.

(A) The design pressure of ASME containers shall include a minimum 5 percent of the absolute vapor pressure of the LP-Gas at the design storage temperature.

(B) The margin (both positive and vacuum) for low-pressure API 620 vessels shall include the following:

(1) Control range of the boil-off handling system
(2) Effects of flash or vapor collapse during filling operations
(3) Flash that can result from withdrawal pump recirculation
(4) Normal range of barometric pressure changes

13.1.2.2 Design Temperature.

(A) The design temperature for those parts of a refrigerated LP-Gas container that are in contact with the liquid or refrigerated vapor shall be equal to or lower than the boiling point of the product to be stored at atmospheric pressure.

(B) A temperature allowance shall be made for the composition of the liquid to be stored when it is flashed into the vapor space of a tank.

13.2 Marking on Refrigerated LP-Gas Containers.

13.2.1 Each refrigerated LP-Gas container shall be identified by the attachment of a nameplate located either on the container or in a visible location.

13.2.2 The nameplate shall be in accordance with API 620, *Design and Construction of Large, Welded, Low-Pressure Storage Tanks*, Section 6.

13.3 Container Installation.

13.3.1 Wind Loading.

13.3.1.1 The design wind loading on refrigerated LP-Gas containers shall be in accordance with the projected area at various height zones above ground in accordance with ASCE/SEI 7, *Minimum Design Loads for Buildings and Other Structures*.

13.3.1.2 Design wind speeds shall be based on a mean occurrence interval of 100 years.

13.3.2 Seismic Loading.

13.3.2.1 The design seismic loading on refrigerated LP-Gas containers shall be in accordance with ASCE/SEI 7, *Minimum Design Loads for Buildings and Other Structures*.

13.3.2.2 A seismic analysis of the proposed installation shall be made that meets the approval of the authority having jurisdiction.

13.3.3 Piping.

13.3.3.1 All piping that is part of a refrigerated LP-Gas container and refrigerated LP-Gas systems, including transfer and process piping, shall be in accordance with ASME B31.3, *Process Piping*.

13.3.3.2 The container piping shall include the following:

(1) All piping internal to the container
(2) All piping within the insulation spaces
(3) All external piping attached or connected to the container up to the first circumferential external joint of the piping

13.3.3.3 Inert gas purge systems wholly within the insulation spaces shall be exempt from the provision in 13.3.3.1.

13.3.3.4 Gaskets used to retain LP-Gas in containers shall be resistant to the action of LP-Gas.

13.3.3.5 Gaskets shall be of metal or other material confined in metal, including spiral-wound metal gaskets, having a melting point over 1500°F (816°C) or shall be protected against fire exposure.

13.3.3.6 When a flange is opened, the gasket shall be replaced.

13.3.4 Foundations.

13.3.4.1 Refrigerated aboveground containers shall be installed on foundations that have been engineered for site soil conditions and loadings.

13.3.4.2* Foundation Design.

(A) Prior to the start of design and construction of the foundation, a subsurface investigation shall be conducted by a soils engineer.

(B) Foundations shall be designed by an engineer who is experienced in foundations and soils.

13.3.4.3 Where product storage is at less than 30°F (−1.1°C), the foundation and the container bottom shall comply with the following:

(1) The foundation design and the container bottom insulation shall prevent damage to the container from frost heave.
(2) If the refrigerated LP-Gas container under bottom foundation and insulation are in contact with the soil, and the soil temperature could be less than 32°F (0°C), a heating system shall be installed to prevent the soil temperature from falling below 32°F (0°C).
(3) The under-container heating system shall be designed to allow both functional and performance monitoring.
(4) The under-container temperature shall be observed and logged at least weekly.
(5) Where the foundation has a discontinuity, such as bottom piping, the heating system in that zone shall be designed for the discontinuity.
(6) The under-container heating system shall be installed so that any heating elements or temperature sensors used for control can be replaced while the container is in service.
(7) Provisions shall be incorporated to minimize the effects of moisture accumulation in the conduit and other forms of deterioration within the conduit or heating element.

13.3.4.4 The refrigerated LP-Gas container foundation shall be periodically monitored for settlement during the life of the facility.

13.3.4.5 The monitoring shall include construction, hydrostatic testing, commissioning, and operation.

13.3.4.6 Any settlement in excess of that anticipated in the design shall be investigated, and corrective action shall be taken if appropriate.

13.3.4.7 For a container having a double wall design, the bottom of the outer wall and the refrigerated LP-Gas container under-container insulation shall be above the groundwater table or protected from contact with groundwater at all times, and it shall also be protected from floodwaters.

13.3.4.8 Where two or more containers are sited in a common dike, the container foundations shall be constructed of material resistant to the effects of refrigerated LP-Gas and the temperatures to which they will be exposed.

13.3.4.9 If the foundation of a refrigerated LP-Gas container is designed to provide air circulation in lieu of a heating system, the foundation and insulating material under the bottom of the container shall be constructed of materials that are resistant to the effects of refrigerated LP-Gas and the temperatures to which they will be exposed.

13.3.4.10 The material in contact with the bottom of the container shall be selected to minimize corrosion.

13.4 Refrigerated LP-Gas Container Instruments and Controls.

13.4.1 Gauging Devices.

13.4.1.1 Each refrigerated LP-Gas container shall be equipped with at least two independent liquid level gauging devices.

13.4.1.2 Liquid level gauging devices shall be installed so that they can be replaced without taking the container out of service.

13.4.1.3 The refrigerated LP-Gas container shall be provided with an audible and visual high–liquid level alarm.

13.4.1.4 The alarm shall be set so that the operator will have sufficient time, based on the maximum allowable filling rate, to stop the flow without exceeding the maximum permissible filling height.

13.4.1.5 The alarm shall be located so that it is visible and audible to the personnel who control the filling.

13.4.1.6 A high–liquid level flow cutoff device shall not be a substitute for the alarm.

13.4.1.7 The refrigerated LP-Gas container shall be equipped with a high-high–liquid level flow cutoff device that is independent from all gauges.

13.4.1.8 Where refrigerated LP-Gas containers of 70,000 gal (265 m^3) or less are attended during the filling operation, they shall be equipped with either liquid trycocks or a high–liquid level alarm, and manual flow cutoff shall be permitted.

13.4.1.9 Each refrigerated LP-Gas container shall be provided with temperature-indicating devices that assist in controlling cooldown rates when placing the tank in service and monitoring product temperatures during operations.

13.4.2 Pressure and Vacuum Control.

13.4.2.1 Provisions shall be made to maintain the container pressure within the limits set by the design specifications by releasing or admitting gas as needed.

Shaded text = Revisions.　**△** = Text deletions and figure/table revisions.　• = Section deletions.　**N** = New material.

13.4.2.2 Provision for admission and release of gas shall be by any means compatible with the gas-handling facilities in the plant.

13.4.2.3 The option of gas admission (or other gas or vapor if so designed) through the vacuum relief valves provided in API 620, *Design and Construction of Large, Welded, Low-Pressure Storage Tanks,* shall not be permitted.

13.5 Refrigerated LP-Gas Container Impoundment.

13.5.1 Each refrigerated LP-Gas container shall be located within an impoundment that complies with Section 13.5.

13.5.2 Enclosed drainage channels for LP-Gas shall be prohibited.

13.5.3 Enclosure of container downcomers used to conduct spilled LP-Gas away from materials subject to failure upon exposure to liquid LP-Gas shall be permitted.

13.5.4 Impoundment for refrigerated LP-Gas containers shall have a volumetric holding capacity, with an allowance made for the displacement of snow accumulation, other containers, or equipment that is equal to the total liquid volume of the largest container served, assuming that container is full to the high–liquid level flow cutoff device.

13.5.5 Where more than one container is installed in a single impoundment, and if an outside container wall is used as a spill containment dike, the material shall be selected to withstand exposure to the temperature of refrigerated LP-Gas liquid.

13.5.6 Impoundment structures and any penetrations thereof shall be designed to withstand the full hydrostatic head of the impounded LP-Gas and the effects of the product composition and the resulting autorefrigeration temperatures.

13.5.7 Impoundment structures shall also be nonporous and resistant to natural forces such as wind, rain, and fire.

13.5.8 Provisions shall be made to clear rain or other water from the impounding area.

13.5.8.1 Sump Pumps.

(A) Where automatically controlled sump pumps are used, they shall be equipped with an automatic shutoff device that prevents their operation when exposed to the flash temperature of liquid LP-Gas.

(B) In addition, the sump pumps shall be de-energized if flammable vapors in excess of 25 percent of the lower flammable limit are detected within the impoundment area.

13.5.8.2 LP-Gas vapors shall not exceed 25 percent of the lower flammable limit or other approved methods of LP-Gas liquid or vapor detection.

13.5.8.3 Gravity drainage utilizing piping penetrations through or below impoundment dikes shall not be permitted.

13.5.9 If the container impounding area is an earthen dike system, the area topography of the impounding area floor shall be graded away from the container to prevent the accumulation of liquid under or around the container.

13.5.9.1 The grading shall move the spilled liquid to the toe of the dike system and as far away from the container as possible.

13.5.9.2 The grading shall move the spilled liquid to a subimpoundment basin that is capable of holding the quantity of liquid spilled from a line rupture, a flange leak, or a source other than container failure.

13.5.9.3 The duration of the incident shall be the amount of time that automatic systems or plant personnel could effect emergency procedures and stop the leak.

13.5.9.4 The subimpoundment basin shall be located as far away from the container as possible.

13.6 Inspection and Testing of Refrigerated LP-Gas Containers and Systems.

13.6.1 During construction and prior to the initial operation or commissioning, each refrigerated LP-Gas container and system shall be inspected or tested in accordance with the provisions of this code and the codes and standards referenced herein.

13.6.2 The inspections or tests required shall be conducted by the operator or a recognized third-party engineering, scientific, insurance, or inspection organization.

13.6.3 Each inspector shall be qualified in accordance with the code or standard that is applicable to the test or inspection being performed.

13.6.4 After acceptance tests are completed, there shall be no field welding on the LP-Gas containers except where allowed by the code under which the container was fabricated.

13.6.5 Retesting shall be required only if the retest tests the element affected and is necessary to demonstrate the adequacy of the repair or modification.

13.7 Container Siting.

13.7.1 Spacing of refrigerated LP-Gas containers designed to operate at greater than 15 psi (103 kPa) from important buildings, storage containers for flammable or combustible liquids or flammable gases, and lines of adjoining property that can be built upon shall be in accordance with Table 13.7.1.

13.7.2 Spacing of refrigerated LP-Gas containers that operate at 15 psi (103 kPa) or less from important buildings, storage containers for flammable or combustible liquids or flammable gases, and lines of adjoining property that can be built upon shall be in accordance with Table 13.7.2.

13.7.3 The edge of a dike, impoundment, or drainage system that is intended for a refrigerated LP-Gas container shall be

Table 13.7.1 Minimum Distances for LP-Gas Containers That Operate Above 15 psi (103 kPa)

Water Capacity per Container		Aboveground Containers	
gal	m³	ft	m
≤70,000	≤265	75	23
70,001–90,000	>265–341	100	30
90,001–120,000	>341–454	125	38
120,001–200,000	>454–757	200	61
200,001–1,000,000	>757–3785	300	91
>1,000,000	>3785	400	122

Shaded text = Revisions.   △ = Text deletions and figure/table revisions.   • = Section deletions.   *N* = New material.

2020 Edition

100 ft (30 m) or more from a property line that can be built upon, a public way, or a navigable waterway.

13.7.4 Nonrefrigerated LP-Gas containers or flammable liquid tanks shall not be located within dikes or impoundments enclosing refrigerated LP-Gas containers.

13.7.5 Refrigerated LP-Gas containers shall not be installed one above the other.

13.7.6 The minimum distance between aboveground refrigerated LP-Gas containers shall be one-half the diameter of the larger container.

13.7.7 The ground within 25 ft (7.6 m) of any aboveground refrigerated LP-Gas container, and all ground within a dike, impoundment, or drainage area, shall be kept clear of readily ignitible materials such as weeds and long, dry grass.

13.8 Relief Devices.

13.8.1 General.

13.8.1.1 All containers shall be equipped with pressure and vacuum relief devices in accordance with Section 13.8.

13.8.1.2 Relief devices shall communicate directly with the atmosphere, and vacuum-relieving devices shall be installed if the container can be exposed to a vacuum lower than that for which the container is designed.

13.8.1.3 Inlet and outlet piping connections to relief devices shall be included in the selection and sizing of relief devices.

13.8.1.4 A manually operated full opening stop valve shall be installed between each pressure and vacuum safety relief valve and the LP-Gas container.

13.8.1.5 All stop valves installed between a relief valve and a container shall be lockable or sealable in the fully open position.

13.8.1.6 A sufficient number of pressure and vacuum relief valves shall be installed on the LP-Gas container to allow each relief valve to be isolated individually while maintaining the full relieving capacities required.

13.8.1.7 Where only one relief device is required, either a full port opening three-way valve shall be installed between the container and two relief devices or separate stop valves shall be beneath each relief device.

13.8.1.8 Stop valves under individual safety relief valves shall be locked or sealed when opened and shall not be opened or closed except by an authorized person.

13.8.1.9 No more than one stop valve shall be closed at one time.

13.8.1.10 Safety relief valve discharge stacks or vents shall be designed and installed to prevent an accumulation of water, ice, snow, or other foreign matter and shall discharge vertically upward.

13.8.1.11 All refrigerated storage container pressure and vacuum relief devices shall be tested or replaced at intervals not to exceed 5 years.

13.8.2 Pressure Relief Device Sizing. The pressure relief devices shall be sized to relieve the flow capacity determined for the largest single contingency or any reasonable and probable combination of the following contingencies:

(1) Fire exposure
(2) Operational upset, such as failure of a control device
(3) Other circumstances resulting from equipment failures and operating errors
(4) Vapor displacement during filling
(5) Flash vaporization during filling, as a result of filling, or as a consequence of mixing of products of different compositions
(6) Loss of refrigeration
(7) Heat input from pump recirculation
(8) Drop in barometric pressure

13.8.3 Vacuum Relief Device Sizing.

13.8.3.1 The vacuum relief devices shall be sized to relieve the flow capacity determined for the largest single contingency or any reasonable and probable combination of the following contingencies:

(1) Withdrawal of liquid or vapor at the maximum rate
(2) Rise in barometric pressure
(3) Reduction in vapor space pressure as a result of filling with subcooled liquid

13.8.3.2 Reduction in the vacuum relief capacity to allow for the rate of vaporization resulting from minimum normal heat gain to the contents of the container shall be allowed.

13.8.3.3 No vacuum relief capacity credit shall be allowed for gas-repressuring or vapor makeup systems.

13.8.4 Fire Exposure Sizing.

13.8.4.1 The pressure-relieving capacity required for fire exposure shall be computed by the following formula:

[13.8.4.1]

$$W = 34,500 \frac{F}{L} A^{0.82} + \frac{H_n}{L}$$

where:
W = relieving capacity in lb/hr or product vapor at relieving conditions
F = environmental factor from Table 13.8.4.1
L = latent heat of vaporization of the stored liquid at the relieving pressure and temperature in Btu/lb
A = exposed wetted surface area of the container in ft^2 [In the case of large containers, the exposed wetted area is the area up to a height of 30 ft (9.1 m) above grade.]
H_n = normal heat leak in refrigerated tanks in Btu/hr

Δ **Table 13.7.2 Minimum Distances for LP-Gas Containers That Operate at 15 psi (103 kPa) or Less**

Water Capacity per Container		Aboveground Containers	
gal	m³	ft	m
≤70,000	≤265	75	25
>70,000	>265	100	30

△ **Table 13.8.4.1 Environmental Factors**

Basis	*F* Factor
Base container	1.0
Water application facilities	1.0
Depressuring and emptying facilities	1.0
Underground container	0
Insulation or thermal protection (U.S.)	$F = \dfrac{U(1660 - T_f)}{34{,}500}$
Insulation or thermal protection (metric)	$F = \dfrac{U(904 - T_f)}{71{,}000}$

Note: U is the overall heat transfer coefficient, Btu/(hr × ft^2 × °F) [W/(m^2 × °C)], of the insulation system using the mean value for the temperature range from T_f to 1660°F (T_f to 904°C). T_f is the temperature [°F (°C)] of vessel content at relieving conditions.

13.8.4.2 Where credit for insulation is taken in sizing of a relief valve for fire exposure, the insulation shall comply with the following:

(1) Resist dislodgment by fire-fighting equipment
(2) Be noncombustible
(3) Not decompose at temperatures up to 1000°F (540°C)

13.8.4.3 If the insulation does not meet the criteria of 13.8.4.2, no credit for the insulation shall be taken.

13.8.4.4 The equivalent airflow for relieving capacity shall be calculated by the following equation:

[13.8.4.4]

$$\text{SCFM (air)} = 3.09 W \left(\frac{ZT}{M} \right)^{0.5}$$

where:
SCFM (air) = equivalent airflow in standard ft^3/min
W = relieving capacity of product vapor at relieving conditions in lb/hr
Z = compressibility factor product vapor at relieving conditions
T = absolute temperature of product vapor at relieving conditions in °R
M = product vapor molecular weight

Chapter 14   Marine Shipping and Receiving

14.1 Scope. This chapter applies to the transfer of LP-Gas between marine vessels and shore facilities.

14.2 Piers.

14.2.1 Design and Construction.

14.2.1.1* Design, construction, and operation of piers, docks, and wharves shall comply with relevant regulations and the requirements of the authorities having jurisdiction.

14.2.1.2 General cargo, flammable liquids, or compressed gases, other than ships' general stores for the LP-Gas tank vessel, shall not be handled over a pier or dock within 100 ft (30 m) of the point of transfer connection while LP-Gas or other flammable liquids are being transferred.

14.2.1.3 Trucks and other motorized vehicles shall be prohibited on the pier or dock within 100 ft (30 m) of the transfer connection while transfer operations are in progress.

14.2.1.4 Authorized parking areas, if provided for in the waterfront area, shall be marked.

14.2.1.5 Warning signs or barricades shall be used to indicate when transfer operations are in progress.

14.2.1.6 Unauthorized individuals shall not be allowed access to the waterfront area while the LP-Gas vessel is alongside the pier or dock.

14.2.1.7 Security personnel shall restrict the entry of visitors, delivery trucks, and service personnel to those authorized by the facility operator.

14.2.1.8 The shore mooring equipment shall be designed and maintained to safely hold the vessel to the pier or dock.

14.2.1.9 If the terminal conducts transfers between sunset and sunrise, the pier or dock area shall have a lighting system that illuminates the following:

(1) Transfer connection area
(2) Control valves
(3) Storage containers
(4) Other equipment
(5) Walkways, fire fighting, and other emergency areas

14.2.1.10 All lighting shall be located or shielded so that it is not confused with any aids to navigation and does not interfere with navigation on the adjacent waterway.

14.2.1.11 Welding and cutting shall be in accordance with NFPA 51B.

14.2.1.12 Smoking shall be prohibited in all areas other than conspicuously marked, designated areas.

14.2.1.13 Medical First-Aid Equipment and Fire Extinguishers.

(A) Medical first-aid equipment and fire extinguishers shall be available at the shore facility.

(B) This equipment shall be in accordance with the following:

(1) Extinguishers shall be ready for use at all times.
(2) Emergency equipment shall be positioned and ready to operate prior to the start of the transfer operation.
(3) The locations of all fire extinguishers shall be marked and readily accessible.

14.2.2 Electrical Equipment. All electrical equipment and wiring installed on the pier or dock shall comply with 6.25.2.1.

14.2.3 Transfer Operations.

14.2.3.1 Prior to the start of the transfer, a warning sign that reads as shown in Figure 14.2.3.1 shall be placed in the marine transfer area and shall be visible from the shoreline and berth areas.

14.2.3.2 A portable LP-Gas detector calibrated to detect LP-Gas shall be readily available for use at the berth.

```
┌─────────────────────────────┐
│                             │
│         WARNING             │
│                             │
│     DANGEROUS CARGO         │
│                             │
│        NO VISITORS          │
│                             │
│       NO SMOKING            │
│                             │
│      NO OPEN LIGHT          │
│                             │
└─────────────────────────────┘
```

FIGURE 14.2.3.1 Warning Sign to Be Placed in Marine Transfer Area.

14.2.3.3 Portable electrical equipment used within 100 ft (30 m) of the transfer connection while transfer operations are in progress either shall be listed for Class I, Division 1 or shall be intrinsically safe.

14.2.3.4 When the transfer operation is completed (secured) and the transfer piping is disconnected, the equipment used shall be in compliance with 6.25.2.1 and 6.25.2.2.

14.2.3.5 The following life safety equipment shall be positioned on the berth and be ready for immediate use while personnel are working on the berth or a vessel is alongside:

(1) Life rings with attendant rope of sufficient length
(2) Approved fire blanket
(3) Flotation vests or immersion suits suitable for the water temperature at the berth and the personnel involved in the work

14.3 Pipelines.

14.3.1* Pipelines shall be located on the dock or pier so that they are not exposed to damage from vehicular traffic or other possible cause of physical damage.

14.3.1.1 Underwater pipelines shall be located or protected so that they are not exposed to damage from marine traffic.

14.3.1.2 The locations of underwater pipelines shall be posted or identified in accordance with federal regulations.

14.3.2 Isolation valving and bleed connections shall be provided at the loading or unloading manifold for both liquid and vapor return lines so that hoses and arms can be blocked off, drained or pumped out, and depressurized before disconnecting.

14.3.2.1 Liquid isolation valves and vapor valves 8 in. (200 mm) and larger in size shall be equipped with powered operators in addition to means for manual operation.

14.3.2.2 Electrical power-operated valves shall be capable of being closed from a remote control station located at least 50 ft (15 m) from the manifold area, as well as locally.

14.3.2.3 Unless the valve will automatically fail closed on loss of power, the valve actuator and its power supply within 50 ft (15 m) of the valve shall be protected against operational failure due to fire exposure of at least 10 minutes.

14.3.2.4 Valves shall be located at the point of hose or arm connection to the manifold.

14.3.2.5 In addition to the isolation valves at the manifold, each vapor return and liquid transfer line shall be provided

with a readily accessible isolation valve located on shore near the approach to the pier or dock.

14.3.2.6 Where more than one line exists, the valves shall be grouped in one location.

14.3.2.7 Valves shall be identified as to their service.

14.3.3 Pipelines used for liquid unloading only shall be provided with a backflow check valve located at the manifold adjacent to the manifold isolation valve.

14.3.4 All pipelines, conduits, and other conductive lines on the berth capable of carrying an electrical charge shall be equipped with insulating flanges or other means to electrically isolate them from stray currents and the rest of the terminal.

14.3.5 If a stray current (bonding) cable is not used between the facility and the vessel, insulating flanges shall be installed in the pipe risers to the off-loading connections between the vessel and the shore facility.

14.3.6 All shore facilities shall provide a low-resistance stray current (bonding) cable to be connected to the vessels.

14.3.6.1 Electrical continuity between the vessel and the berth shall be verified prior to transfer operations.

14.3.6.2 The cable shall be connected to the vessel prior to the connection of the unloading hose/arms and shall remain connected until after the hose/arms have been disconnected.

14.4 Inspections Prior to Transfer.

14.4.1* Prior to starting transfer operations, the officer in charge of the vessel transfer operation and the person in charge of the shore facility shall inspect their respective facilities.

14.4.1.1 The inspection shall ensure that all cargo transfer equipment and hose have been maintained and tested and are in operating condition.

14.4.1.2 Following the inspection, the officers in charge shall meet to discuss the transfer procedures, and, when ready, each will notify the other that each facility is ready in all respects to start transfer operations.

14.4.2 The shore facility transfer system shall be equipped with a remotely operated emergency shutdown system.

14.4.3 A facility's emergency procedures manual shall be readily available and shall contain the following information:

(1) LP-Gas release response and emergency shutdown procedures
(2) Telephone number for all emergency response organizations, U.S. Coast Guard, emergency medical facilities, and hospital(s)
(3) Description and location of the facility fire systems and emergency equipment

14.4.4 A facility's standard operating procedures manual shall be readily available and shall contain the following information:

(1) Procedures for start-up, operation, and shutdown of the transfer system and equipment
(2) Procedures for cooling down the transfer hose and line where refrigerated LP-Gas is transferred

(3) Telephone numbers for all emergency response organizations, U.S. Coast Guard, emergency medical facilities, and hospital(s)

(4) Description, location, and operational guidelines for the facility fire systems and emergency equipment

14.4.5 Each transfer operation shall be conducted in accordance with the operations manual.

14.4.6 At the completion of the transfer, and prior to disconnect of the transfer hose or arm, the transfer connection shall be purged of all liquid and depressurized.

(A) The liquid and vapor pressure shall be returned either to the vessel or to the shore facility.

(B) LP-Gas shall not be vented to the atmosphere.

Chapter 15 Operations and Maintenance

15.1* Scope. This chapter includes requirements related to the operations and maintenance of bulk plant, industrial plant, refrigerated, marine, and pipeline LP-Gas systems not regulated by the U.S. Department of Transportation.

15.1.1 The provisions of this chapter apply to all new and existing installations

15.1.2 If stated elsewhere in the code, operation and maintenance requirements are referenced to those sections.

15.1.3* Containers or equipment at bulk plants and industrial plants that have been determined to be unsuitable for continued service shall be taken out of service.

15.2 Operating Requirements.

15.2.1* Operating Procedures.

△ 15.2.1.1 Operating procedure shall address all aspects of LP-Gas transfer, as appropriate for the facility, including inspection of hose and fittings and connection and disconnection procedures.

15.2.1.2 Operating procedures shall include operator actions to be taken if flammable concentrations of flammable liquids or gases are detected in the facility using fixed detectors, portable detectors, operating malfunctions, or the human senses.

△ 15.2.1.3 Each facility shall prepare and maintain in a common location or locations written operating procedure manuals that contain the written operating procedures.

15.2.1.4* Facilities that are not attended shall have the internal valves and emergency shutoff valves of the container closed unless the facility is in use or the valve is required to be open to maintain a process or system.

15.2.1.5* Container openings serving an engine fuel (LP-Gas) refueling system shall be exempt from the requirements of 15.2.1.4.

15.2.2 Content of Operating Procedures. Written procedures shall be the basis for conducting activities associated with the systems referenced in Section 15.1.

15.2.2.1 Operating procedures shall be updated whenever a change occurs that affects the operation of a system and prior to its start-up.

15.2.2.2 The written procedures shall address the requirements in Section 15.3 and Section 15.4, where applicable.

N 15.3 Operating Requirements for Bulk Plants and Industrial Plants.

N 15.3.1 Container Operations.

N 15.3.1.1 Containers that show excessive denting, bulging, gouging, or corrosion shall be removed from service in accordance with 5.2.1.4.

N 15.3.1.2 Storage of combustible materials shall be in accordance with 6.5.3.3.

N 15.3.1.3 The surface on which temporary containers are placed shall be maintained in accordance with 6.8.5.2.

N 15.3.1.4 Temperature-sensitive elements of emergency shutoff valves shall not be painted or coated in accordance with 6.14.7.

N 15.3.1.5 Welding on containers shall be in accordance with 6.8.1.3.

N 15.3.1.6 Venting of containers shall be in accordance with Section 7.3.

N 15.3.1.7 The quantity of LP-Gas in containers shall be in accordance with Section 7.4.

N 15.3.1.8 Paint and coatings on containers shall be maintained.

N 15.3.2 Cylinder Operations.

N 15.3.2.1 A cylinder with an expired requalification date shall not be refilled until it is requalified in accordance with 5.2.2.3.

N 15.3.2.2 Where LP-Gas cylinders are to be stored or used in the same area with other compressed gases, the requirements of 6.5.3.12 shall be followed.

N 15.3.3 Hose Inspection. Inspection of hose assemblies shall be in accordance with 7.2.4.

N 15.3.4 Transfer Operations.

N 15.3.4.1 Transfer personnel requirements shall be in accordance with 7.2.1.

N 15.3.4.2 Filling and evacuation of containers shall be in accordance with 7.2.2.

N 15.3.4.3 Control of sources of ignition and smoking during transfer operations shall be in accordance with 7.2.3.2 and 9.4.10.

N 15.3.4.4 The arrangement and operation of transfer systems shall be in accordance with 7.2.3.

N 15.3.4.5 Transfers to containers serving industrial equipment requiring refueling in the field shall be in accordance with 7.2.3.5.

N 15.3.4.6 Public access to storage and transfer areas shall be in accordance with 7.2.3.1.

N 15.3.4.7 Transfer hose at dispensing stations shall be secured in accordance with 6.27.4.1(3).

N 15.3.4.8 Railcar transfer operations shall be in accordance with 7.2.3.6, 7.2.3.7, and 7.2.3.8.

Shaded text = Revisions. △ = Text deletions and figure/table revisions. • = Section deletions. N = New material.

2020 Edition

N **15.3.5 Cargo Tank Motor Vehicle Operations.**

N **15.3.5.1** Parking of cargo tank motor vehicles at bulk plants and industrial plants shall be in accordance with 6.26.8.4.

N **15.3.5.2** The use of wheel stops shall be in accordance with 9.4.8.

N **15.3.5.3** Cargo tank motor vehicles unloading into storage containers shall be located and oriented in accordance with 7.2.3.3.

N **15.3.6 Vaporizer Operating Procedures.**

N **15.3.6.1** Operating procedures for vaporizers shall include maintenance of vaporization rate, pressure control, and temperature.

N **15.3.6.2** Procedures shall include specific actions to be taken when parameters exceed normal operating limits and criteria for emergency shutdown.

N **15.3.7 Fire Response Operations.** LP-Gas fires shall not be extinguished until the source of the burning gas has been shut off.

N **15.3.8 Refrigerated Liquid Operating Procedures.**

N **15.3.8.1** In facilities where propane is stored as a refrigerated liquid, operating procedures shall include monitoring of liquid temperature and pressure and procedures to be taken if the temperature or pressure exceeds operating limits.

N **15.3.8.2** The procedures required in 15.3.8.1 shall minimize the release of flammable gases to the atmosphere.

N **15.4 Operations Requirements for Marine Shipping and Receiving.**

N **15.4.1 Propane Transfer at Marine Terminals.** Marine transfer requirements shall be in accordance with Section 14.4.

N **15.4.2 Medical First-Aid Equipment and Fire Extinguishers at Marine Terminals.** Medical first-aid equipment and fire extinguishers shall be in accordance with 14.2.1.13.

15.5* Maintenance Manuals and Procedures.

15.5.1 Maintenance Procedures. Written maintenance procedures shall be the basis for maintaining the mechanical integrity of LP-Gas systems.

15.5.1.1 Procedures shall be updated whenever a change occurs that affects the maintenance of a system.

15.5.1.2 Persons who perform maintenance on LP-Gas systems shall be trained in the hazards of the system and in the maintenance and testing procedures applicable to the installation.

15.5.1.3 Any maintenance contractor shall ensure that each contract maintenance employee is so trained or under the immediate supervision of such a trained person to perform the maintenance procedures.

N **15.6 Maintenance Procedures for Bulk Plants and Industrial Plants.**

N **15.6.1 Container Maintenance.**

N **15.6.1.1** Paint and coatings on containers shall be maintained.

N **15.6.1.2** The part of an ASME container in contact with saddles, foundations, or masonry shall be in accordance with 6.8.3.5.

N **15.6.1.3** Sacrificial anode cathodic protection systems shall be monitored by testing, the results shall be documented, and confirming tests shall be conducted in accordance with 6.19.3.1 and 6.19.3.2.

N **15.6.1.4** Impressed current cathodic protection systems shall be monitored and tested in accordance with 6.19.3.3.

N **15.6.1.5** Containers that have been involved in a fire and show no distortion shall be requalified in accordance with 5.2.1.2.

N **15.6.2 Hose Maintenance.**

N **15.6.2.1** Hose assemblies shall be inspected as specified in 7.2.4 and shall be replaced, repaired, or continued in service based on the results of the inspection.

N **15.6.2.2 Flexible Hose Connectors.** Flexible hose connectors on cargo tank motor vehicles shall be replaced in accordance 9.4.3.7.

N **15.6.3 Valve Maintenance.** Emergency shutoff valves required by the code shall be tested annually in accordance with 6.14.10.

Chapter 16   Pipe and Tubing Sizing Tables

△ **16.1* Sizing Pipe and Tubing.** When the pipe sizing method of 6.11.2.2 is used, Table 16.1(a) through Table 16.1(p), or other approved piping tables, shall be used to size piping systems. To convert to SI units, the following conversions shall be used: 1 ft^3 = 0.028 m^3; 1 ft = 0.305 m; 1 in. water column = 2.49 kPa; 1 psi = 6.894 kPa; and 1000 Btu/hr = 0.203 kW.

△ Table 16.1(a) Schedule 40 Metallic Pipe

	Gas:	Undiluted Propane
	Inlet Pressure:	10.0 psi
	Pressure Drop:	1.0 psi
	Specific Gravity:	1.50

INTENDED USE: Pipe Sizing Between Single- or Second-Stage (Low-Pressure) Regulator and Appliance.

Nominal:	½	¾	1	1¼	1½	2	2½	3	4
Actual:	0.622	0.824	1.049	1.380	1.610	2.067	2.469	3.068	4.026
Length (ft)	Capacity in Thousands of Btu per Hour								
10	3,320	6,950	13,100	26,900	40,300	77,600	124,000	219,000	446,000
20	2,280	4,780	9,000	18,500	27,700	53,300	85,000	150,000	306,000
30	1,830	3,840	7,220	14,800	22,200	42,800	68,200	121,000	246,000
40	1,570	3,280	6,180	12,700	19,000	36,600	58,400	103,000	211,000
50	1,390	2,910	5,480	11,300	16,900	32,500	51,700	91,500	187,000
60	1,260	2,640	4,970	10,200	15,300	29,400	46,900	82,900	169,000
70	1,160	2,430	4,570	9,380	14,100	27,100	43,100	76,300	156,000
80	1,080	2,260	4,250	8,730	13,100	25,200	40,100	70,900	145,000
90	1,010	2,120	3,990	8,190	12,300	23,600	37,700	66,600	136,000
100	956	2,000	3,770	7,730	11,600	22,300	35,600	62,900	128,000
125	848	1,770	3,340	6,850	10,300	19,800	31,500	55,700	114,000
150	768	1,610	3,020	6,210	9,300	17,900	28,600	50,500	103,000
175	706	1,480	2,780	5,710	8,560	16,500	26,300	46,500	94,700
200	657	1,370	2,590	5,320	7,960	15,300	24,400	43,200	88,100
250	582	1,220	2,290	4,710	7,060	13,600	21,700	38,300	78,100
300	528	1,100	2,080	4,270	6,400	12,300	19,600	34,700	70,800
350	486	1,020	1,910	3,930	5,880	11,300	18,100	31,900	65,100
400	452	945	1,780	3,650	5,470	10,500	16,800	29,700	60,600
450	424	886	1,670	3,430	5,140	9,890	15,800	27,900	56,800
500	400	837	1,580	3,240	4,850	9,340	14,900	26,300	53,700
550	380	795	1,500	3,070	4,610	8,870	14,100	25,000	51,000
600	363	759	1,430	2,930	4,400	8,460	13,500	23,900	48,600
650	347	726	1,370	2,810	4,210	8,110	12,900	22,800	46,600
700	334	698	1,310	2,700	4,040	7,790	12,400	21,900	44,800
750	321	672	1,270	2,600	3,900	7,500	12,000	21,100	43,100
800	310	649	1,220	2,510	3,760	7,240	11,500	20,400	41,600
850	300	628	1,180	2,430	3,640	7,010	11,200	19,800	40,300
900	291	609	1,150	2,360	3,530	6,800	10,800	19,200	39,100
950	283	592	1,110	2,290	3,430	6,600	10,500	18,600	37,900
1,000	275	575	1,080	2,230	3,330	6,420	10,200	18,100	36,900
1,100	261	546	1,030	2,110	3,170	6,100	9,720	17,200	35,000
1,200	249	521	982	2,020	3,020	5,820	9,270	16,400	33,400
1,300	239	499	940	1,930	2,890	5,570	8,880	15,700	32,000
1,400	229	480	903	1,850	2,780	5,350	8,530	15,100	30,800
1,500	221	462	870	1,790	2,680	5,160	8,220	14,500	29,600
1,600	213	446	840	1,730	2,590	4,980	7,940	14,000	28,600
1,700	206	432	813	1,670	2,500	4,820	7,680	13,600	27,700
1,800	200	419	789	1,620	2,430	4,670	7,450	13,200	26,900
1,900	194	407	766	1,570	2,360	4,540	7,230	12,800	26,100
2,000	189	395	745	1,530	2,290	4,410	7,030	12,400	25,400

Note: All table entries are rounded to 3 significant digits.
[54:Table 6.3.1(a)]

Shaded text = Revisions.   △ = Text deletions and figure/table revisions.   • = Section deletions.   N = New material.

2020 Edition

△ **Table 16.1(b) Schedule 40 Metallic Pipe**

						Gas:	Undiluted Propane
						Inlet Pressure:	2.0 psi
						Pressure Drop:	1.0 psi
						Specific Gravity:	1.50

INTENDED USE: Pipe Sizing Between 2 psig Service and Line Pressure Regulator.

	Pipe Size (in.)								
Nominal:	½	¾	1	1¼	1½	2	2½	3	4
Actual:	0.622	0.824	1.049	1.380	1.610	2.067	2.469	3.068	4.026
Length (ft)	Capacity in Thousands of Btu per Hour								
10	2,680	5,590	10,500	21,600	32,400	62,400	99,500	176,000	359,000
20	1,840	3,850	7,240	14,900	22,300	42,900	68,400	121,000	247,000
30	1,480	3,090	5,820	11,900	17,900	34,500	54,900	97,100	198,000
40	1,260	2,640	4,980	10,200	15,300	29,500	47,000	83,100	170,000
50	1,120	2,340	4,410	9,060	13,600	26,100	41,700	73,700	150,000
60	1,010	2,120	4,000	8,210	12,300	23,700	37,700	66,700	136,000
70	934	1,950	3,680	7,550	11,300	21,800	34,700	61,400	125,000
80	869	1,820	3,420	7,020	10,500	20,300	32,300	57,100	116,000
90	815	1,700	3,210	6,590	9,880	19,000	30,300	53,600	109,000
100	770	1,610	3,030	6,230	9,330	18,000	28,600	50,600	103,000
125	682	1,430	2,690	5,520	8,270	15,900	25,400	44,900	91,500
150	618	1,290	2,440	5,000	7,490	14,400	23,000	40,700	82,900
175	569	1,190	2,240	4,600	6,890	13,300	21,200	37,400	76,300
200	529	1,110	2,080	4,280	6,410	12,300	19,700	34,800	71,000
250	469	981	1,850	3,790	5,680	10,900	17,400	30,800	62,900
300	425	889	1,670	3,440	5,150	9,920	15,800	27,900	57,000
350	391	817	1,540	3,160	4,740	9,120	14,500	25,700	52,400
400	364	760	1,430	2,940	4,410	8,490	13,500	23,900	48,800
450	341	714	1,340	2,760	4,130	7,960	12,700	22,400	45,800
500	322	674	1,270	2,610	3,910	7,520	12,000	21,200	43,200
550	306	640	1,210	2,480	3,710	7,140	11,400	20,100	41,100
600	292	611	1,150	2,360	3,540	6,820	10,900	19,200	39,200
650	280	585	1,100	2,260	3,390	6,530	10,400	18,400	37,500
700	269	562	1,060	2,170	3,260	6,270	9,990	17,700	36,000
750	259	541	1,020	2,090	3,140	6,040	9,630	17,000	34,700
800	250	523	985	2,020	3,030	5,830	9,300	16,400	33,500
850	242	506	953	1,960	2,930	5,640	9,000	15,900	32,400
900	235	490	924	1,900	2,840	5,470	8,720	15,400	31,500
950	228	476	897	1,840	2,760	5,310	8,470	15,000	30,500
1,000	222	463	873	1,790	2,680	5,170	8,240	14,600	29,700
1,100	210	440	829	1,700	2,550	4,910	7,830	13,800	28,200
1,200	201	420	791	1,620	2,430	4,680	7,470	13,200	26,900
1,300	192	402	757	1,550	2,330	4,490	7,150	12,600	25,800
1,400	185	386	727	1,490	2,240	4,310	6,870	12,100	24,800
1,500	178	372	701	1,440	2,160	4,150	6,620	11,700	23,900
1,600	172	359	677	1,390	2,080	4,010	6,390	11,300	23,000
1,700	166	348	655	1,340	2,010	3,880	6,180	10,900	22,300
1,800	161	337	635	1,300	1,950	3,760	6,000	10,600	21,600
1,900	157	327	617	1,270	1,900	3,650	5,820	10,300	21,000
2,000	152	318	600	1,230	1,840	3,550	5,660	10,000	20,400

All table entries are rounded to 3 significant digits.
[**54:**Table 6.3.1(c)]

△ **Table 16.1(c) Schedule 40 Metallic Pipe**

		Gas:	Undiluted Propane
		Inlet Pressure:	11.0 in. w.c.
		Pressure Drop:	0.5 in. w.c.
		Specific Gravity:	1.50

INTENDED USE: Pipe Sizing Between Single- or Second-Stage (Low-Pressure) Regulator and Appliance.

	Pipe Size (in.)								
Nominal:	½	¾	1	1¼	1½	2	2½	3	4
Actual:	0.622	0.824	1.049	1.380	1.610	2.067	2.469	3.068	4.026
Length (ft)	Capacity in Thousands of Btu per Hour								
10	291	608	1,150	2,350	3,520	6,790	10,800	19,100	39,000
20	200	418	787	1,620	2,420	4,660	7,430	13,100	26,800
30	160	336	632	1,300	1,940	3,750	5,970	10,600	21,500
40	137	287	541	1,110	1,660	3,210	5,110	9,030	18,400
50	122	255	480	985	1,480	2,840	4,530	8,000	16,300
60	110	231	434	892	1,340	2,570	4,100	7,250	14,800
80	101	212	400	821	1,230	2,370	3,770	6,670	13,600
100	94	197	372	763	1,140	2,200	3,510	6,210	12,700
125	89	185	349	716	1,070	2,070	3,290	5,820	11,900
150	84	175	330	677	1,010	1,950	3,110	5,500	11,200
175	74	155	292	600	899	1,730	2,760	4,880	9,950
200	67	140	265	543	814	1,570	2,500	4,420	9,010
250	62	129	243	500	749	1,440	2,300	4,060	8,290
300	58	120	227	465	697	1,340	2,140	3,780	7,710
350	51	107	201	412	618	1,190	1,900	3,350	6,840
400	46	97	182	373	560	1,080	1,720	3,040	6,190
450	42	89	167	344	515	991	1,580	2,790	5,700
500	40	83	156	320	479	922	1,470	2,600	5,300
550	37	78	146	300	449	865	1,380	2,440	4,970
600	35	73	138	283	424	817	1,300	2,300	4,700
650	33	70	131	269	403	776	1,240	2,190	4,460
700	32	66	125	257	385	741	1,180	2,090	4,260
750	30	64	120	246	368	709	1,130	2,000	4,080
800	29	61	115	236	354	681	1,090	1,920	3,920
850	28	59	111	227	341	656	1,050	1,850	3,770
900	27	57	107	220	329	634	1,010	1,790	3,640
950	26	55	104	213	319	613	978	1,730	3,530
1,000	25	53	100	206	309	595	948	1,680	3,420
1,100	25	52	97	200	300	578	921	1,630	3,320
1,200	24	50	95	195	292	562	895	1,580	3,230
1,300	23	48	90	185	277	534	850	1,500	3,070
1,400	22	46	86	176	264	509	811	1,430	2,930
1,500	21	44	82	169	253	487	777	1,370	2,800
1,600	20	42	79	162	243	468	746	1,320	2,690
1,700	19	40	76	156	234	451	719	1,270	2,590
1,800	19	39	74	151	226	436	694	1,230	2,500
1,900	18	38	71	146	219	422	672	1,190	2,420
2,000	18	37	69	142	212	409	652	1,150	2,350

Note: All table entries are rounded to 3 significant digits.

[**54:**Table 6.3.1(d)]

Shaded text = Revisions.   △ = Text deletions and figure/table revisions.   • = Section deletions.   *N* = New material.

2020 Edition

△ **Table 16.1(d) Pipe Sizing Between First-Stage and Second-Stage Regulators: Nominal Pipe Size, Schedule 80**

	Gas:	Undiluted Propane
	Inlet Pressure:	10.0 psi
	Pressure Drop:	1.0 psi
	Specific Gravity:	1.50

INTENDED USE: Pipe Sizing Between First-Stage (High-Pressure) Regulator and Second-Stage (Low-Pressure) Regulator.

Pipe Length (ft)	½ in. 0.546	¾ in. 0.742	1 in. 0.957	1¼ in. 1.278	1½ in. 1.5	2 in. 1.939	3 in. 2.9	3½ in. 3.364	4 in. 3.826
30	1309	2927	5706	12185	18548	36368	104539	154295	216246
40	1121	2505	4884	10429	15875	31127	89472	132057	185079
50	993	2221	4328	9243	14069	27587	79297	117039	164032
60	900	2012	3922	8375	12748	24996	71849	106046	148625
70	828	1851	3608	7705	11728	22996	66100	97561	136733
80	770	1722	3357	7168	10911	21393	61494	90762	127204
90	723	1616	3149	6725	10237	20073	57697	85159	119351
100	683	1526	2975	6353	9670	18960	54501	80440	112738
150	548	1226	2389	5105	7765	15236	43766	64596	90533
200	469	1049	2045	4366	6646	13031	37458	55286	77484
250	416	930	1812	3870	5890	11549	33198	48999	68673
300	377	842	1642	3506	5337	10465	30080	44397	62223
350	347	775	1511	3226	4910	9627	27673	40844	57244
400	322	721	1405	3001	4568	8956	25745	37998	53255
450	303	676	1318	2816	4286	8403	24155	35652	49967
500	286	639	1245	2660	4048	7938	22817	33677	47199
600	259	579	1128	2410	3668	7192	20674	30514	42765
700	238	533	1038	2217	3375	6617	19020	28072	39344
800	222	495	966	2062	3139	6156	17694	26116	36602
900	208	465	906	1935	2946	5776	16602	24504	34342
1000	196	439	856	1828	2782	5456	15682	23146	32439
1500	158	353	687	1468	2234	4381	12593	18587	26050
2000	135	302	588	1256	1912	3750	10778	15908	22295

Notes:

(1) Capacities are in 1000 Btu/hr.

(2) To convert to capacities at a gauge pressure of 5 psi setting with 10 percent (0.5 psig) pressure drop, multiply values by 0.606. To convert to capacities at a gauge pressure of 15 psi with 10 percent (1.5 psig) pressure drop, multiply values by 1.380.

Δ **Table 16.1(e) Pipe Sizing Between Second-Stage Regulator and Appliance: Nominal Pipe Size, Schedule 80**

									Gas:	Undiluted Propane
									Inlet Pressure:	11 in. w.c.
									Pressure Drop:	0.5 in.
									Specific Gravity:	1.50

INTENDED USE: Pipe Sizing Between Single- or Second-Stage (Low-Pressure) Regulator and Appliance.

Pipe Length (ft)	½ in. 0.546	¾ in. 0.742	1 in. 0.957	1¼ in. 1.278	1½ in. 1.5	2 in. 1.939	3 in. 2.9	3½ in. 3.364	4 in. 3.826
10	207	462	901	1924	2928	5741	16503	24357	34137
20	142	318	619	1322	2012	3946	11342	16740	23462
30	114	255	497	1062	1616	3169	9108	13443	18841
40	98	218	426	909	1383	2712	7795	11506	16125
50	87	193	377	805	1226	2404	6909	10197	14292
60	78	175	342	730	1111	2178	6260	9239	12949
80	67	150	292	625	951	1864	5358	7908	11083
100	59	133	259	553	842	1652	4748	7009	9823
125	53	118	230	491	747	1464	4208	6212	8706
150	48	107	208	444	677	1327	3813	5628	7888
200	41	91	178	380	579	1135	3264	4817	6751
250	36	81	158	337	513	1006	2892	4269	5983
300	33	73	143	305	465	912	2621	3868	5421
350	30	68	132	281	428	839	2411	3559	4987
400	28	63	122	261	398	780	2243	3311	4640

Note: Capacities are in 1000 Btu/hr.

Shaded text = Revisions. Δ = Text deletions and figure/table revisions. • = Section deletions. N = New material.

2020 Edition

Δ Table 16.1(f) Semirigid Copper Tubing

		Gas:	Undiluted Propane
		Inlet Pressure:	10.0 psi
		Pressure Drop:	1.0 psi
		Specific Gravity:	1.50

INTENDED USE: Tube Sizing Between First-Stage (High-Pressure) Regulator and Second-Stage (Low-Pressure) Regulator.

						Tube Size (in.)				
Nominal:	**K & L:**	¼	⅜	½	⅝	¾	1	1¼	1½	2
	ACR:	⅜	½	⅝	¾	⅞	1⅛	1⅜	—	—
Outside:		0.375	0.500	0.625	0.750	0.875	1.125	1.375	1.625	2.125
Inside:*		0.305	0.402	0.527	0.652	0.745	0.995	1.245	1.481	1.959
Length (ft)					Capacity in Thousands of Btu per Hour					
10		513	1,060	2,150	3,760	5,330	11,400	20,500	32,300	67,400
20		352	727	1,480	2,580	3,670	7,830	14,100	22,200	46,300
30		283	584	1,190	2,080	2,940	6,290	11,300	17,900	37,200
40		242	500	1,020	1,780	2,520	5,380	9,690	15,300	31,800
50		215	443	901	1,570	2,230	4,770	8,590	13,500	28,200
60		194	401	816	1,430	2,020	4,320	7,780	12,300	25,600
70		179	369	751	1,310	1,860	3,980	7,160	11,300	23,500
80		166	343	699	1,220	1,730	3,700	6,660	10,500	21,900
90		156	322	655	1,150	1,630	3,470	6,250	9,850	20,500
100		147	304	619	1,080	1,540	3,280	5,900	9,310	19,400
125		131	270	549	959	1,360	2,910	5,230	8,250	17,200
150		118	244	497	869	1,230	2,630	4,740	7,470	15,600
175		109	225	457	799	1,130	2,420	4,360	6,880	14,300
200		101	209	426	744	1,060	2,250	4,060	6,400	13,300
250		90	185	377	659	935	2,000	3,600	5,670	11,800
300		81	168	342	597	847	1,810	3,260	5,140	10,700
350		75	155	314	549	779	1,660	3,000	4,730	9,840
400		70	144	292	511	725	1,550	2,790	4,400	9,160
450		65	135	274	480	680	1,450	2,620	4,130	8,590
500		62	127	259	453	643	1,370	2,470	3,900	8,120
550		59	121	246	430	610	1,300	2,350	3,700	7,710
600		56	115	235	410	582	1,240	2,240	3,530	7,350
650		54	111	225	393	558	1,190	2,140	3,380	7,040
700		51	106	216	378	536	1,140	2,060	3,250	6,770
750		50	102	208	364	516	1,100	1,980	3,130	6,520
800		48	99	201	351	498	1,060	1,920	3,020	6,290
850		46	96	195	340	482	1,030	1,850	2,920	6,090
900		45	93	189	330	468	1,000	1,800	2,840	5,910
950		44	90	183	320	454	970	1,750	2,750	5,730
1,000		42	88	178	311	442	944	1,700	2,680	5,580
1,100		40	83	169	296	420	896	1,610	2,540	5,300
1,200		38	79	161	282	400	855	1,540	2,430	5,050
1,300		37	76	155	270	383	819	1,470	2,320	4,840
1,400		35	73	148	260	368	787	1,420	2,230	4,650
1,500		34	70	143	250	355	758	1,360	2,150	4,480
1,600		33	68	138	241	343	732	1,320	2,080	4,330
1,700		32	66	134	234	331	708	1,270	2,010	4,190
1,800		31	64	130	227	321	687	1,240	1,950	4,060
1,900		30	62	126	220	312	667	1,200	1,890	3,940
2,000		29	60	122	214	304	648	1,170	1,840	3,830

Note: All table entries are rounded to 3 significant digits.

*Table capacities are based on Type K copper tubing inside diameter (shown), which has the smallest inside diameter of the copper tubing products.
[54:Table 6.3.1(e)]

△ Table 16.1(g) Semirigid Copper Tubing

Gas:	**Undiluted Propane**
Inlet Pressure:	**11.0 in. w.c.**
Pressure Drop:	**0.5 in. w.c.**
Specific Gravity:	**1.50**

INTENDED USE: Tube Sizing Between Single- or Second-Stage (Low-Pressure) Regulator and Appliance.

		\multicolumn{9}{c}{Tube Size (in.)}								
Nominal:	**K & L:**	¼	⅜	½	⅝	¾	1	1¼	1½	2
	ACR:	⅜	½	⅝	¾	⅞	1⅛	1⅜	—	—
Outside:		0.375	0.500	0.625	0.750	0.875	1.125	1.375	1.625	2.125
Inside:*		0.305	0.402	0.527	0.652	0.745	0.995	1.245	1.481	1.959
Length (ft)	\multicolumn{10}{c}{Capacity in Thousands of Btu per Hour}									
10		45	93	188	329	467	997	1,800	2,830	5,890
20		31	64	129	226	321	685	1,230	1,950	4,050
30		25	51	104	182	258	550	991	1,560	3,250
40		21	44	89	155	220	471	848	1,340	2,780
50		19	39	79	138	195	417	752	1,180	2,470
60		17	35	71	125	177	378	681	1,070	2,240
70		16	32	66	115	163	348	626	988	2,060
80		15	30	61	107	152	324	583	919	1,910
90		14	28	57	100	142	304	547	862	1,800
100		13	27	54	95	134	287	517	814	1,700
125		11	24	48	84	119	254	458	722	1,500
150		10	21	44	76	108	230	415	654	1,360
175		NA	20	40	70	99	212	382	602	1,250
200		NA	18	37	65	92	197	355	560	1,170
250		NA	16	33	58	82	175	315	496	1,030
300		NA	15	30	52	74	158	285	449	936
350		NA	14	28	48	68	146	262	414	861
400		NA	13	26	45	63	136	244	385	801
450		NA	12	24	42	60	127	229	361	752
500		NA	11	23	40	56	120	216	341	710
550		NA	11	22	38	53	114	205	324	674
600		NA	10	21	36	51	109	196	309	643
650		NA	NA	20	34	49	104	188	296	616
700		NA	NA	19	33	47	100	180	284	592
750		NA	NA	18	32	45	96	174	274	570
800		NA	NA	18	31	44	93	168	264	551
850		NA	NA	17	30	42	90	162	256	533
900		NA	NA	17	29	41	87	157	248	517
950		NA	NA	16	28	40	85	153	241	502
1,000		NA	NA	16	27	39	83	149	234	488
1,100		NA	NA	15	26	37	78	141	223	464
1,200		NA	NA	14	25	35	75	135	212	442
1,300		NA	NA	14	24	34	72	129	203	423
1,400		NA	NA	13	23	32	69	124	195	407
1,500		NA	NA	13	22	31	66	119	188	392
1,600		NA	NA	12	21	30	64	115	182	378
1,700		NA	NA	12	20	29	62	112	176	366
1,800		NA	NA	11	20	28	60	108	170	355
1,900		NA	NA	11	19	27	58	105	166	345
2,000		NA	NA	11	19	27	57	102	161	335

NA: A flow of less than 10,000 Btu/hr.

Note: All table entries are rounded to 3 significant digits.

*Table capacities are based on Type K copper tubing inside diameter (shown), which has the smallest inside diameter of the copper tubing products.
[**54:**Table 6.3.1(f)]

Shaded text = Revisions.   △ = Text deletions and figure/table revisions.   • = Section deletions.   **N** = New material.

2020 Edition

△ Table 16.1(h) Semirigid Copper Tubing

		Gas:	Undiluted Propane
		Inlet Pressure:	2.0 psi
		Pressure Drop:	1.0 psi
		Specific Gravity:	1.50

INTENDED USE: Tube Sizing Between 2 psig Service and Line Pressure Regulator.

Nominal:	K & L:	¼	⅜	½	⅝	¾	1	1¼	1½	2
	ACR:	⅜	½	⅝	¾	⅞	1⅛	1⅜	—	—
Outside:		0.375	0.500	0.625	0.750	0.875	1.125	1.375	1.625	2.125
Inside:*		0.305	0.402	0.527	0.652	0.745	0.995	1.245	1.481	1.959
Length (ft)		Capacity in Thousands of Btu per Hour								
10		413	852	1,730	3,030	4,300	9,170	16,500	26,000	54,200
20		284	585	1,190	2,080	2,950	6,310	11,400	17,900	37,300
30		228	470	956	1,670	2,370	5,060	9,120	14,400	29,900
40		195	402	818	1,430	2,030	4,330	7,800	12,300	25,600
50		173	356	725	1,270	1,800	3,840	6,920	10,900	22,700
60		157	323	657	1,150	1,630	3,480	6,270	9,880	20,600
70		144	297	605	1,060	1,500	3,200	5,760	9,090	18,900
80		134	276	562	983	1,390	2,980	5,360	8,450	17,600
90		126	259	528	922	1,310	2,790	5,030	7,930	16,500
100		119	245	498	871	1,240	2,640	4,750	7,490	15,600
125		105	217	442	772	1,100	2,340	4,210	6,640	13,800
150		95	197	400	700	992	2,120	3,820	6,020	12,500
175		88	181	368	644	913	1,950	3,510	5,540	11,500
200		82	168	343	599	849	1,810	3,270	5,150	10,700
250		72	149	304	531	753	1,610	2,900	4,560	9,510
300		66	135	275	481	682	1,460	2,620	4,140	8,610
350		60	124	253	442	628	1,340	2,410	3,800	7,920
400		56	116	235	411	584	1,250	2,250	3,540	7,370
450		53	109	221	386	548	1,170	2,110	3,320	6,920
500		50	103	209	365	517	1,110	1,990	3,140	6,530
550		47	97	198	346	491	1,050	1,890	2,980	6,210
600		45	93	189	330	469	1,000	1,800	2,840	5,920
650		43	89	181	316	449	959	1,730	2,720	5,670
700		41	86	174	304	431	921	1,660	2,620	5,450
750		40	82	168	293	415	888	1,600	2,520	5,250
800		39	80	162	283	401	857	1,540	2,430	5,070
850		37	77	157	274	388	829	1,490	2,350	4,900
900		36	75	152	265	376	804	1,450	2,280	4,750
950		35	72	147	258	366	781	1,410	2,220	4,620
1,000		34	71	143	251	356	760	1,370	2,160	4,490
1,100		32	67	136	238	338	721	1,300	2,050	4,270
1,200		31	64	130	227	322	688	1,240	1,950	4,070
1,300		30	61	124	217	309	659	1,190	1,870	3,900
1,400		28	59	120	209	296	633	1,140	1,800	3,740
1,500		27	57	115	201	286	610	1,100	1,730	3,610
1,600		26	55	111	194	276	589	1,060	1,670	3,480
1,700		26	53	108	188	267	570	1,030	1,620	3,370
1,800		25	51	104	182	259	553	1,000	1,570	3,270
1,900		24	50	101	177	251	537	966	1,520	3,170
2,000		23	48	99	172	244	522	940	1,480	3,090

Note: All table entries are rounded to 3 significant digits.

*Table capacities are based on Type K copper tubing inside diameter (shown), which has the smallest inside diameter of the copper tubing products.

[**54:**Table 6.3.1(g)]

△ Table 16.1(i) Corrugated Stainless Steel Tubing (CSST)

														Gas:	Undiluted Propane
														Inlet Pressure:	5-10 psi
														Pressure Drop:	3.5 psi
														Specific Gravity:	1.50

Nominal Size	Tube Size													
	³⁄₈"	³⁄₈"	½"	½"	¾"	¾"	1"	1"	1¼"	1¼"	1½"	1½"	2"	2"
EHD	13	15	18	19	23	25	30	31	37	39	46	48	60	62
Length (ft)	Capacity in Thousands of Btu per Hour													
10	826	1,070	1,710	2,060	3,150	4,000	7,830	8,950	13,100	14,441	28,600	31,200	54,400	63,800
25	509	664	1,090	1,310	2,040	2,550	4,860	5,600	8,400	9,339	18,000	19,900	34,700	40,400
30	461	603	999	1,190	1,870	2,340	4,430	5,100	7,680	8,564	16,400	18,200	31,700	36,900
40	396	520	867	1,030	1,630	2,030	3,820	4,400	6,680	7,469	14,200	15,800	27,600	32,000
50	352	463	777	926	1,460	1,820	3,410	3,930	5,990	6,717	12,700	14,100	24,700	28,600
75	284	376	637	757	1,210	1,490	2,770	3,190	4,920	5,539	10,300	11,600	20,300	23,400
80	275	363	618	731	1,170	1,450	2,680	3,090	4,770	5,372	9,990	11,200	19,600	22,700
100	243	324	553	656	1,050	1,300	2,390	2,760	4,280	4,830	8,930	10,000	17,600	20,300
150	196	262	453	535	866	1,060	1,940	2,240	3,510	3,983	7,270	8,210	14,400	16,600
200	169	226	393	464	755	923	1,680	1,930	3,050	3,474	6,290	7,130	12,500	14,400
250	150	202	352	415	679	828	1,490	1,730	2,740	3,124	5,620	6,390	11,200	12,900
300	136	183	322	379	622	757	1,360	1,570	2,510	2,865	5,120	5,840	10,300	11,700
400	117	158	279	328	542	657	1,170	1,360	2,180	2,498	4,430	5,070	8,920	10,200
500	104	140	251	294	488	589	1,050	1,210	1,950	2,247	3,960	4,540	8,000	9,110

EHD: Equivalent hydraulic diameter. A measure of the relative hydraulic efficiency between different tubing sizes. The greater the value of EHD, the greater the gas capacity of the tubing.

Notes:

(1) Table does not include effect of pressure drop across the line regulator. Where regulator loss exceeds ½ psi (based on 13 in. w.c. outlet pressure), do not use this table. Consult with regulator manufacturer for pressure drops and capacity factors. Pressure drops across a regulator may vary with flow rate.

(2) CAUTION: Capacities shown in table may exceed maximum capacity for a selected regulator. Consult with regulator or tubing manufacturer for guidance.

(3) Table includes losses for four 90 degree bends and two end fittings. Where additional fittings are used, increase the length of tubing according to the following equation: $L = 1.3n$, where L is additional length (ft) of tubing and n is the number of additional fittings and/or bends.

(4) All table entries are rounded to 3 significant digits.

Table 16.1(j) Corrugated Stainless Steel Tubing (CSST)

							Gas:	Undiluted Propane
							Inlet Pressure:	2.0 psi
							Pressure Drop:	1.0 psi
							Specific Gravity:	1.50

INTENDED USE: CSST Sizing Between 2 psig Service and Line Pressure Regulator.

	Tube Size (EHD)													
Nominal Size:	³⁄₈"	³⁄₈"	½"	½"	¾"	¾"	1"	1"	1¼"	1¼"	1½"	1½"	2"	2"
Flow Designation:	13	15	18	19	23	25	30	31	37	39	46	48	60	62
Length (ft)	Capacity in Thousands of Btu per Hour													
10	426	558	927	1,110	1,740	2,170	4,100	4,720	7,130	7,958	15,200	16,800	29,400	34,200
25	262	347	591	701	1,120	1,380	2,560	2,950	4,560	5,147	9,550	10,700	18,800	21,700
30	238	316	540	640	1,030	1,270	2,330	2,690	4,180	4,719	8,710	9,790	17,200	19,800
40	203	271	469	554	896	1,100	2,010	2,320	3,630	4,116	7,530	8,500	14,900	17,200
50	181	243	420	496	806	986	1,790	2,070	3,260	3,702	6,730	7,610	13,400	15,400
75	147	196	344	406	663	809	1,460	1,690	2,680	3,053	5,480	6,230	11,000	12,600
80	140	189	333	393	643	768	1,410	1,630	2,590	2,961	5,300	6,040	10,600	12,200
100	124	169	298	350	578	703	1,260	1,450	2,330	2,662	4,740	5,410	9,530	10,900
150	101	137	245	287	477	575	1,020	1,180	1,910	2,195	3,860	4,430	7,810	8,890
200	86	118	213	248	415	501	880	1,020	1,660	1,915	3,340	3,840	6,780	7,710
250	77	105	191	222	373	448	785	910	1,490	1,722	2,980	3,440	6,080	6,900
300	69	96	173	203	343	411	716	829	1,360	1,578	2,720	3,150	5,560	6,300
400	60	82	151	175	298	355	616	716	1,160	1,376	2,350	2,730	4,830	5,460
500	53	72	135	158	268	319	550	638	1,030	1,237	2,100	2,450	4,330	4,880

EHD: Equivalent hydraulic diameter. A measure of the relative hydraulic efficiency between different tubing sizes. The greater the value of EHD, the greater the gas capacity of the tubing.

Notes:

(1) Table does not include effect of pressure drop across the line regulator. Where regulator loss exceeds ½ psi (based on 13 in. w.c. outlet pressure), do not use this table. Consult with regulator manufacturer for pressure drops and capacity factors. Pressure drops across a regulator may vary with flow rate.

(2) CAUTION: Capacities shown in table may exceed maximum capacity for a selected regulator. Consult with regulator or tubing manufacturer for guidance.

(3) Table includes losses for four 90 degree bends and two end fittings. Tubing runs with larger number of bends and/or fittings shall be increased by an equivalent length of tubing according to the following equation: $L = 1.3n$, where L is additional length (ft) of tubing and n is the number of additional fittings and/or bends.

(4) All table entries are rounded to 3 significant digits.

Shaded text = Revisions.   Δ = Text deletions and figure/table revisions.   • = Section deletions.   *N* = New material.

Table 16.1(k) Corrugated Stainless Steel Tubing (CSST)

														Undiluted
												Gas:		Propane
												Inlet Pressure:		11.0 in. w.c.
												Pressure Drop:		0.5 in. w.c.
												Specific Gravity:		1.50

INTENDED USE: CSST Sizing Between Single- or Second-Stage (Low-Pressure) Regulator and Appliance Shutoff Valve.

	Tube Size (EHD)													
Nominal Size:	⅜"	⅜"	½"	½"	¾"	¾"	1"	1"	1¼"	1¼"	1½"	1½"	2"	2"
Flow Designation:	13	15	18	19	23	25	30	31	37	39	46	48	60	62
Length (ft)	Capacity in Thousands of Btu per Hour													
5	72	99	181	211	355	426	744	863	1,420	1,638	2,830	3,270	5,780	6,550
10	50	69	129	150	254	303	521	605	971	1,179	1,990	2,320	4,110	4,640
15	39	55	104	121	208	248	422	490	775	972	1,620	1,900	3,370	3,790
20	34	49	91	106	183	216	365	425	661	847	1,400	1,650	2,930	3,290
25	30	42	82	94	164	192	325	379	583	762	1,250	1,480	2,630	2,940
30	28	39	74	87	151	177	297	344	528	698	1,140	1,350	2,400	2,680
40	23	33	64	74	131	153	256	297	449	610	988	1,170	2,090	2,330
50	20	30	58	66	118	137	227	265	397	548	884	1,050	1,870	2,080
60	19	26	53	60	107	126	207	241	359	502	805	961	1,710	1,900
70	17	25	49	57	99	117	191	222	330	466	745	890	1,590	1,760
80	15	23	45	52	94	109	178	208	307	438	696	833	1,490	1,650
90	15	22	44	50	90	102	169	197	286	414	656	787	1,400	1,550
100	14	20	41	47	85	98	159	186	270	393	621	746	1,330	1,480
150	11	15	31	36	66	75	123	143	217	324	506	611	1,090	1,210
200	9	14	28	33	60	69	112	129	183	283	438	531	948	1,050
250	8	12	25	30	53	61	99	117	163	254	390	476	850	934
300	8	11	23	26	50	57	90	107	147	234	357	434	777	854

EHD: Equivalent hydraulic diameter. A measure of the relative hydraulic efficiency between different tubing sizes. The greater the value of EHD, the greater the gas capacity of the tubing.

Notes:

(1) Table includes losses for four 90 degree bends and two end fittings. Tubing runs with larger numbers of bends and/or fittings shall be increased by an equivalent length of tubing to the following equation: $L = 1.3n$, where L is additional length (ft) of tubing and n is the number of additional fittings and/or bends.

(2) All table entries are rounded to 3 significant digits.

△ Table 16.1(l) Corrugated Stainless Steel Tubing (CSST)

		Gas:	Undiluted Propane
		Inlet Pressure:	2.0 psi
		Pressure Drop:	1.0 psi
		Specific Gravity:	1.50

INTENDED USE: CSST Sizing Between 2 psig Service and Line Pressure Regulator.

	Tube Size (EHD)													
Nominal Size:	3/8"	3/8"	1/2"	1/2"	3/4"	3/4"	1"	1"	1¼"	1¼"	1½"	1½"	2"	2"
Flow Designation:	13	15	18	19	23	25	30	31	37	39	46	48	60	62
Length (ft)	Capacity in Thousands of Btu per Hour													
10	426	558	927	1,110	1,740	2,170	4,100	4,720	7,130	7,958	15,200	16,800	29,400	34,200
25	262	347	591	701	1,120	1,380	2,560	2,950	4,560	5,147	9,550	10,700	18,800	21,700
30	238	316	540	640	1,030	1,270	2,330	2,690	4,180	4,719	8,710	9,790	17,200	19,800
40	203	271	469	554	896	1,100	2,010	2,320	3,630	4,116	7,530	8,500	14,900	17,200
50	181	243	420	496	806	986	1,790	2,070	3,260	3,702	6,730	7,610	13,400	15,400
75	147	196	344	406	663	809	1,460	1,690	2,680	3,053	5,480	6,230	11,000	12,600
80	140	189	333	393	643	768	1,410	1,630	2,590	2,961	5,300	6,040	10,600	12,200
100	124	169	298	350	578	703	1,260	1,450	2,330	2,662	4,740	5,410	9,530	10,900
150	101	137	245	287	477	575	1,020	1,180	1,910	2,195	3,860	4,430	7,810	8,890
200	86	118	213	248	415	501	880	1,020	1,660	1,915	3,340	3,840	6,780	7,710
250	77	105	191	222	373	448	785	910	1,490	1,722	2,980	3,440	6,080	6,900
300	69	96	173	203	343	411	716	829	1,360	1,578	2,720	3,150	5,560	6,300
400	60	82	151	175	298	355	616	716	1,160	1,376	2,350	2,730	4,830	5,460
500	53	72	135	158	268	319	550	638	1,030	1,237	2,100	2,450	4,330	4,880

EHD: Equivalent hydraulic diameter. A measure of the relative hydraulic efficiency between different tubing sizes. The greater the value of EHD, the greater the gas capacity of the tubing.

Notes:

(1) Table does not include effect of pressure drop across the line regulator. Where regulator loss exceeds ½ psi (based on 13 in. w.c. outlet pressure), do not use this table. Consult with regulator manufacturer for pressure drops and capacity factors. Pressure drops across a regulator may vary with flow rate.

(2) CAUTION: Capacities shown in table may exceed maximum capacity for a selected regulator. Consult with regulator or tubing manufacturer for guidance.

(3) Table includes losses for four 90 degree bends and two end fittings. Tubing runs with larger number of bends and/or fittings shall be increased by an equivalent length of tubing according to the following equation: $L = 1.3n$, where L is additional length (ft) of tubing and n is the number of additional fittings and/or bends.

(4) All table entries are rounded to 3 significant digits.

Δ **Table 16.1(m) Corrugated Stainless Steel Tubing (CSST)**

	Gas:	**Undiluted Propane**		
	Inlet Pressure:	**11.0 in. w.c.**		
	Pressure Drop:	**0.5 in. w.c.**		
	Specific Gravity:	**1.50**		

INTENDED USE: CSST Sizing Between Single- or Second-Stage (Low-Pressure) Regulator and Appliance Shutoff Valve.

	Tube Size (EHD)													
Nominal Size:	⅜"	⅜"	½"	½"	¾"	¾"	1"	1"	1¼"	1¼"	1½"	1½"	2"	2"
Flow Designation:	**13**	**15**	**18**	**19**	**23**	**25**	**30**	**31**	**37**	**39**	**46**	**48**	**60**	**62**
Length (ft)	**Capacity in Thousands of Btu per Hour**													
5	72	99	181	211	355	426	744	863	1,420	1,638	2,830	3,270	5,780	6,550
10	50	69	129	150	254	303	521	605	971	1,179	1,990	2,320	4,110	4,640
15	39	55	104	121	208	248	422	490	775	972	1,620	1,900	3,370	3,790
20	34	49	91	106	183	216	365	425	661	847	1,400	1,650	2,930	3,290
25	30	42	82	94	164	192	325	379	583	762	1,250	1,480	2,630	2,940
30	28	39	74	87	151	177	297	344	528	698	1,140	1,350	2,400	2,680
40	23	33	64	74	131	153	256	297	449	610	988	1,170	2,090	2,330
50	20	30	58	66	118	137	227	265	397	548	884	1,050	1,870	2,080
60	19	26	53	60	107	126	207	241	359	502	805	961	1,710	1,900
70	17	25	49	57	99	117	191	222	330	466	745	890	1,590	1,760
80	15	23	45	52	94	109	178	208	307	438	696	833	1,490	1,650
90	15	22	44	50	90	102	169	197	286	414	656	787	1,400	1,550
100	14	20	41	47	85	98	159	186	270	393	621	746	1,330	1,480
150	11	15	31	36	66	75	123	143	217	324	506	611	1,090	1,210
200	9	14	28	33	60	69	112	129	183	283	438	531	948	1,050
250	8	12	25	30	53	61	99	117	163	254	390	476	850	934
300	8	11	23	26	50	57	90	107	147	234	357	434	777	854

EHD: Equivalent hydraulic diameter. A measure of the relative hydraulic efficiency between different tubing sizes. The greater the value of EHD, the greater the gas capacity of the tubing.

Notes:

(1) Table includes losses for four 90 degree bends and two end fittings. Tubing runs with larger numbers of bends and/or fittings shall be increased by an equivalent length of tubing to the following equation: $L = 1.3n$, where L is additional length (ft) of tubing and n is the number of additional fittings and/or bends.

(2) All table entries are rounded to 3 significant digits.

△ Table 16.1(n) Polyethylene Plastic Pipe — IPS

					Gas:	Undiluted Propane
					Inlet Pressure:	10.0 psig
					Pressure Drop:	1.0 psig
					Specific Gravity:	1.52

Plastic Pipe Length (ft)	½ in. SDR 9.33 (0.660)	¾ in. SDR 11 (0.860)	1 in. SDR 11 (1.007)	1¼ in. SDR 11 (1.328)	1½ in. SDR 11 (1.554)	2 in. SDR 11 (1.943)
INTENDED USE: Sizing Between First-Stage Pressure Regulator and Second-Stage (Low-Pressure) Regulator						
30	2140	2390	7740	13420	20300	36400
40	1840	3670	6630	11480	17300	31200
50	1630	3260	5870	10180	15400	27600
60	1470	2950	5320	9220	13900	25000
70	1360	2710	4900	8480	12800	23000
80	1260	2530	4560	7890	11900	21400
90	1180	2370	4270	7400	11200	20100
100	1120	2240	4040	6990	10600	19000
125	990	990	3580	6200	9360	16800
150	897	897	3240	5620	8480	15200
175	826	826	2980	5170	7800	14000
200	778	778	2780	4810	7260	13000
225	721	721	2600	4510	6810	12200
250	681	681	2460	4260	6430	11600
275	646	646	2340	4050	6110	11000
300	617	617	2230	3860	5830	10470
350	567	567	2050	3550	5360	9640
400	528	528	1910	3300	4990	8970
450	495	495	992	3100	4680	8410
500	468	468	937	2930	4420	7950
600	424	424	849	2650	4010	7200
700	390	390	781	2440	3690	6620
800	363	363	726	2270	3430	6160
900	340	340	682	2130	3220	5780
1000	322	322	644	2010	3040	5460
1500	258	258	517	933	1616	4390
2000	221	221	443	498	1383	3750

IPS: Iron Pipe Size.
SDR: Standard Dimension Ratio
Notes:
(1) Capacities are in 1000 Btu/hr.
(2) Dimensions in parentheses are inside diameter.

△ Table 16.1(o) Polyethylene Plastic Tubing — CTS

Plastic Pipe Length (ft.)	Gas:	Undiluted Propane
	Inlet Pressure:	10.0 psig
	Pressure Drop:	1.0 psig
	Specific Gravity:	1.52
Plastic Pipe Length (ft.)	½ in. SDR 7.00 (0.445 OD)	1 in. SDR 11 (1.007 OD)
INTENDED USE: Sizing Between First-Stage Pressure Regulator and Second-Stage (Low-Pressure) Regulator		
30	762	5230
40	653	4470
50	578	3960
60	524	3590
70	482	3300
80	448	3070
90	421	2880
100	397	2720
125	352	2410
150	319	2190
175	294	2010
200	273	1870
225	256	1760
250	242	1660
275	230	1580
300	219	1500
350	202	1380
400	188	1290
450	176	1210
500	166	1140
600	151	1030
700	139	951
800	129	884
900	121	830
1000	114	784
1500	92	629
2000	79	539

CTS: Copper Tube Size
SDR: Standard Dimension Rating
Notes:
(1) Capacities are in 1000 Btu/hr.
(2) Dimensions in Parentheses are inside diameter.

△ Table 16.1(p) Polyethylene Plastic Tubing

	Gas:	Undiluted Propane
	Inlet Pressure:	11.0 in. w.c.
	Pressure Drop:	0.5 in. w.c.
	Specific Gravity:	1.50

INTENDED USE: Sizing Between Integral 2-Stage Regulator at Tank or Second-Stage (Low-Pressure Regulator) and the Building.

Plastic Tubing Size (CTS) (in.)

Nominal OD:	½	1
Designation:	SDR 7	SDR 11
Actual ID:	0.445	0.927
Length (ft)	Capacity in Thousands of Btu per Hour	
10	121	828
20	83	569
30	67	457
40	57	391
50	51	347
60	46	314
70	42	289
80	39	269
90	37	252
100	35	238
125	31	211
150	28	191
175	26	176
200	24	164
225	22	154
250	21	145
275	20	138
300	19	132
350	18	121
400	16	113
450	15	106
500	15	100

CTS: Copper tube size.
Note: All table entries are rounded to 3 significant digits.
[**54**:Table 6.3.1(m)]

Annex A   Explanatory Material

Annex A is not a part of the requirements of this NFPA document but is included for informational purposes only. This annex contains explanatory material, numbered to correspond with the applicable text paragraphs.

A.1.1 *General Properties of LP-Gas.* Liquefied petroleum gases (LP-Gases), as defined in this code *(see 3.3.44)*, are gases at normal room temperature and atmospheric pressure. They liquefy under moderate pressure and readily vaporize upon release of the pressure. It is this property that allows the transportation and storage of LP-Gases in concentrated liquid form, although they normally are used in vapor form.

For additional information on other properties of LP-Gases, see Annex B.

Federal Regulations. Regulations of the U.S. Department of Transportation (DOT) are referenced throughout this code. Prior to April 1, 1967, these regulations were promulgated by the Interstate Commerce Commission (ICC). The Federal Hazardous Substances Act (15 U.S.C. 1261) requires cautionary labeling of refillable cylinders of liquefied petroleum gases distributed for consumer use. They are typically 40 lb (13 kg) and less and are used with outdoor cooking appliances, portable lamps, camp stoves, and heaters. The Federal Hazardous Substances Act is administered by the U.S. Consumer Product Safety Commission under regulations codified at 16 CFR 1500, "Commercial Practices," Chapter 11, "Consumer Product Safety Commission."

A.1.3.1(4) For further information on the storage and handling of LP-Gas at natural gas processing plants, refineries, and petrochemical plants, see API 2510, *Design and Construction of LP-Gas Installations*.

A.1.3.2(4) The exclusion of the use of LP-Gas as a chemical reactant (feedstock) or in processes recognizes the unique and complex fire hazard problems that often exist in a chemical plant. The term *chemical plant* includes all facilities owned by chemical companies where LP-Gas is used primarily as a chemical reactant, process solvent gas, or solvent. However, there is no standard definition of a chemical plant, and facilities in which few or no chemical reactions are carried out might be called chemical plants.

A.1.3.2(5) For information on the use of LP-Gas with oxygen, see NFPA 51 and AWS Z49.1, *Safety in Welding, Cutting, and Allied Processes*.

A.1.3.2(6) Several types of LP-Gas systems are not covered by NFPA 54 as noted. These include, but are not restricted to, most portable applications; many farm installations; vaporization, mixing, and gas manufacturing; temporary systems, for example, in construction; and systems on vehicles.

A.1.3.2(8) For information on the use of LP-Gas in vessels, see NFPA 302.

A.3.2.1 Approved. The National Fire Protection Association does not approve, inspect, or certify any installations, procedures, equipment, or materials; nor does it approve or evaluate testing laboratories. In determining the acceptability of installations, procedures, equipment, or materials, the authority having jurisdiction may base acceptance on compliance with NFPA or other appropriate standards. In the absence of such standards, said authority may require evidence of proper installation, procedure, or use. The authority having jurisdiction may also refer to the listings or labeling practices of an organization that is concerned with product evaluations and is thus in a position to determine compliance with appropriate standards for the current production of listed items.

A.3.2.2 Authority Having Jurisdiction (AHJ). The phrase "authority having jurisdiction," or its acronym AHJ, is used in NFPA documents in a broad manner, since jurisdictions and approval agencies vary, as do their responsibilities. Where public safety is primary, the authority having jurisdiction may be a federal, state, local, or other regional department or individual such as a fire chief; fire marshal; chief of a fire prevention bureau, labor department, or health department; building official; electrical inspector; or others having statutory authority. For insurance purposes, an insurance inspection department, rating bureau, or other insurance company representative may be the authority having jurisdiction. In many circumstances, the property owner or his or her designated agent assumes the role of the authority having jurisdiction; at government installations, the commanding officer or departmental official may be the authority having jurisdiction.

△ **A.3.2.3 Code.** The decision to designate a standard as a "code" is based on factors such as the size and scope of the document, its intended use and form of adoption, and whether it contains substantial enforcement and administrative provisions.

A.3.2.5 Listed. The means for identifying listed equipment may vary for each organization concerned with product evaluation; some organizations do not recognize equipment as listed unless it is also labeled. The authority having jurisdiction should utilize the system employed by the listing organization to identify a listed product.

N A.3.3.9 Assembly Occupancy. Assembly occupancies might include the following:

(1)   Armories
(2)   Assembly halls
(3)   Auditoriums
(4)   Bowling lanes
(5)   Club rooms
(6)   College and university classrooms, 50 persons and over
(7)   Conference rooms
(8)   Courtrooms
(9)   Dance halls
(10) Drinking establishments
(11) Exhibition halls
(12) Gymnasiums
(13) Libraries
(14) Mortuary chapels
(15) Motion picture theaters
(16) Museums
(17) Passenger stations and terminals of air, surface, underground, and marine public transportation facilities
(18) Places of religious worship
(19) Pool rooms
(20) Recreation piers
(21) Restaurants
(22) Skating rinks
(23) Special amusement buildings, regardless of occupant load
(24) Theaters
[*101*, 2018]

Assembly occupancies are characterized by the presence or potential presence of crowds with attendant panic hazard in case of fire or other emergency. These are generally open or occasionally open to the public, and the occupants, who are present voluntarily, are not ordinarily subject to discipline or control. Such buildings are ordinarily occupied by able-bodied persons and are not used for sleeping purposes. Special conference rooms, snack areas, and other areas incidental to, and under the control of, the management of other occupancies, such as offices, fall under the 50-person limitation. [*101*, 2018]

Restaurants and drinking establishments with an occupant load of fewer than 50 persons should be classified as mercantile occupancies. For special amusement buildings, see 12.4.8 and 13.4.8 of NFPA *101*. [*101*, 2018]

Note that, in addition to assembly occupancy, the term *public assembly* would also apply to outdoor areas where members of the public assemble.

A.3.3.10 Bulk Plant. Bulk plants receive gas through a variety of methods, such as railroad tank car, transport, cargo tank vehicle, gas piping, or watercraft. These plants generally store LP-Gas prior to being sent on for domestic, commercial, agricultural, institutional, and industrial applications or for the storage of product awaiting delivery to the end user. Such plants could have container-filling and truck loading/unloading facilities on the premises. Normally, no persons other than the plant management or plant employees have access to these facilities. It is not the intent of the definition to exclude facilities that use propane at the site, such as for building heating.

A.3.3.22 Dispenser. A dispenser can include, but is not limited to, the following devices (mechanical or electronic): a pressure relief device, vapor separator, strainer, metering assembly, differential valve, meter register, control valves, hose, hose nozzle, controls, interlocking mechanism, locking mechanism, weigh scale and associated wiring, and pipe fittings and housing.

A.3.3.27 Fire Protection. The term *fire prevention* covers measures directed at avoiding the inception of fire or the escalation of an incident following the accidental or inadvertent release of LP-Gas. Such measures could include product control equipment and the insulation, mounding, or burial of containers.

The term *fire detection* covers equipment that detects the presence of fire or heat either to initiate automated operation of the product control or other process equipment or to initiate local or remote alarms.

The term *fire suppression* covers means of supplying water or other agents providing for fire control, exposure protection, or fire extinguishment.

A.3.3.32 Gas. The more specific terms *liquid LP-Gas* or *vapor LP-Gas* are used for clarity.

A.3.3.33 Gas-Air Mixer. A gas-air mixture normally is used in industrial or commercial facilities as a substitute for another fuel gas.

A.3.3.34.6 Slip Tube Gauge. The installation fitting for the tube is designed so that the tube can be slipped in and out of the container and the liquid level at the inner end of the tube can be determined by observing when the shutoff valve vents liquid.

N A.3.3.34.7 Variable Liquid Level Gauge. Examples of variable liquid level gauges include a float gauge, rotary gauge, and slip tube gauge.

A.3.3.35 Ground Snow Load. For regions where the ground snow load is not provided in ASCE/SEI 7, *Minimum Design Loads for Buildings and Other Structures* (CS or case studies regions), the ground snow load is determined based on the provisions of Section 7.2 of ASCE/SEI 7 or by any method approved by the local authority having jurisdiction. Figure A.3.3.35(a), Figure A.3.3.35(b), and Table A.3.3.35 show the ground snow load data from ASCE/SEI 7.

A.3.3.40 Industrial Plant. *Industrial plant* is a term used in NFPA 58 to include all LP-Gas storage facilities that use the gas on site. Industrial plants are found at industrial facilities, farms, engine fueling stations, schools, hotels, and other locations. It is not the intent of the definition to exclude facilities that have a small use of propane off the site, such as for vehicles, where such use is not the major use of the gas stored.

Table A.3.3.35 Ground Snow Loads, p_g, for Alaskan Locations

Location	p_g lb/ft^2	p_g kN/m^2	Location	p_g lb/ft^2	p_g kN/m^2	Location	p_g lb/ft^2	p_g kN/m^2
Adak	30	1.4	Galena	60	2.9	Petersburg	150	7.2
Anchorage	50	2.4	Gulkana	70	3.4	St. Paul	40	1.9
Angoon	70	3.4	Homer	40	1.9	Seward	50	2.4
Barrow	25	1.2	Juneau	60	2.9	Shemya	25	1.2
Barter	35	1.7	Kenai	70	3.4	Sitka	50	2.4
Bethel	40	1.9	Kodiak	30	1.4	Talkeetna	120	5.8
Big Delta	50	2.4	Kotzebue	60	2.9	Unalakleet	50	2.4
Cold Bay	25	1.2	McGrath	70	3.4	Valdez	160	7.7
Cordova	100	4.8	Nenana	80	3.8	Whittier	300	14.4
Fairbanks	60	2.9	Nome	70	3.4	Wrangell	60	2.9
Fort Yukon	60	2.9	Palmer	50	2.4	Yakutat	150	7.2

Source: Reprinted with permission from ASCE/SEI 7.

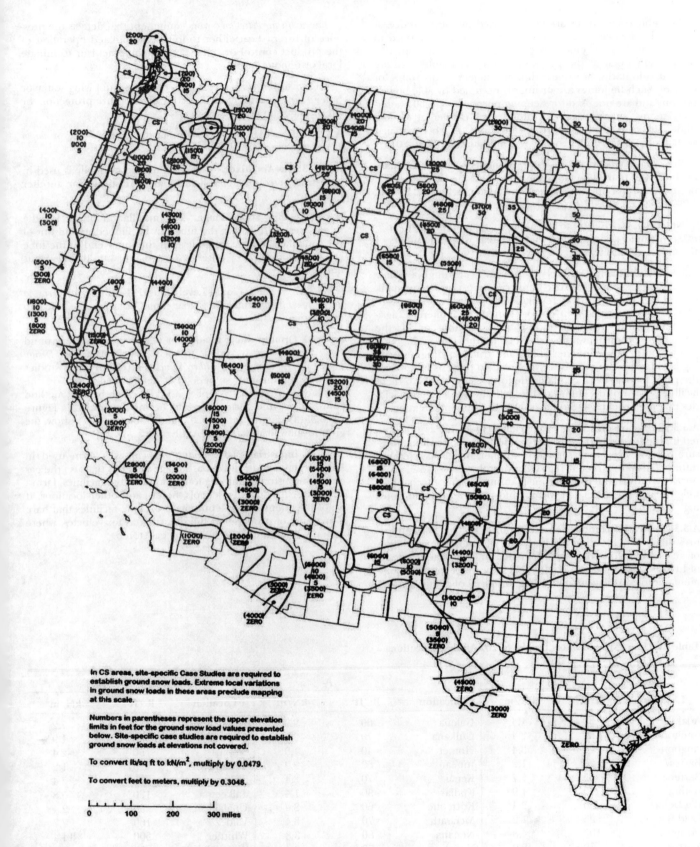

△ FIGURE A.3.3.35(a)   Ground Snow Loads, p_g, for the United States (lb/ft²).
(*Source*: Reprinted with permission from ASCE/SEI 7.)

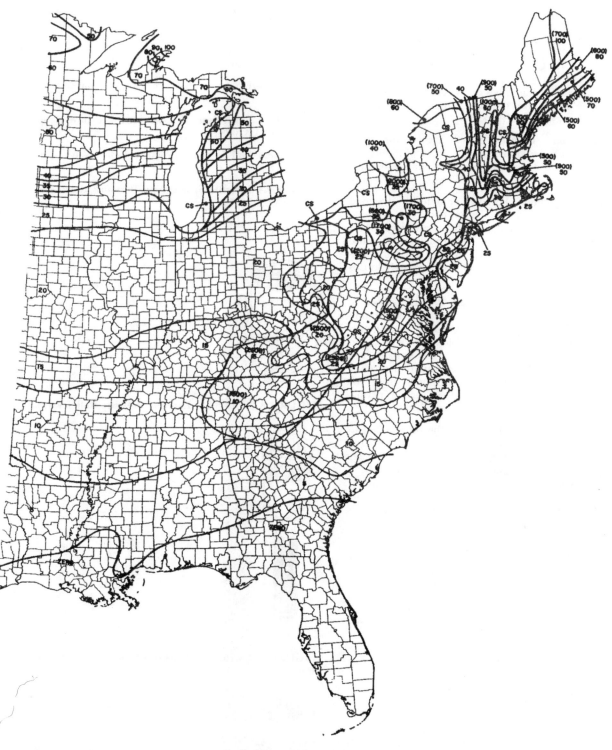

△ **FIGURE A.3.3.35(b)   Ground Snow Loads, p_g, for the United States (lb/ft²).**
(*Source:* **Reprinted with permission from ASCE/SEI 7.)**

A.3.3.44 Liquefied Petroleum Gas (LP-Gas). In the pure state propylene (Chemical Abstract Service 105-07-01) has a vapor pressure of 132.8 psig (915.72 kPa) at 70°F (21.1°C). The vapor pressure of commercial propane (Chemical Abstract Service 74-98-6) at 70°F (21.1°C) is 124 psig (855 kPa). Although commercial propane can contain some propylene, as in impurity, propylene in the pure state does not meet the definition of LP-Gas. Propylene in the pure state is commonly found in use as an industrial fuel gas. *(See NFPA 51.)*

A.3.3.45 Low-Emission Transfer. Specifications for low-emission transfer might be employed to comply with environmental regulations or to determine certain minimum distance requirements.

A.3.3.60 Portable Container. Portable containers, designed for transportation, include cylinders, cargo tanks, and portable tanks, which are defined separately in this code. Containers that are designed to be readily moved from one location of use to another but that are substantially empty of product are portable storage containers and are also defined separately in this code.

A.3.3.61 Portable Storage Container. Portable storage containers have legs or other supports attached or are mounted on running gear (such as trailer or semitrailer chassis), with suitable supports that can be of the fold-down type. Such supports allow the containers to be placed on a reasonably firm and level surface. For large-volume, limited-duration product usage (such as at construction sites normally used for 12 months or less), portable storage containers serve as permanently installed stationary containers.

A.3.3.69 Refrigerated LP-Gas. LP-Gas can be refrigerated to reduce its vapor pressure to near atmospheric up to 15 psig (103 kPa). Refrigerated LP-Gas containers are typically constructed to API 620 and are maintained at less than ½ psig (3.4 kPa) and use a container fabricated of significantly thinner steel than a pressure vessel. Refrigerated LP-Gas can also be stored in ASME containers above 15 psig (103 kPa) and this is called semirefrigerated LP-Gas.

A.3.3.70.1 Automatic Changeover Regulator. An automatic changeover regulator incorporates two inlet connections and a service-reserve indicator. The system automatically changes the LP-Gas vapor withdrawal from the designated service cylinder(s) when depleted to the designated reserve cylinder(s) without interruption of service. The service reserve indicator gives a visual indication of the cylinder(s) that is supplying the system.

A.3.3.73 Special Protection. Where required in this code, special protection consists of one of the following:

(1) Applied insulating coating
(2) Mounding
(3) Burial
(4) Water spray fixed systems
(5) Fixed monitor nozzles that meet the criteria specified in this code
(6) Any means listed for this purpose

See Section 6.29 for more information on fire protection and special protection.

A.3.3.78.6 Internal Valve. An internal valve has provision for the addition of a means of remote closure. An internal valve closes when flow through the valve exceeds its rated excess-flow capacity or when the pump actuation differential pressure drops to a predetermined point.

A.3.3.78.8.1 External Pressure Relief Valve. See Figure A.3.3.78.8.1.

A.3.3.78.8.2 Flush-Type Full Internal Pressure Relief Valve. See Figure A.3.3.78.8.2.

A.3.3.78.8.3 Full Internal Pressure Relief Valve. See Figure A.3.3.78.8.3.

A.3.3.78.8.4 Internal Spring-Type Pressure Relief Valve. See Figure A.3.3.78.8.4.

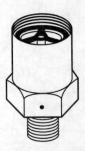

FIGURE A.3.3.78.8.1   External Pressure Relief Valve.

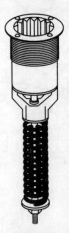

FIGURE A.3.3.78.8.2   Flush-Type Full Internal Pressure Relief Valve.

FIGURE A.3.3.78.8.3   Full Internal Pressure Relief Valve.

FIGURE A.3.3.78.8.4   Internal Spring-Type Pressure Relief Valve.

A.3.3.81 Vehicular Barrier Protection (VBP). Numerous effective means to provide protection for LP-Gas installations from impact by motor vehicles are available. The system or method selected depends on local conditions with regard to the kinds of traffic that can be reasonably expected and the environment surrounding the location. Examples of such protection include, but are not limited to, the following:

(1)   Guard rails
(2)   Steel bollards
(3)   Raised sidewalks [minimum of 6 in. (150 mm) in height]
(4)   Fencing
(5)   Ditches
(6)   Berms (not to exceed 50 percent of the container perimeter)
(7)   Jersey barriers
(8)   Parking bumpers [minimum of 6 in. (150 mm) in height]
(9)   Fencing/gates

A.4.2.1 It is recognized that no odorant will be completely effective as a warning agent in every circumstance.

It is recommended that odorants be qualified as to compliance with 4.2.1 by tests or experience. Where qualifying is by tests, such tests should be certified by an approved laboratory not associated with the odorant manufacturer. Experience has shown that ethyl mercaptan in the ratio of 1.0 lb (0.45 kg) per 10,000 gal (37.9 m^3) of liquid LP-Gas has been recognized as an effective odorant. Other odorants and quantities meeting the provisions of 4.2.1 can be used. Research on odorants has shown that thiophane (tetrahydrothiophene) in a ratio of at least 6.4 lb (2.9 kg) per 10,000 gal (37.9 m^3) of liquid LP-Gas might satisfy the requirements of 4.2.1.

NOTE: Odorant research includes *A New Look at Odorization Levels for Propane Gas*, BERC/RI-77/1, United States Energy Research and Development Administration, Technical Information Center, September 1977.

A.4.2.3 Another method of determining the presence of odorant is the stain tube test. This method uses a small handheld pump to draw a sample through a stain tube (a glass tube filled with a chemical indicator), and it requires reading the resulting length of color change. For additional information, see ASTM D5305, *Standard Test Method for Determination of Ethyl Mercaptan in LP-Gas Vapor*, and CAN/CGSB-3.0 No. 18.5, *Test for*

Ethyl Mercaptan Odorant in Propane, Field Method. The method found in ASTM D5305 indicates the concentration of ethyl mercaptan in the vapor. Stain tube manufacturers' instructions should be followed.

Due to the boiling point difference between ethyl mercaptan and propane, the concentration of ethyl mercaptan within propane vapor will be less than that found in the same sample of liquid propane. For example, a liquid concentration of 1 lb (0.5 kg) of ethyl mercaptan per 10,000 gal (37.85 m^3) of propane will result in a stain tube value of 3.0 ppmv of the vapor sample at 32°F (0°C) and will be greater at higher temperatures. For more information, see the supplement on fuel gas odorization in the *National Fuel Gas Code Handbook*. The appendix of ASTM D5305 addresses the corrections required to determine the concentration within the liquid. The ethyl mercaptan concentration cited in A.4.2.1 is the liquid concentration. The Canadian method (CAN/CGSB-3.0) will yield a value approximately equal to the liquid concentration.

A.4.4 Examples of training programs are as follows:

(1)   Certified Employee Training Program available from the Propane Education and Research Council (PERC), www.propanecouncil.org
(2)   Programs developed by propane companies
(3)   Programs developed by government entities

The term *refresher* indicates that the periodic training could be less intensive than the original training, since the primary purpose of periodic training is to reinforce initial training rather than repeat it.

A.4.4.3 Refresher training should review important concepts but concentrate on changes in procedures, requirements, or applications that affect the employee's primary duties that fall within the scope of this document.

A.4.5 To test for the presence of ammonia, allow a moderate vapor stream of the product to be tested to escape from the container. A rotary, slip tube, or fixed level gauge is a convenient vapor source. Wet a piece of red litmus paper by pouring distilled water over it while holding it with clean tweezers. Hold the wet litmus paper in the vapor stream from the container for 30 seconds. The appearance of any blue color on the litmus paper indicates that ammonia is present in the product.

NOTE: Because red litmus paper will turn blue when exposed to any basic (alkaline) solution, care is required in performing the test and interpreting the results. Contact with tap water, saliva, perspiration, or hands that have been in contact with water having a pH greater than 7, or with any alkaline solution, will produce erroneous results.

A.4.6 The installation of safety-enhancing equipment that is not otherwise required by the code is permitted by the code. This includes any device that performs a safety-related function even though the device is designed or named to perform a required function. For example, an emergency shutoff valve (ESV) is installed in a location where it is not required to provide all the safety functions of an ESV. Even though the installer uses it to provide a specific feature that can be common to all ESVs, the code would still not require compliance with all of the ESV provisions — for example, the closing requirements described in 5.14.2.3.

N A.4.7 NFPA 10 provides general guidance for selecting, installing, maintaining, recharging, and testing portable fire extinguishers and is not intended to negate the specific requirements of other NFPA standards. Various NFPA standards acknowledge it is often undesirable to attempt the extinguishment of pressurized Class B fires unless the source of fuel can be shut off promptly. NFPA 10 defers to the knowledge and experience reflected within fire safety standards written for each product or material; however, Section 5.5 of NFPA 10 provides requirements for specific minimum fire extinguisher capacities and agent discharge rates of 1 lb/sec (0.45 kg/sec) or more for properly addressing various types of specific Class B hazards, including pressurized, three-dimensional, and obstacle fires. All are possibilities when considering the various applications of NFPA 58 stated in 1.3.1.

Emergency responders, fire service personnel, and gas industry representatives might find it necessary to extinguish a fire in certain situations.

Employees and other personnel working where propane containers and equipment are located should understand the need to quickly extinguish any nearby incipient fires before they spread to areas where propane is handled or stored. The specific requirements for fire extinguishers within this code are intended to anticipate and properly address all the various potential fire scenarios that might be encountered.

N A.4.9 The provisions of Section 4.9 do not require inherently noncombustible materials to be tested in order to be classified as noncombustible materials. [*101*:A.4.6.13]

N A.4.9.1(1) Examples of such materials include steel, concrete, masonry, and glass. [*101*:A.4.6.13.1(1)]

A.5.1 The field assembly of components, subassemblies, container assemblies, or complete container systems into complete LP-Gas systems is addressed in Chapter 6. (*See 3.3.46, LP-Gas System.*)

A.5.2.1.1 Prior to April 1, 1967, regulations of the U.S. Department of Transportation were promulgated by the Interstate Commerce Commission. In Canada, the regulations of the Canadian Transport Commission apply and are available from the Canadian Transport Commission, Union Station, Ottawa, Canada.

Construction of containers to the API-ASME *Code for Unfired Pressure Vessels for Petroleum Liquids and Gases* has not been authorized after July 1, 1961.

△ A.5.2.2.1 See CGA C-6, *Standard for Visual Inspection of Steel Compressed Gas Cylinders*, or CGA C-6.3, Standard *for Visual Inspection of Low Pressure Aluminum Alloy Compressed Gas Cylinders*, for further information regarding cylinder inspection.

△ A.5.2.2.2 See CGA C-6, *Standard for Visual Inspection of Steel Compressed Gas Cylinders*, or CGA C-6.3, Standard *for Visual Inspection of Low Pressure Aluminum Alloy Compressed Gas Cylinders*, for further information regarding cylinder inspection.

A.5.2.4.6 ASME mobile fuel containers constructed prior to April 1, 2001, were required to have a maximum allowable working pressure (MAWP) pf 250 psig (1.7 MPag).

A.5.2.5.3 Prior to December 1, 1963, ASME containers of greater than 30 gal (0.1 m^3) water capacity, up to and including 2000 gal (7.6 m^3) water capacity, were not required to be equipped for filling into the vapor space of the container.

A.5.2.5.4 Containers fabricated on or before July 1, 1961, are exempt from this requirement.

A.5.2.5.5 See 5.9.8.7 for the pressure gauge requirement.

A.5.2.5.7 Containers fabricated on or before December 31, 1965, are exempt from this requirement.

A.5.2.8.2 The tare weight is the cylinder weight plus the weight of all permanently attached valves and other fittings but does not include the weight of protecting devices that are removed in order to load the cylinder.

A.5.2.8.3 Head design refers to the shape of the head. Shapes include hemispherical, semi-ellipsoidal, and others. (*Refer to the API-ASME Code for Unfired Pressure Vessels for Petroleum Liquids and Gases for more information.*)

A.5.9.1.2 Materials with melting points exceeding 1500°F (816°C) include steel, ductile (nodular) iron, malleable iron, or brass, as follows:

(1) Ductile iron should meet the requirements of ASTM A395/A395M, *Standard Specification for Ferritic Ductile Iron Pressure-Retaining Castings for Use at Elevated Temperatures,* or equivalent and malleable iron should meet the requirements of ASTM A47/A47M, *Standard Specification for Ferritic Malleable Iron Castings,* or equivalent.
(2) Approved or listed variable liquid level gauges used in containers of 3500 gal (13.2 m^3) water capacity or less are exempt from the minimum melting point requirement.
(3) Cast-iron should not be used.
(4) Nonmetallic materials should not be used for bonnets or bodies of valves or regulators.

A.5.9.2.1 Experience has indicated that a vertical and unimpeded vent of high-velocity hydrocarbon gases will entrain sufficient air within a very short distance so that the resultant plume will be diluted below the lower flammable limit. This behavior is documented in ANSI/API 521, *Guide for Pressure-Relieving and Depressuring Systems.* This document was based, in part, on an API-commissioned study by Battelle Memorial Institute, "The Effect of Velocity, Temperature, and Gas Molecular Weight on Flammability Limits in Wind-Blown Jets of Hydrocarbon Gases."

These reports clearly indicate that a vertical and unimpeded jet will be diluted below its lower flammable limit within 50 pipe diameters of the issuing jet and that the effects of "wind-tilt" can be safely neglected if a 50 ft (15 m) horizontal clearance is provided between the jet and a source of ignition. High-velocity jet is defined as a jet having an exit velocity in excess of 100 ft/sec (30.5 m/sec), which is slightly more than an order of magnitude less than the acoustic velocity that can be anticipated at the throat of an operating relief valve. ANSI/API 521 also indicates that a partially open relief valve will produce a velocity sufficient to achieve the necessary dilution.

Once such a mixture has been diluted below its flammable limit, there are no known natural forces (including gravitational forces) that will cause the reconcentration of the LP-Gases so as to create a flammable cloud. The application of water, as either a fog or a heavy stream, will not hasten and can actually inhibit the dilution of the jet stream. It is recommended that this information be included in any emergency procedure manual and that the responding emergency services be made aware of this information.

A.5.9.3.2 Example: When the dip tube length marked on the cylinder is 3.8 in. (97 mm), use a 4.0 in. (100 mm) dip tube for the retrofit.

If the dip tube length is not marked on the cylinder, contact the manufacturer for the recommended dip tube length.

A.5.9.4.3 The list of required appurtenances for containers over 4000 gal (15.2 kg) provides safety and operational needs. Other appurtenances are not prohibited. Larger installations, such as rail and marine terminals, are sometimes required to take liquid propane samples to analyze the gas, to determine the level of odorant, and to verify that the specifications for the gas are met. A sampling valve can be added to the container where sampling is anticipated.

A.5.9.5.3 Containers fabricated on or before December 1, 1965, were exempt from this requirement.

𝑵 **A.5.9.8.1(H)** The opening of a container is equipped with a device that stops flow in case of a pipe break leading to or from that opening. A back check valve can be used where flow is only into the container. An excess-flow check valve is often used as a discrete component or as part of an internal valve where flow might be into or out of the container. For piping from the container, the excess-flow capacity is determined so that flow can be stopped in case of a complete line break. Restrictions downstream from an excess flow valve (e.g., pipe reducers, filters, pipe fittings) might render the excess flow valve incapable of stopping flow from a complete line break.

If the piping system includes branches with smaller pipe sizes, an additional excess flow valve is needed where the size reduction is made.

A.5.9.8.4(A) The requirement is intended to ensure that the point of discharge and hose connection points will not become submerged by groundwater during normal operations. It does not require the installation to resist flooding conditions that might occur.

A.5.9.9 Container refurbishment includes activities such as sand blasting and spray painting.

△ **A.5.10.3** Listed rigid PVC electrical conduit in accordance with UL 651, *Standard for Schedule 40, 80, Type EB and A Rigid PVC Conduit and Fittings,* has been designed, manufactured, and tested for use in a wide variety of operating conditions, including low temperatures and exposure to sunlight and outdoor weather. UL 651 conduit is widely available and can be purchased in hardware and electrical supply stores, where it is usually sold as electrical conduit.

A.5.11.5.1 Persons joining polyethylene pipe should be trained under the applicable joining procedure established by the manufacturer, including the following:

(1) Appropriate training in the use of joining procedures
(2) Making a specimen joint from pipe sections joined according to the procedures
(3) Visually examining these joints during and after assembly

A.5.11.5.5 49 CFR 192.281(e) states the following:

Mechanical joints — Each compression-type mechanical joint on plastic pipe must comply with the following:

(1) The gasket material in the coupling must be compatible with the plastic.

(2) A rigid internal tubing stiffener, other than a split tubular stiffener, must be used in conjunction with the coupling.

49 CFR 192.283(b) states the following:
Mechanical joints — Before any written procedure established under 192.273(b) is used for plastic making mechanical plastic pipe joints that are designed to withstand tensile forces, the procedure must be qualified by subjecting five specimen joints made according to the procedure to the following tensile test:

(1) Use an apparatus for the test as specified in ASTM D638, *Standard Test Method for Tensile Properties of Plastics* (except for conditioning).
(2) The specimen must be of such length that the distance between the grips of the apparatus and the end of the stiffener does not affect the joint strength.
(3) The speed of testing is 0.2 in. (5.0 mm) per minute, plus or minus 25 percent.
(4) Pipe specimens less than 4 in. (102 mm) in diameter are qualified if the pipe yields to an elongation less than 25 percent or failure initiates outside the joint area.
(5) Pipe specimens 4 in. (102 mm) and larger in diameter shall be pulled until the pipe is subjected to a tensile stress equal to or greater than the maximum thermal stress that would be produced by a temperature change of 100°F (55°C) or until the pipe is pulled from the fitting. If the pipe pulls from the fitting, the lowest value of the five test results or the manufacturer's rating, whichever is lower, must be used in the design calculations for stress.
(6) Each specimen that fails at the grips must be retested using new pipe.
(7) Results obtained pertain only to the outside diameter and material of the pipe tested, except where testing of a heavier wall pipe is used to qualify pipe of the same material but with a lesser wall thickness.

A.5.23.6 See NFPA 1192 for additional requirements where used on recreational vehicles.

A.5.23.7 Combustion air inlets and flue gas outlets should be included in the listing of the appliance.

A.5.24.5.9 See NFPA 61 for ignition and combustion controls applicable to vaporizing burners associated with grain dryers.

A.6.1.1 Section 6.5 includes general provisions that are applicable to most stationary systems. Sections 6.7 through 6.15 extend and modify Section 6.5 for systems installed for specific purposes.

A.6.1.3 This installation of safety-enhancing equipment that is not otherwise required by the code is permitted by the code. This includes any device that performs a safety-related function even though the device is designed or designated to perform a required function. For example, if an emergency shutoff valve (ESV) is installed in a location where it is not required, and the installation is not intended to perform the function of an ESV but is to provide a function or feature that is available in the ESV, the valve is not required to comply with all of the closing requirements described in 5.14.2.3.

A.6.4.1.1 When applying Table 6.4.1.1 to cylinders, which have their capacities expressed in pounds, the first table entry, <125 gal (<0.5 m³), includes all cylinders. Cylinders have a maximum capacity of 1000 lb or 119 gal (454 kg or 3.8 m³) (water capacity).

The "Line of Adjoining Property That Can Be Built Upon" refers to the property boundaries of the property adjacent to the one where the container is located. This is illustrated in Figure A.6.4.1.1, Figure I.1(a), Figure I.1(b), and Figure I.1(c) taking into consideration a condition that involves property on the other side of a street, highway, navigable waterway, or other right of way. The minimum distance limitation is from the container to the property line where that property line is common to plots of ground of different ownership and would also apply between the container and the property line of the far side of a street or other public right of way.

Regarding "Important Building," a building can be important for any number of reasons, including the following:

(1) Human occupancy
(2) Replacement value
(3) Value of the contents
(4) Vital role of its production equipment or business records to a business
(5) The effect of building location on product release and fire control activities by fire fighters and other emergency responders

Human occupancy in a building does not automatically make it important. Occupancy for brief periods, such as one might find in a garage while a vehicle is being loaded, should not be a factor in classifying a building as important.

Clearly, buildings that house assembly occupancies, such as theaters and churches, are "important" because the general public will be there, as well as at mercantile occupancies (stores). Homes, apartments, hotels, dormitories, and prisons should also be considered "important." Storage occupancies might not be considered "important" if workers only occasionally enter the building.

Buildings with characteristics that (1) hinder emergency responders from being able to gain access to a position where they can safely apply water to a tank or (2) act as an impediment to applying water should also be considered a part of this category. There is such a wide assortment of physical configurations of industrial and bulk plant sites that each location must be considered on its own. Items such as railroad tracks, containers for storage of other fuels, fences obstructing access from preferred directions, topography, and even rows of trees can present unique challenges for access and, with the location of buildings on congested sites, can by themselves, or in combination, make applying water on the tanks extremely difficult.

N A.6.4.3(4) Figure A.6.4.3(4)(a) and Figure A.6.4.3(4)(b) depict the requirements of 6.4.3(4).

A.6.4.4.3 Building openings in the context of 6.4.4.3 are any opening that communicates air from the exterior to the interior of the building, including windows, doors, or dryer vent terminations below the level of the relief valve discharge.

A.6.5.3.3 Clearance is required between combustible materials and propane containers in order to minimize the effects of fires on the container. The requirement to maintain separation between the container and stored combustible materials is needed so that an accumulation of materials that might represent a hazard to the container does not occur. The term *stored* is intended to denote materials that are purposely placed. The term *accumulate* is intended to denote materials that are there by other than being purposely placed. Vegetation of any type

located near or under the container is not considered to be a hazard.

A.6.5.3.4 For information on determination of flash points, see NFPA 30.

A.6.5.3.5 Examples of Class I flammable liquids are gasoline and methanol. Examples of Class II combustible liquids are diesel, kerosene, or fuel oils.

A.6.5.3.9 Also see NFPA 51.

A.6.5.4 The presence of such structures can create significant hazards, such as the following:

(1) Pocketing of escaping gas
(2) Interference with application of cooling water by fire departments
(3) Redirection of flames against containers
(4) Impeding the egress of personnel in an emergency

A.6.7.1.1 It is the intent to allow transfer of liquid into containers in open areas under canopies or roofs where 50 percent or more of the perimeter is not enclosed.

Δ A.6.7.2.1 Examples of Class I flammable liquids, as referenced in Table 6.7.2.1 Part J, are gasoline and methanol; examples of Class II combustible liquids, as referenced in Table 6.7.2.1 Part K, are diesel, kerosene, and fuel oils.

A.6.8.1.4 Generally, a light-reflecting color paint is preferred unless the system is installed in an extremely cold climate.

A.6.8.3.5.1 For example, if the ground snow load is 50 lb/ft^2, then the snow density is 20.5 lb/ft^3 and the snow depth is 2.44 ft.

A.6.8.6.1 See Annex K.

A.6.8.6.1(G)(2) If vapor is vented too rapidly, the pressure drop due to the refrigeration of the liquid can lead to the erroneous conclusion that no liquid remains in the container.

A.6.8.6.1(H) See A.5.9.8.4(A).

A.6.8.6.1(I) Installing cathodic corrosion protection systems on new installations will help ensure the integrity of underground storage systems. Technical reports or other data can be presented to the authority having jurisdiction in support of waiving the requirement for a cathodic protection system.

For information on the proper sizing and installation of corrosion protection systems for containers and piping systems, see the following:

(1) National Association of Corrosion Engineers Standard SP0169, *Control of External Corrosion on Underground or Submerged Metallic Piping Systems*
(2) National Association of Corrosion Engineers Standard SP0285, *External Corrosion Control of Underground Storage Tank Systems by Cathodic Protection*
(3) API RP 1632, *Cathodic Protection of Underground Petroleum Storage Tanks and Piping Systems*, 3rd ed.

For information on complete cathodic protection systems installed on containers at the factory, see the following:

(1) UL LLC, ANSI/UL 1746, *External Corrosion Protection Systems for Steel Underground Storage Tanks*
(2) Underwriters Laboratories of Canada, CAN/ULC S603.1, *Standard for External Corrosion Protection Systems for Steel Underground Tanks for Flammable and Combustible Liquids*

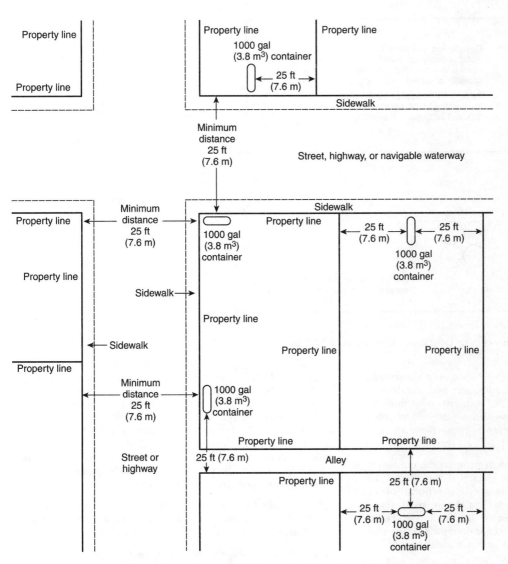

FIGURE A.6.4.1.1   Illustration of Separation Distances from Containers to Line of Adjoining Property That Can Be Built Upon.

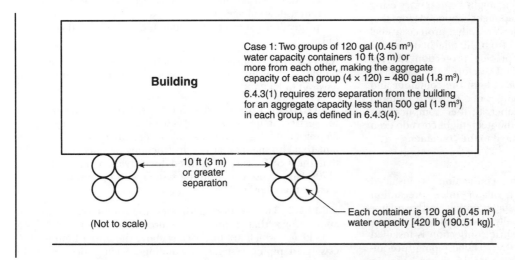

FIGURE A.6.4.3(4)(a)   Separation Between Containers 10 ft (3 m) or Greater.

Shaded text = Revisions.   Δ = Text deletions and figure/table revisions.   • = Section deletions.   **N** = New material.

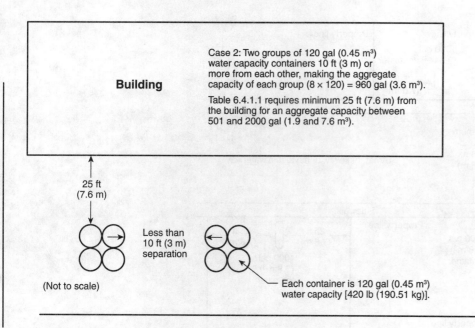

Case 2: Two groups of 120 gal (0.45 m³) water capacity containers 10 ft (3 m) or more from each other, making the aggregate capacity of each group (8 × 120) = 960 gal (3.6 m³).

Table 6.4.1.1 requires minimum 25 ft (7.6 m) from the building for an aggregate capacity between 501 and 2000 gal (1.9 and 7.6 m³).

Building

25 ft
(7.6 m)

Less than 10 ft (3 m) separation

(Not to scale)

Each container is 120 gal (0.45 m³) water capacity [420 lb (190.51 kg)].

FIGURE A.6.4.3(4)(b)   Separation Between Containers Less Than 10 ft (3 m).

Corrosion protection systems include not only the anode system, but also the coating on the container and a means to test the performance of the system. All elements contribute to the overall performance of the system and are needed in order to provide the most comprehensive protection to the container.

The sacrificial galvanic anode system protects the container from corrosion by generating a low voltage electrical current that protects the container while the anode deteriorates over time. While impressed current systems can also be used, those systems are typically used on containers larger than 2000 gal (7.6 m³) water capacity and are not found on typical residential or commercial ASME underground container installations.

It is important that, when a cathodic protection system is designed, there is a clear understanding of the limits of the surface area and materials being protected. Electrical isolation of the container from metallic piping might be necessary using a dielectric fitting or other component designed for that purpose. For example, the cathodic system that protects a steel tank that is not electrically isolated from the attached metallic piping system will be forced to provide protection for the connected piping system as well. Therefore, the sacrificial anode will have to be sized to protect both the container and the piping. Additionally, if the piping is of a different material (such as copper) from the container, further complications could result, and it is possible that the steel might corrode even though a sacrificial anode is connected to the container.

A.6.8.6.1(K) Firm earth can be used.

A.6.8.6.1(L) Where the dielectric connection is installed between the service valve and regulator inlet, precaution should be taken such that the metallic piping and regulator casing are not in contact or electrically connected to the underground container. When the dielectric connection is installed between the regulator outlet and the metallic piping, precaution should be taken to ensure the metallic piping is not in contact or electrically connected to the underground

container. Electrical isolation of the piping from the container is achieved by using materials that can prevent low amperage current at low voltage. If such contact is made with the underground container, the container or metallic piping could be subject to a higher rate of corrosion since there will not be electrical isolation between the buried metallic piping and underground. The dielectric connection is advantageous since the design of cathodic protection systems is typically intended to protect the underground container only.

Nonmetallic tubing such as polyethylene tubing, recommended for LP-Gas service and rated for the operating pressure, accomplishes the function of a dielectric union.

A.6.8.6.3(A) Noncombustible, noncorrosive materials include vermiculite and perlite.

A.6.10.1.3 Electrical isolation of the piping from the container is achieved by using materials that can prevent low amperage current at low voltage. This is necessary when designing cathodic protection systems that include the underground container only.

A.6.11.1.1(D) Construction of buildings or separate areas of buildings housing certain internal combustion engines is covered in NFPA 37.

A.6.11.1.1(E) Corrugated stainless steel (CSST) can be listed for service at up to 5 psig (34.5 kPag) or for service up to 25 psig (170 kPag) at the manufacturer's discretion. It is important that the manufacturer's instructions be checked to verify that the CSST product is listed for service at up to 25 psig (170 kPag) if used in a piping system with operating pressure greater than 5 psig (34.5 kPag).

A.6.11.1.2 This section addresses the numerous industrial applications that require pressures higher than 20 psig (138 kPag), which are historically above the upper limit for LP-Gas fixed piping systems in buildings. Such processes could include flame cutting, heat treating, and fuel for microturbines used to generate electricity.

Any installation with design pressures of 20 psig through 50 psig (138 kPag through 345 kPag) must first receive the approval of the authority having jurisdiction. Such approval need not be based on buildings or separate areas of buildings that are constructed in accordance with Chapter 10, because the low-temperature shutoff control system precludes the reliquefaction of the LP-Gas vapor.

In designing the systems permitted by this section, it is necessary for one to be knowledgeable of, and experienced with, the properties and behavior of LP-Gases, especially with respect to reliquefaction of vapor in closed fixed piping systems. For this reason, the text requires a low-temperature shutoff control system if low temperatures are anticipated. The most appropriate location for the low temperature sensor is determined by the system designer.

A.6.11.3.1 Normal fluid service is described in ASME B31.3, *Process Piping*, as any fluid service covered by ASME B31.3, other than toxic fluids, flammable fluids, and fluids under high pressure.

A.6.11.4.5 Polyethylene will expand or contract 1 in. for every 10°F (25 mm for every 18°C) temperature change for every 100 ft (30 m) of pipe.

A.6.12.1(3) If LP-Gas vapor is supplied at container pressure and there is no flow, an ambient temperature drop below the container liquid temperature will result in condensation of the LP-Gas vapor. If the system is activated, the presence of liquid could result in a delay or malfunction of the system operation.

A.6.14.8 Anchorage can be accomplished by the use of concrete bulkheads or equivalent anchorage or by the use of a weakness or shear fitting.

A.6.17.1 The pressure threshold of 20 psig (138 kPag) is established in recognition that systems operating at pressures higher than 20 psig (34.5 kPag) are likely to be specially designed and supervised systems that do not utilize two-stage regulation and for which a leak check requirement would be impractical, with little or no benefit gained.

A.6.17.2 Refer to Annex L for suggested methods for performing a leak check. A leak check differs from a pressure test in that the leak check procedure is used to prove that a system is free of leaks that could pose a hazard, such as uncapped piping ends or piping corrosion failure, whereas a pressure test is used to test the integrity of the piping system at normal or elevated pressure at the time of installation or after modification. NFPA 54 requires a leak check to be performed on new systems and immediately after reintroducing gas into a system following an interruption of service. An "interruption of service" is commonly interpreted to mean that the pressure in the fuel gas piping has dropped to a point that the appliances can no longer operate.

A.6.17.4 LP-Gas systems operating under 49 CFR 192 are exempted from leak check requirements because they are already subject to periodic inspections and maintenance as mandated by Part 192.

A.6.18.1 The variables that affect the potential for damage to outdoor gas system components present in areas where heavy snowfalls occur are numerous. Therefore, the selection of an appropriate method to mitigate potential damage from snow

and ice should be based upon the characteristics of the installation site and the forces that are anticipated. Some alternatives include the following:

(1) Locating aboveground piping, regulators, and meters above snow levels
(2) Locating aboveground piping, regulators, and meters on the gable end of buildings
(3) Adding support to aboveground piping, regulators, and meters or securing them to the structure to withstand snow and ice load
(4) Installing dedicated covers for regulators and meters that are designed to withstand a vertical static load equal to two times the ground snow load (psf) for the area but not less than 350 psf
(5) Locating aboveground piping, regulators, and meters in an elevated and protected location under extended roof overhangs and eaves. The equipment should be located near the elevation of the bottom of the eave or overhang. If the equipment is located too far below the eave or overhang, snow shedding from the roof can curl back under the eave and impact equipment. See Figure A.6.18.1.

A.6.19 For information on protection of underground components, see NACE SP0169, *Control of External Corrosion on Underground or Submerged Metallic Piping Systems.*

FIGURE A.6.18.1   Snow Shedding Example with Roof Overhang.

A.6.19.3.1 Once the monitoring tests required by 6.19.3.1 have been performed, the results can be compared to the criteria listed in this paragraph. The system is functioning properly if it develops -0.85 volt or greater negative voltage when tested with a copper–copper sulfate reference electrode.

The use of a copper–copper sulfate half cell to confirm that the cathodic protection system is functioning properly is anticipated to be the most common method of testing sacrificial anode systems on propane containers. Other standard reference half cells can be substituted for the saturated copper–copper sulfate half cell. In addition to the standard reference half cells, other means of testing cathodic systems can be employed, and they are explained in more detail in 49 CFR 192, Appendix D.

A.6.19.3.2 The installation of a cathodic protection system on an underground container introduces a need to periodically verify that the system is functioning properly and protecting the container from corrosion. Sacrificial anode systems are anticipated to be the most frequently installed systems for propane underground storage containers. The testing program required for sacrificial anode systems is consistent with nationally recognized practices (*see A.6.19.3.1*). Initial testing is required as soon as practical after installing the system, and then the verification test is required approximately 12 to 18 months after the initial testing was done. The time periods for the initial and verification tests are allowed to be adjusted to accommodate installations that, due to inclement weather, unsuitable soil conditions, or other environmental conditions, cannot be tested immediately.

If the initial test and verification test are successful, a suitable period for follow-up testing of the system should be established. A review of available standards, federal and state regulations, and recommended practices indicates that a maximum time period of 3 years is an acceptable interval for periodic testing. Should a test of the installation not achieve the required results, the sacrificial anode system must be repaired and the testing program begun again.

Training material on the installation and testing of cathodic protection systems can be found in the following publications:

(1) Propane Education and Research Council (PERC) video titled "Cathodic Protection Systems"
(2) Propane Education and Research Council (PERC) publication *Cathodic Protection Manual and Quiz #20689590*

The requirement in A.6.19.3.1 is to provide protection for the container owner and to permit the AHJ to verify that the container is in compliance with the code. Retaining test results also permits easy verification of the continued effectiveness of the cathodic protection system. The retention of the two most recent tests will permit comparison with the current test results, resulting in a trend curve of performance for the system. The observed trend can be used to increase the testing frequency as needed.

A.6.19.3.3 Impressed current cathodic protection systems are typically engineered systems that must be maintained and inspected according to a more frequent schedule. The requirements contained in this section are based on information published in the NACE documents referenced in A.6.8.6.1(I). In 6.19.3.3(A), evidence of proper functioning might be current output, normal power consumption, or a signal indicating normal operation. In 6.19.3.3(B), a preventive maintenance program to minimize in-service failure is necessary.

Inspections should include a check for electrical shorts, ground connections, meter accuracy, efficiency, and circuit resistance. The effectiveness of isolating devices and continuity bonds should be evaluated during the periodic surveys. This can be accomplished by on-site inspection or by evaluating corrosion test data.

A.6.21.2.5 Debris and foreign material can enter a propane system from hose and connectors used to fill containers. Using strainers or screens is one method to prevent debris from interfering with the action of valves and other components.

A.6.21.2.6(3) The intent of the emergency discharge control system is to prevent the discharge of product in the event of a complete hose separation. Compliance with the requirement for emergency discharge control can be accomplished using a mechanical, pneumatic, or electronic device or any combination thereof.

A.6.22.2.6 The requirement for a pilot or an electronic ignition system became effective for heaters with inputs over 50,000 Btu/hr (53 MJ/hr) manufactured on or after May 17, 1967.

A.6.22.9.3 The weight of the cylinders will be affected by the specific gravity of the LP-Gas. Weights varying from 16.0 oz to 16.8 oz (454 g to 476 g) are recognized as being within the range of what is nominal.

A.6.22.10.3 The use of LP-Gas containers inside of assembly occupancies for flame effects before a proximate audience requires compliance with this code and NFPA 160. Storage of idle cylinders should be in accordance with Chapter 8. In cases where the minimum 20 ft (6.1 m) separation distance required by 6.22.10 cannot be satisfied, the authority having jurisdiction, in determining equivalency, can consider additional safety controls such as the following:

(1) Construction of a noncombustible line-of-sight barrier to protect adjacent cylinders from fire exposure
(2) Installation of piped flammable gas fixed piping systems instead of hose

A.6.24.4.6 Tank heaters in general are capable of elevating the pressure inside the storage container and as such should not be installed on containers exhibiting corrosion either to the container base metal or to the coating. If the coating is damaged but the underlying base metal is not significantly corroded, the material should be properly cleaned and then the coating should be repaired in accordance with the coating manufacturer's instructions, prior to installation of a direct-type tank heater.

A corroded container might have reduced metal thickness that could lead to an unsafe condition. Upon annual inspection the surfaces covered by the tank heater should be inspected for damage to the container coating and to the base material. An assessment should be made to determine the viability of the container for continued use with the tank heater. Direct-type tank heaters should be designed not to cause damage to the container coating or base metal. If a heater is causing damage to the coating, the heater should be repaired or replaced and any corrective measures necessary should be taken to repair the coating prior to continued use.

A.6.25.1.2 For information on lightning protection, see NFPA 780.

A.6.25.1.3 Because LP-Gas is contained in a closed system of piping and equipment, the system need not be electrically conductive or electrically bonded for protection against static electricity. For information on grounding and bonding for protection against static electricity, see NFPA 77.

A.6.25.2.2 When classifying the extent of hazardous areas, consideration should be given to possible variations in the spotting of railroad tank cars and cargo tank vehicles at the unloading points and the effect these variations of actual spotting point can have on the point of connection.

Where specified for the prevention of fire or explosion during normal operation, ventilation is considered adequate where provided in accordance with the provisions of this code.

A.6.25.2.3 See Figure A.6.25.2.3.

A.6.26.1 Typical nonengine fuel systems include those on commercial, industrial, construction, and public service vehicles such as trucks, semitrailers, trailers, portable tar kettles, road surface heating equipment, mobile laboratories, clinics, and mobile cooking units (such as catering and canteen vehicles).

A.6.26.7.6 Requirements for the design of containers are located in Section 5.2. Requirements for container appurtenances are located in Section 5.9.

A.6.27.3.6 This provision intends to mitigate the uncontrolled discharge of liquid from the system should a hose fail in service. An excess flow valve is one method of achieving this result. Other methods could include using sensing devices installed within the system (as part of the meter or elsewhere) that stop the flow. The predetermined flow rate typically exceeds the maximum design flow rate of the fuel delivery system.

A.6.29.2 The wide range in size, arrangement, and location of LP-Gas installations covered by this code precludes the inclusion of detailed fire protection provisions completely applicable to all installations. Provisions in Section 6.29 are subject to verification or modification through analysis of local conditions.

The National Fire Protection Association, American Petroleum Institute, and National Propane Gas Association publish material, including visual aids, useful in such planning.

A.6.29.3 In recent years, the concept of total product control systems has been developed. Facilities that have redundant automatic product control systems provide a high level of confidence that propane will not be released during an emergency. Therefore, not only will the storage be protected from a fire that could lead to container rupture, but major fires at the facility would be prevented. The public would be protected, fire-fighting operations would be safer, and applications of large quantities of water would not be needed to prevent tank failure.

A fire safety analysis should include the following:

(1) Effectiveness of product control measures
(2) Analysis of local conditions of hazard within the container site
(3) Exposure to or from other properties, population density, and congestion within the site
(4) Probable effectiveness of plant fire brigades or local fire departments, based on adequate water supply, response time, and training
(5) Consideration for the adequate application of water by hose stream or other method for effective control of leakage, fire, or other exposures
(6) If necessary, designated time period for review of the fire safety analysis with local emergency response agencies to ensure preplanning and emergency response plans for the installation are current

The National Fire Protection Association and the National Propane Gas Association, through a grant with the Propane Education and Research Council, have developed and published the *Fire Safety Analysis Manual for LP-Gas Storage Facilities* in order to provide a format and guidance for propane industry personnel or competent persons to perform a fire safety analysis in conjunction with the requirements of NFPA 58.

A.6.29.3.1 Where there are multiple containers of 4000 gal (15.2 m³) water capacity or less each, the term *aggregate water capacity* refers to the total capacity of a group of aboveground containers located closer than the minimum separation required between containers and property lines prescribed by Table 6.4.1.1. Under no circumstances should containers be located closer to each other than as specified in Table 6.4.1.1.

A.6.29.5.1 For LP-Gas fixed storage facilities of 60,000 gal (227 m³) water capacity or less, a fire safety analysis could indicate that applied insulating coatings are quite often the most practical solution for special protection. It is recommended that insulation systems be evaluated on the basis of experience or listings by an approved testing laboratory.

A.7.1 Ignition source control at transfer locations is covered in Section 6.25. Fire protection is covered in Section 6.29.

A.7.2.1.4 An FAA-certificated balloon pilot meets the qualification requirements of Section 4.4 for container filling. A crew member for the pilot that has been trained for container filling and carries a card documenting that training also meets the qualification requirements. The acceptability of a hot air balloon container for filling can be verified by finding the container listed in the flight log for that aircraft.

A.7.2.2.5 Examples of an effective seal are a POL plug or cap. Listed quick-closing couplings with CGA V-1 connection numbers 790 (fork lift ACME connection), 791 (portable cylinder ACME/POL connection), and 810 (socket/plug quick

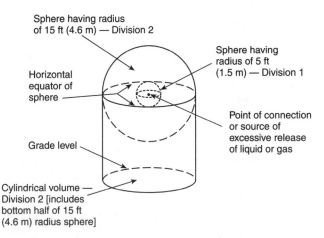

FIGURE A.6.25.2.3   Extent of Electrically Classified Area.
(See Table 6.25.2.2.)

connection) have secondary seals. Therefore, plugs or caps for these connections are not required or recommended.

N A.7.2.2.7 CGA 791 and 793 connections are primarily used on consumer LP-Gas equipment. Both connection designs employ the use of a face seal to seal the male and female sides of the connection before gas flow occurs. Damage to the face seal (e.g., cracking, gouging, tearing, roping) affects the sealing surfaces and could result in a leak. Examples of cracking, gouging/tearing, roping, and filling double seal are shown in Figure A.7.2.2.7.

The CGA 791 and 793 connections as manufactured do not permit the replacement of the face seal, and the face seal design is not the same for all manufacturers. Therefore, if the face seal has been compromised, the cylinder should not be filled.

A.7.2.3.5(A) Air-moving equipment includes large blowers on crop dryers, space heaters, and some central heating equipment. Equipment employing open flames includes flame cultivators, weed burners, and tar kettles.

N A.7.2.3.6(3) This requirement could be satisfied by securing each switch that provides access to the unloading area against movement with an effective locking device or by using derails, portable bumper blocks, or other equipment that provides an equivalent level of safety, as required by DOT regulations.

A.7.4.2.2 The maximum permitted filling limit in percent by weight should be as shown in Table 7.4.2.2.

A.7.4.2.3 The maximum permitted LP-Gas volume of any container depends on the size of the container, whether it is installed above ground or under ground, the specific gravity,

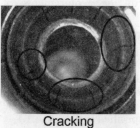
Cracking

Gouging/tearing

Roping

Filling double seal

N FIGURE A.7.2.2.7 Examples of Defects.

and the temperature of the liquid. *[See Table 7.4.2.2, Table 7.4.2.3(a), Table 7.4.2.3(b), and Table 7.4.2.3(c).]*

See F.5.1.2 for the method of computing the values in Table 7.4.2.3(a), Table 7.4.2.3(b), and Table 7.4.2.3(c).

A.7.4.4 The overfilling prevention device is intended to be a backup safety device to prevent overfilling of cylinders. Other means as provided in the chapter must be used when filling containers, even if an overfilling prevention device is present and expected to stop flow into the container before the other means indicate the container is properly filled.

A.8.4.1 The filling process in 8.4.1.4 refers to the time period beginning when a cylinder or cylinders are brought to a dispensing system to be filled and ending when the last cylinder is filled and all the cylinders are removed from the filling area. This is meant to define a continuous process, with the cylinders being unattended for only brief periods, such as operator breaks or lunch.

N A.8.4.2.1 It has been shown that when tested in accordance with ASTM E84, *Standard Test Method for Surface Burning Characteristics of Building Materials*, or ANSI/UL 723, *Standard for Test for Surface Burning Characteristics of Building Materials*, materials such as steel, concrete, gypsum board, and aluminum will meet the requirements of a flame spread index of 25 or less. In contrast, the flame spread indices of some combustible materials can be much higher. Typically, untreated wood products will exhibit a flame spread index ranging between 50 and 200.

A.8.4.2.3 Research conducted demonstrated that lockable, ventilated enclosures of aluminum or steel construction protect cylinders stored within those cabinets from potentially catastrophic damage due to impact from a motor vehicle. The report, "Evaluation of Collision Protection Provided by Vehicle Impact Bollards and Propane Cylinder Exchange Cabinets," was prepared for the National Propane Gas Association and is available from NFPA.

Where cylinders are not stored in lockable, ventilated metal enclosures, 8.4.2.2(1) requires them to be stored in a fenced enclosure *(see 6.21.4.2)*, which could provide sufficient protection for the cylinders. Where fenced enclosures warrant additional vehicular barrier protection (VBP), the following provide such protection:

(1) Guard rails
(2) Steel bollards
(3) Raised sidewalks [minimum of 6 in. (150 mm) in height]
(4) Fencing
(5) Ditches
(6) Berms (not to exceed 50 percent of the container perimeter)
(7) Jersey barriers
(8) Parking bumpers [minimum of 6 in. (150 mm) in height]
(9) Fencing/gates

N A.8.5.1 Although fire extinguishers are required in locations where cylinders are stored and awaiting use or resale, the specific site characteristics should be considered. For example, where the installation is a retail exchange cabinet, cylinders will be locked inside and will typically contain either a CGA 791, CGA 793, or CGA 810 valve connection, all of which have redundancy built into them that prevents the flow of gas unless connected to an appliance. As such, any cylinder fire in a retail facility cabinet should never be extinguished by anyone other than fire service personnel because the source of the gas

Shaded text = Revisions.   Δ = Text deletions and figure/table revisions.   • = Section deletions.   *N* = New material.

cannot be turned off. The sole function for fire extinguishers in these locations is to extinguish incipient fires in the vicinity of the cabinet.

A.9.1.1(3) Most truck transportation of LP-Gas is subject to regulation by the U.S. Department of Transportation (DOT). Many of the provisions of this chapter are identical or similar to DOT regulations and are intended to extend these provisions to areas not subject to DOT regulation.

A.9.1.2(3) LP-Gas systems used for engine fuel are covered by Chapter 11.

A.9.4.8 A wheel stop might consist of a chock block, curb, or parking barrier at the parking point or other means to prevent the cargo tank vehicle from unintended movement. Wheel stops are intended to prevent or restrict movement caused by gravity, from impact by vehicles, and from improper actions by drivers such as an attempt to move the vehicle before a delivery or transfer hose has been disconnected. A wheel stop is not a substitute for an operable parking brake. Use of a single wheel stop placed between wheels on tandem axles could be appropriate if the gap between the tire and the stop does not allow enough momentum to build up to roll over the stop.

A.9.7.2.2 The term *congested area* is intended to describe situations where access to the vehicle during an emergency would be impeded or where moving the vehicle away from an emergency would be prevented.

N A.10.2.1.2 For information on explosion venting, see NFPA 68.

N A.10.3.2.5 For information on explosion venting, see NFPA 68.

A.10.3.2.6 See NFPA 80.

A.11.1.1 Chapter 11 covers engine fuel systems for engines installed on vehicles for any purpose, as well as fuel systems for portable engines. This includes containers, container appurtenances, carburetion equipment, piping, hose, and fittings.

A.11.1.3 Containers for engine fuel systems can be of the permanently installed or exchange type.

A.11.3.1 Prior to April 1, 1967, these regulations were promulgated by the Interstate Commerce Commission (ICC). In Canada, the regulations of the Canadian Transport Commission apply and are available from the Canadian Transport Commission, Union Station, Ottawa, Canada.

N A.11.3.3.1 Excessive denting, bulging, gouging, and corrosion can be determined using either CGA C-6, *Standard for Visual Inspection of Steel Compressed Gas Cylinders*, or CGA C-6.3, *Standard for Visual Inspection of Low Pressure Aluminum Alloy Compressed Gas Cylinders*, for cylinders or NBBI NB23, *National Board Inspection Code*, for ASME containers.

A.11.3.7 See A.6.8.1.4.

A.11.4.1.16 Paragraph 5.9.4.1 and Table 5.9.4.1(B) require a fixed maximum liquid level gauge and an overfilling prevention device to be installed on all ASME engine fuel containers.

A.11.8.4.3 The intent of 11.8.4.3 does not limit the location of the valve as long as it is protected in accordance with 11.8.2.2 and does not require the use of any tools.

A.11.9.1.2 The luggage compartment (trunk) of a vehicle can constitute such an enclosure, provided that it meets all these requirements.

N A.11.10.1.2 Installing piping in a manner that protects it from damage can include specific routing of the pipe or tubing within the frame or shielding with external protection or other methods.

A.12.1.1 The need for a new chapter to address over-the-road vehicles became apparent when the requirements in NFPA 58 were no longer in step with the technologies that modern LP-Gas fuel systems now utilize.

A.12.3.1.2 Cylinders are permitted to be used temporarily for the purposes of shipping a vehicle, transporting it between assembly lines/areas, or testing the vehicle.

A.12.3.1.3 ECE R67.01 is one of the most commonly used standards in the world for the approval and installation of equipment used in LP-Gas vehicle fuel systems. Where no performance or specification standard is referenced in NFPA 58 for materials or equipment within the scope of Chapter 12, NFPA 58 will defer to the requirements in R67.01. Compliance to R67.01 is demonstrated by a homologation report issued by a country who is signatory to the UN standards. A list of these countries can be found in Annex 3 of this document: http://www.unece.org/fileadmin/DAM/trans/main/wp29/wp29resolutions/ECE-TRANS-WP29-78-r3e.pdf.

The reason for specifying cold weather testing to at least –40°F (–40°C) is due to the fact that R67.01 requires testing to only –20°F (–28.9°C), which is not sufficient to provide assurance of safe performance in many locations in North America. The choice of –40°F (–40°C) was based on the fact that other standards already referenced in NFPA 58 use that temperature for cold weather testing.

N A.12.3.1.3(A) The National Voluntary Laboratory Accreditation Program (NVLAP), operated by NIST, provides third-party accreditation to testing and calibration laboratories in response to legislative actions or requests from government agencies or private-sector organizations. Information can be found at https://www.nist.gov/nvlap.

A.12.3.2.5 The industry has utilized various purging practices that include the following:

(1) A five-cycle vapor purge by adding 14.7 psig (101 kPag) LP-Gas vapor to the container and venting down to 0 psig (0 kPag)
(2) A vacuum purge procedure to achieve a vacuum of 26 in. Hg (–88 kPag)
(3) Any method that reduces the concentration of air in the container to no more than 4 percent by volume and does not increase container pressures above MAWP or create an internal ignitable atmosphere

A.12.3.9.3 Properly soldered connections using sealed heat shrink are considered to be automotive-grade connections.

A.12.3.9.5 Fuel rails and distribution blocks are typically manufactured using metal, composite materials, synthetic materials, or a combination of these.

A.12.3.9.8 Pressure relief can be provided using either an internal relief device that returns liquid to the container, or a hydrostatic relief device that is piped away from the engine compartment and any sources of ignition.

A.12.3.12.10 Methods of protecting hoses from excessive temperature include the use of radiation shields or insulation.

A.12.3.14.1 The use of wire nuts and other connectors not intended for automotive use should not be used.

A.12.4.2.1 Training of technicians is needed on three levels. The first level is to train the technician in the proper handling and emergency response procedures associated with LP-Gas as required by 4.4.1. The next level of training would be to ensure that the technician is familiar with and can identify the basic components of all LP-Gas engine fuel systems. The third level would be to qualify the individual to install the specific fuel delivery system. This third level of training typically relies upon an organized and managed program developed and administered by the manufacturer or distributor of the system brand or technology being installed. This training typically addresses the installation, diagnosis, maintenance, and repair of the specific system.

Δ **A.12.4.4(1)** This requirement permits deformation of the structural components attached to the ASME container. This allows the components to absorb part of the forces that would be generated upon impact to the vehicle that could be traveling at relatively higher speeds than those addressed in Chapter 11.

A.12.4.4(3) One resource for conducting inspections is the NBBI NB23, *National Board Inspection Code.*

A.12.4.4(5) The term *mounting brackets* is intended to mean the welded mounting structure on the container or another component affixed directly to the container.

A.12.4.5.1 The luggage compartment (trunk) of a vehicle can constitute such an enclosure, provided that it meets all of the requirements in 12.4.5.1. Any sealant used should provide the following performance attributes:

(1) Nonshrinking and nonswelling
(2) Resistant to damage by LP-Gas, road salt, and vehicle vibration
(3) Effective for use from −40°F (−40°C) to 135°F (55°C)
(4) Should not deteriorate over the useful life of the vehicle

N **A.12.4.13** The fuel pump can run for a predetermined amount of time when the ignition switch is turned to the "engine on" position before the electric starter motor is engaged, or as required by specific system start protocols that utilize other systems to activate the fuel pump.

An appropriate wiring insulation material to comply with 12.4.13(7) is THHN or TFFN.

N **A.12.5.8** Soldered connections using sealed heat shrink are considered automotive grade connections. This provision will help prevent cross connections that could create a source of ignition.

N **A.12.5.9** See SAE J2618, *Recommended Testing Methods for Physical Protection of Wiring Harnesses,* for examples of such methods.

A.12.6.1 Threaded connections should not be over tightened to the extent that could break or weaken the structural integrity of the fitting or the component into which it is threaded.

A.13.3.4.2 See API 620, *Design and Construction of Large, Welded, Low-Pressure Storage Tanks,* Annex C, for further information.

A.14.2.1.1 Federal regulations applicable to marine terminals are contained in 33 CFR.

A.14.3.1 Refer to 49 CFR 195.

A.14.4.1 For guidance, refer to 33 CFR.

Δ **A.15.1** The operations and maintenance chapter provides specific reference to operations and maintenance requirements located in other chapters to make it simpler for users to locate these requirements for individual operations.

In addition to the requirements in this code, some LP-Gas storage facilities with a capacity of 10,000 lb (454 kg) or more [about 2381 gal (9 m³)] come under the requirements of the U.S. Environmental Protection Agency's Risk Management Planning. The EPA requirements do not apply if the LP-Gas is not used as a fuel at the facility at which it is stored or if it is stored at a retail facility where more than half the income is obtained from direct sales to end users or if more than half the fuel sold, by volume, is sold through a cylinder exchange program.

A.15.1.3 This can be accomplished by using a "lock-out, tag-out" method that prevents operation of the piping connections and controls. This also serves to inform any person who might be attempting to use equipment or containers at bulk plants and industrial occupancies that have been removed from service. There are other methods that can be used to prevent the operation of unsuitable equipment as well.

A.15.2.1 The procedures should address normal start-up, operations, shutdown, emergency shutdown and operations, start-up following a major change to the system, consequences of deviations and steps required to correct or avoid deviations, and equipment inspections.

A.15.2.1.4 The term *in use* can address containers at facilities that are feeding a process, system, or engine fuel (LP-Gas) refueling facility through the liquid opening primary shutoff valve. For some applications a system might be considered to be in use even though gas is not continuously flowing through the valve. The facility is considered to be attended when a qualified employee of the company or operator is on site and is able to activate the emergency shutdown system in the event of an emergency.

A.15.2.1.5 Engine fuel (LP-Gas) refueling systems are exempt because the container primary shutoff valve must remain open for the system to function properly. Persons who operate engine fuel (LP-Gas) refueling systems are required to be trained in accordance with Section 11.2. Engine fuel (LP-Gas) refueling systems are considered to be "in operation" continuously whether or not they are attended or whether gas is continuously flowing through the valve. The internal valves and emergency shutoff valves are required to be tested annually for proper operation per 6.27.3.11.

A.15.5 As the basis for maintenance procedures, the owner or operator can use procedures or instructions provided by equipment vendors, procedures found in industrial codes, or procedures prepared by persons or organizations knowledgeable about the process and equipment.

A.16.1 Use of Table 16.1(i) for pressures between 5 psig and 10 psig could provide larger CSST sizes than necessary. This provides some extra capacity. As pressures of 5 psig to 10 psig are used between the first stage pressure regulator and the second stage pressure regulator, most applications will be at residences where a small tubing size provides sufficient capacity. For larger capacities than typically used at residences, sizing information may be available from CSST manufacturers.

Annex B Properties of LP-Gases

This annex is not a part of the requirements of this NFPA document but is included for informational purposes only.

B.1 Approximate Properties of LP-Gases.

B.1.1 Source of Property Values.

B.1.1.1 The property values for the LP-Gases are based on average industry values and include values for LP-Gases coming from natural gas liquid plants as well as petroleum refineries. Thus, any particular commercial propane or butane might have properties varying slightly from the values shown. Similarly, any propane–butane mixture might have properties varying from those obtained by computation from these average values (*see B.1.2 for computation method used*). Because these are average values, the interrelationships between them (e.g., pounds per gallon, specific gravity) will not cross-check perfectly in all cases.

B.1.1.2 The variations specified in B.1.1.1 are not sufficient to prevent the use of average values for most engineering and design purposes. They stem from minor variations in composition. The commercial grades are not chemically pure (CP) propane or butane, or mixtures of the two, but they might also contain small and varying percentages of ethane, ethylene, propylene, isobutane, or butylene, which can cause slight variations in property values. There are limits to the accuracy of even the most advanced testing methods used to determine the percentages of these minor components in any LP-Gas.

B.1.2 Approximate Properties of Commercial LP-Gases. The principal properties of commercial propane and commercial butane are shown in Table B.1.2(a) and Table B.1.2(b). Reasonably accurate property values for propane–butane mixtures can be obtained by computation, applying the percentages by weight of each in the mixture to the values for the property desired to be obtained. Slightly more accurate results for vapor pressure are obtained by using the percentages by volume. Very accurate results can be obtained using data and methods explained in petroleum and chemical engineering data books.

B.1.3 Specifications of LP-Gases. Specifications of LP-Gases covered by this code are listed in GPA 2140, *Liquefied Petroleum Gas Specifications and Test Methods*, or ASTM D1835, *Standard Specification for Liquefied Petroleum (LP) Gases*.

Δ **Table B.1.2(a) Approximate Properties of LP-Gases (English)**

Property	Commercial Propane	Commercial Butane
Vapor pressure in psi (absolute pressure) at:		
70°F	145	32
100°F	218	52
105°F	233	56
130°F	315	84
Specific gravity of liquid at 60°F	0.504	0.582
Initial boiling point (°F) at 14.7 psia	−44	31
Weight (lb) per gallon of liquid at 60°F	4.20	4.81
Specific heat of liquid (Btu/lb) at 60°F	0.630	0.549
Cubic feet of vapor per gallon at 60°F	36.38	31.26
Cubic feet of vapor per pound at 60°F	8.66	6.51
Specific gravity of vapor (air = 1) at 60°F	1.50	2.01
Ignition temperature (°F) in air	920–1,120	900–1,000
Maximum flame temperature (°F) in air	3,595	3,615
Limits of flammability in air, percent of vapor in air–gas mixture:		
Lower	2.15	1.55
Upper	9.60	8.60
Latent heat of vaporization at boiling point:		
Btu per pound	184	167
Btu per gallon	773	808
Total heating values after vaporization:		
Btu per cubic foot	2,488	3,280
Btu per pound	21,548	21,221
Btu per gallon	91,502	102,032

Note: To obtain gauge pressures at sea level, subtract 14.7 psi.

△ Table B.1.2(b) Approximate Properties of LP-Gases (Metric)

Property	Commercial Propane	Commercial Butane
Vapor pressure in kPa (absolute pressure) at:		
20°C	1,000	220
40°C	1,570	360
45°C	1,760	385
55°C	2,170	580
Specific gravity of liquid at 15.56°C	0.504	0.582
Initial boiling point (°C) at 1.00 atm pressure	−42	−1
Weight (kg) per cubic meter of liquid at 15.56°C	504	582
Specific heat (kJ/kg) of liquid at 15.56°C	1.464	1.276
Cubic meter of vapor per liter of liquid at 15.56°C	0.271	0.235
Cubic meter of vapor per kilogram of liquid at 15.56°C	0.539	0.410
Specific gravity of vapor (air = 1) at 15.56°C	1.50	2.01
Ignition temperature (°C) in air	493–549	482–538
Maximum flame temperature (°C) in air	1,980	2,008
Limits of flammability in air, percent of vapor in air–gas mixture:		
Lower	2.15	1.55
Upper	9.60	8.60
Latent heat of vaporization at boiling point:		
Kilojoules per kilogram	428	388
Kilojoules per liter	216	226
Total heating value after vaporization:		
Kilojoules per cubic meter	92,430	121,280
Kilojoules per kilogram	49,920	49,140
Kilojoules per liter	25,140	28,100

Note: To obtain gauge pressures at sea level, subtract 101.3 kPa.

Annex C Design, Construction, and Requalification of DOT (ICC) Cylinders

This annex is not a part of the requirements of this NFPA document but is included for informational purposes only.

C.1 Scope.

C.1.1 Application.

C.1.1.1 This annex provides general information on cylinders referred to in this code. For complete information, consult the applicable specification *(see C.2.1).* The water capacity of such cylinders is not permitted to be more than 1000 lb (454 kg).

C.1.1.2 This annex is not applicable to Department of Transportation (DOT) specifications for tank cars, portable tank containers, or cargo tanks. Portable and cargo tanks are basically ASME containers and are covered in Annex D.

C.1.1.3 Prior to April 1, 1967, these specifications were promulgated by the Interstate Commerce Commission (ICC). On this date, certain functions of the ICC, including the promulgation of specifications and regulations dealing with LP-Gas cylinders, were transferred to DOT. Throughout this annex, both ICC and DOT are used, ICC applying to dates prior to April 1, 1967, and DOT to subsequent dates.

C.2 LP-Gas Cylinder Specifications.

C.2.1 Publishing of DOT Cylinder Specifications. DOT cylinder specifications are published in 49 CFR 178, "Specifications for Packaging," available from the U.S. Government Publishing Office, Washington, DC. The information in this publication is also issued as Tariff No. BOE-6000 by the Bureau of Explosives, American Railroads Building, 1920 L Street, NW, Washington, DC 20036.

C.2.2 DOT Specification Nomenclature.

△ **C.2.2.1** The specification designation consists of a one-digit number, sometimes followed by one or more capital letters, then by a dash and a three-digit number. The one-digit number alone or with one or more capital letters designates the specification number. The three-digit number following the dash shows the service pressure for which the cylinder is designed. Thus, "4B–240" indicates a cylinder built to Specification 4B for a 240 psig (1650 kPag) service pressure. *(See C.2.2.3.)*

C.2.2.2 The specification gives the details of cylinder construction, such as material used, method of fabrication, tests required, and inspection method, and prescribes the service pressure or range of service pressures for which that specification can be used.

C.2.2.3 The term *service pressure* is analogous to, and serves the same purpose as, the ASME design pressure. However, it is not identical, representing instead the highest pressure to which the cylinder will normally be subjected in transit or in use, but not necessarily the maximum pressure to which it might be subjected under emergency conditions in transportation. The service pressure stipulated for the LP-Gases is based on the vapor pressures exerted by the product in the cylinder at two different temperatures, the higher pressure of the two becoming the service pressure, as follows:

Shaded text = Revisions. △ = Text deletions and figure/table revisions. • = Section deletions. *N* = New material.

(1) The pressure in the cylinder at 70°F (21°C) must be less than the service pressure for which the cylinder is marked.

(2) The pressure in the container at 130°F (54.4°C) must not exceed ⅝ times the pressure for which the cylinder is marked.

Example: Commercial propane has a vapor pressure at 70°F (21°C) of 132 psig (910 kPag). However, its vapor pressure at 130°F (54.4°C) is 300 psig (2070 kPag), so service pressure [⅝ times, which must not exceed 300 psig (2070 kPag)] is 300 divided by ⅝, or 240 psig (1650 kPag). Thus, commercial propane requires at least a 240 psig (1650 kPag) service pressure cylinder.

C.2.3 DOT Cylinder Specifications Used for LP-Gas.

C.2.3.1 A number of different specifications were approved by DOT (and its predecessor, ICC) for use with LP-Gases. Some of these are no longer published or used for new construction. It should be noted that recently DOT has elected to remove certain old cylinder specifications from the list of specification cylinders that can be requalified. *(See 49 CFR 180.209.)*

C.2.3.2 DOT specifications cover primarily safety in transportation. However, for the product to be used, it is necessary for it to come to rest at the point of use and serve as LP-Gas storage during the period of use. Cylinders adequate for transportation are also deemed to be adequate for use as provided in this code. Because small-size ASME containers were not available at the time cargo tank vehicle delivery was started, ICC (now DOT) cylinders have been equipped for cargo tank vehicle deliveries and permanently installed.

C.2.3.3 The DOT cylinder specifications most widely used for the LP-Gases are shown in Table C.2.3.3. The differing materials of construction, the method of fabrication, and the date of the specification reflect the progress made in knowledge of the products to be contained and the improvement in metallurgy and methods of fabrication.

C.3 Requalification, Retesting, and Repair of DOT Cylinders.

C.3.1 Application. This section outlines the requalification, retesting, and repair requirements for cylinders but should be used only as a guide. For official information, the applicable DOT regulations should be consulted.

C.3.2 Requalification (Including Retesting) of DOT Cylinders.

C.3.2.1 DOT rules prohibit cylinders from being refilled, continued in service, or transported unless they are properly qualified or requalified for LP-Gas service in accordance with DOT regulations.

Table C.2.3.3 DOT Cylinder Specifications

Specification No. and Marking	Material of Construction	Method of Fabrication
3B-300	Steel	Seamless
4B-300	Steel	2-piece welded and brazed
4B-240	Steel	2-piece welded and brazed
4BA-240	Alloy steel	2-piece welded and brazed
4E-240	Aluminum	Welded and brazed
4BW-240	Steel	3-piece welded

Note: The term *service pressure* had a different connotation at the time the specification was adopted.

C.3.2.2 DOT rules require a careful examination of every cylinder each time it is to be filled, and a cylinder must be rejected if there is evidence of exposure to fire or if there are bad gouges or dents, seriously corroded areas, leaks, or other conditions indicating possible weaknesses that might render it unfit for service. The following disposition is to be made of rejected cylinders:

(1) Cylinders subjected to fire are required to be requalified, reconditioned, or repaired in accordance with C.3.3 or permanently removed from service, except that DOT 4E (aluminum) cylinders and composite material cylinders used under a special permit issued by DOT must be permanently removed from service.

(2) Cylinders showing serious physical damage or leaks or showing a reduction in the marked tare weight of 5 percent or more are required to be retested in accordance with C.3.2.4.1(1) or C.3.2.4.1(2) and, if necessary, repaired in accordance with C.3.3.

C.3.2.3 All cylinders, including those apparently undamaged, are required to be periodically requalified for continued service. The first requalification for a new cylinder is required within 12 years after the date of manufacture. Subsequent requalifications are required within the periods specified under the requalification method used. Composite material cylinders used under a special permit issued by DOT must be requalified in accordance with the terms of the permit.

C.3.2.4 DOT regulations permit three alternative methods of requalification for most commonly used LP-Gas cylinders *(see DOT regulations for permissible requalification methods for specific cylinder specifications).* Two methods use hydrostatic testing, and the third uses a carefully made and duly recorded visual examination by a competent person. DOT regulations cite in detail the data to be recorded for the hydrostatic test methods, the observations to be made during the visual examination for the hydrostatic and visual inspection methods, and the marking of cylinders to indicate the requalification date and the method used. The three methods — the volumetric expansion method, the proof pressure method, and the external visual inspection method — are outlined in C.3.2.4.1 through C.3.2.4.3.

△ C.3.2.4.1 Volumetric Expansion Method. The volumetric expansion method test, with determination of expansion readings, can be used to requalify cylinders for 12 years before the next requalification is due. A pressure of twice the marked service pressure is applied, using a water jacket (or the equivalent) so that the total expansion of the cylinder during the application of the test pressure can be observed and recorded for comparison with the permanent expansion of the cylinder after depressurization. The following disposition is made of cylinders tested in this manner:

(1) Cylinders that pass the retest and the visual examination required with it *(see C.3.2.4)* are marked with the retester identification number (RIN) and retest date. The RIN (e.g., A123) is set in a square pattern between the month and the year of the test date (e.g., 5/96). The first character of the RIN is positioned at the upper left corner of the square pattern, the second character in the upper right, the third character in the lower right, and the fourth character in the lower left. Minimum character size is ⅛ in. (3 mm) [¼ in. (6 mm) minimum height is recommended for the month and year]. Following marking, cylinders can be placed back into service.

(2) Cylinders that leak, or for which the permanent expansion exceeds 10 percent of the total expansion (12 percent for Specification 4E aluminum cylinders), must be rejected. If rejected for leakage, cylinders can be repaired in accordance with C.3.3.

C.3.2.4.2 Proof Pressure Method. Cylinders are requalified for 7 years before the next requalification is due, using the proof pressure method. A pressure of twice the marked service pressure is applied, but no provision is made for measuring total and permanent expansion during the test outlined in C.3.2.4.1. The cylinder is carefully observed while under the test pressure for leaks, undue swelling, or bulging indicating weaknesses. The following disposition is made of cylinders tested in this manner:

(1) Cylinders that pass the test and the visual examination required with it *(see C.3.2.4)* are marked with the retester identification number (RIN) and retest date. The RIN (e.g., A123) is set in a square pattern between the month and the year of the test date (e.g., 5/96), followed by an S. The first character of the RIN is positioned at the upper left corner of the square pattern, the second character in the upper right, the third character in the lower right, and the fourth character in the lower left. Minimum character size is ⅛ in. (3 mm) [¼ in. (6 mm) minimum height is recommended for the month and year]. Following marking, cylinders can be placed back into service.

(2) Cylinders that are developing leaks or showing undue swelling or bulging must be rejected. If rejected for leaks, cylinders are permitted to be repaired in accordance with C.3.3.

△ C.3.2.4.3 External Visual Inspection Method. The recorded external visual inspection method can be used to requalify cylinders for 5 years before the next qualification is due, provided that the cylinder has been used exclusively for LP-Gas commercially free of corroding components. Inspection is to be made by a competent person, using CGA C-6, *Standard for Visual Inspection of Steel Compressed Gas Cylinders*, for steel cylinders and CGA C-6.3, *Standard for Visual Inspection of Low Pressure Aluminum Alloy Compressed Gas Cylinders*, for aluminum cylinders and recording the inspection results as required by DOT regulations. The following disposition is to be made of cylinders inspected in this manner:

(1) Cylinders that pass the visual examination are marked with the retester identification number (RIN) and retest date and year of the examination, followed by an E (e.g., 6-07 A123 E, indicating requalification by the specific cylinder retester using the visual examination method in June 2007), and can be placed back into service. In certain situations, DOT has issued visual requalifier identification numbers (VRIN). Those issued this identification number must place the VRIN in a straight line (e.g., V108231), followed by the month and year and the letter E.

(2) Cylinders that leak or show serious denting or gouging or excessive corrosion must be either scrapped or repaired in accordance with C.3.3.

C.3.3 Repair of DOT Cylinders. Repair of DOT cylinders is required to be performed by a manufacturer of the type of cylinder to be repaired or by a repair facility authorized by DOT.

Repairs normally made are for fire damage, leaks, denting, and gouges and for broken or detached valve-protecting collars or foot rings.

Annex D Design of ASME and API-ASME Containers

This annex is not a part of the requirements of this NFPA document but is included for informational purposes only.

D.1 General.

D.1.1 Application.

D.1.1.1 This annex provides general information on containers designed and constructed in accordance with ASME or API-ASME codes, usually referred to as ASME containers. For complete information on either ASME or API-ASME containers, the applicable code should be consulted. Construction of containers to the API-ASME *Code for Unfired Pressure Vessels for Petroleum Liquids and Gases* has not been authorized since July 1, 1961.

D.1.1.2 Department of Transportation (DOT) and Interstate Commerce Commission (ICC) specifications for portable tanks and cargo tanks are for either ASME or API-ASME containers. In writing these specifications, which should be consulted for complete information, additions were made to ASME and API-ASME pressure vessel codes to cover the following:

(1) Protection of tank valves and appurtenances against physical damage in transportation

(2) Hold-down devices for securing cargo tanks to conventional vehicles

(3) Attachments to relatively large [6000 gal (22.7 m^3) or more water capacity] cargo tanks in which the tank serves as a stress member in lieu of a frame

D.1.2 Development of ASME and API-ASME Codes.

D.1.2.1 ASME-type containers of approximately 12,000 gal (45.4 m^3) or more water capacity were initially used for bulk storage in processing, distribution, and industrial plants. As the industry expanded and residential and commercial usage increased, the need grew for small ASME containers with capacities greater than the upper limit for cylinders. This ultimately resulted in the development of cargo containers for cargo tank vehicles and the wide use of ASME containers ranging in size from less than 25 gal to 120,000 gal (0.1 m^3 to 454 m^3) water capacity.

D.1.2.2 In 1911, the American Society of Mechanical Engineers (ASME) set up the Boiler and Pressure Vessel Committee to formulate "standard rules for the construction of steam boilers and other pressure vessels." The ASME *Boiler and Pressure Vessel Code*, first published in 1925, has been revised regularly since that time. During this period, changes have been made to the code as materials of construction improved and more was known about them and as fabrication methods changed and inspection procedures were refined.

D.1.2.3 One major change involved the so-called "factor of safety" (the ratio of the ultimate strength of the metal to the design stress used). Prior to 1946, a 5:1 safety factor was used. Fabrication changed from the riveting widely used when the code was first written (some forge welding was used) to fusion welding. This latter method was incorporated into the code as welding techniques were perfected, and it now predominates.

D.1.2.4 The safety factor change in the ASME Code was based on the technical progress made since 1925 and on experience with the use of the API-ASME Code. This offshoot of the ASME Code, initiated in 1931, was formulated and published by the American Petroleum Institute (API) in cooperation with ASME. It justified the 4:1 safety factor on the basis of certain quality and inspection controls not incorporated at that time in the ASME Code editions. In 1998, ASME reduced the safety factor or design margin from 4:1 to 3.5:1, noting improvements in metal manufacturing, welding techniques, x-ray quality, and pressure vessel manufacturer's quality systems.

D.1.2.5 ASME Code case interpretations and addenda are published between code editions and normally become part of the code in the new edition. Adherence to these interpretations and addenda is considered compliance with the code. *[See 5.2.1.1(B).]*

D.2 Design of Containers for LP-Gas.

D.2.1 ASME Container Design.

D.2.1.1 When ASME containers were first used to store LP-Gas, the properties of the chemically pure (CP) grades of the principal constituents were available, but the average properties for the commercial grades of propane and butane were not. Also, there was no experience that demonstrated the expected temperatures and pressures for product stored in areas with high atmospheric temperatures. A 200 psig (1378 kPag) design pressure was for propane [the CP grade of which has a gauge vapor pressure of 176 psig (1210 kPag) at 100°F (37.8°C)] and 80 psig (550 kPag) for butane [CP grade has a vapor pressure of 37 psig (255 kPag) at 100°F (37.8°C)] were deemed appropriate. These containers were built with a 5:1 safety factor. *(See D.1.2.3.)*

D.2.1.2 Pressure vessel codes, following boiler pressure relief valve practice, require that the pressure relief valve start-to-leak setting be the maximum allowable working pressure (MAWP) of the container. In specifying pressure relief valve capacity, however, they stipulate that this relieving capacity be adequate to prevent the internal pressure from rising above 120 percent of the design pressure under fire exposure conditions.

D.2.1.3 Containers built in accordance with D.2.1.1 were entirely adequate for the commercial grades of the LP-Gases [the vapor pressure of propane at 100°F (37.8°C) is 220 psig (1515 kPag); the gauge vapor pressure of commercial butane at 100°F (37.8°C) is 37 psig (255 kPag)]. However, because they were equipped with pressure relief valves set to start-to-leak at the MAWP of the container, these relief valves occasionally opened on an unusually warm day. Because any unnecessary release of a flammable gas is potentially dangerous, and considering the recommendations of fire prevention and insurance groups as well as the favorable experience with API-ASME containers *(see D.2.2.1)*, relief valve settings above the design pressure [up to 250 psig (1720 kPag) for propane and 100 psig (690 kPag) for butane] were widely used.

D.2.1.4 In determining safe filling limits for compressed liquefied gases, DOT (ICC) uses the criterion that the container not become liquid full at the highest temperature the liquid is expected to reach due to the normal atmospheric conditions to which the container can be exposed. For containers of more than 1200 gal (4.5 m^3) water capacity, the liquid temperature selected is 115°F (46°C). The vapor pressure of the gas to be contained at 115°F (46°C) is specified by DOT as the minimum design pressure for the container. The gauge vapor pressure of CP propane and commercial propane at 115°F (46.1°C) is 211 psig (1450 kPag) and 255 psig (1756 kPag), respectively. The gauge vapor pressure of both normal butane and commercial butane at 115°F (46.1°C) is 51 psig (350 kPag).

D.2.1.5 The ASME *Boiler and Pressure Vessel Code* editions generally applicable to LP-Gas containers, and the design pressures, safety factors, and exceptions to these editions for LP-Gas use, are shown in Table D.2.1.5. They reflect the use of the information in D.2.1.1 through D.2.1.4.

D.2.2 API-ASME Container Design.

D.2.2.1 The API-ASME Code was first published in 1931. Based on petroleum industry experience using certain material quality and inspection controls not incorporated at that time in the ASME Code, the 4:1 safety factor was first used. Many LP-Gas containers were built under this code with design pressures of 125 psig (860 kPag) [100 psig (690 kPag) until December 31, 1947] for butane and 250 psig (1725 kPag) for propane. Containers constructed in accordance with the API-ASME Code were not required to comply with Section 1 or with the annex to Section 1. Paragraphs W-601 through W-606 of the 1943 and earlier editions were not applicable to LP-Gas containers.

D.2.2.2 By changing the safety factor from 5:1 to 4:1 through consideration of the factors described in D.2.1.1 through D.2.1.4, the ASME Code became, in effect, nearly identical to the API-ASME Code by the 1950s. Thus, the API-ASME Code was phased out, and construction was not authorized after July 1, 1961.

D.2.3 Design Criteria for LP-Gas Containers. To prevent confusion in earlier editions of this code, the container type nomenclature was used to designate the pressure rating of the container to be used for various types of LP-Gases. With the adoption of the 4:1 safety factor in the ASME Code and the phasing out of the API-ASME Code, the need for container type ceased to exist.

D.2.4 DOT (ICC) Specifications Utilizing ASME or API-ASME Containers.

D.2.4.1 DOT (ICC) specifications for portable tanks and cargo tanks require ASME or API-ASME construction for the tank proper *(see D.1.1.2)*. Several such specifications were written by the ICC prior to 1967, and DOT has continued this practice.

D.2.4.2 ICC specifications written prior to 1946, and to some extent through 1952, used ASME containers with a 200 psig (1380 kPag) design pressure for propane and 80 psig (550 kPag) for butane [100 psi (690 kPa) after 1947] with a 5:1 safety factor. During this period and until 1961, ICC specifications also permitted API-ASME containers with a 250 psig (1720 kPag) design pressure for propane and 100 psig (690 kPag) for butane [125 psig (862 kPag) after 1947].

Table D.2.1.5 Container Pressure and Safety Factors/Design Margin for Various Editions of the ASME Code

| Year ASME Code Edition Published | Maximum Allowable Working Pressure (MAWP) | | | | Safety Factor/ Design Margin |
| | Butane | | Propane | | |
	psig	MPag	psig	MPag	
1931 through 1946[a]	100[a]	0.7	200	1.4	5:1
1949, paragraphs U-68 and U-69[b]	100	0.7	200	1.4	5:1
1949, paragraphs U-200 and U-201[c]	125	0.9	250	1.7	4:1
1952 through 1998	125	0.9	250	1.7	4:1
1998 to current					3.5:1

[a]Until December 31, 1947, containers designed for 80 psig (0.6 MPag) under prior (5:1 safety factor) codes were authorized for butane. Since that time, either 100 psig (0.7 MPag) (under prior codes) or 125 psig (0.9 MPag) (under present codes) is required.

[b]Containers constructed in accordance with the 1949 edition and prior editions of the ASME Code were not required to be in compliance with paragraphs U-2 to U-10, inclusive, or with paragraph U-19. Construction in accordance with paragraph U-70 of these editions was not authorized.

[c]Higher MAWP [312.5 psig (2.2 MPag)] is required for small ASME containers used for vehicular installations, because they can be exposed to higher temperatures and, consequently, develop higher internal pressure.

D.2.4.3 To prevent any unnecessary release of flammable vapor during transportation *(see D.2.1.3)*, the use of safety relief valve settings 25 percent above the MAWP was common for ASME 5:1 safety factor containers. To eliminate confusion, and in line with the good experience with API-ASME containers, the ICC permitted the rerating of these particular ASME containers used under its specifications to 125 percent of the originally marked MAWP.

D.2.4.4 DOT (ICC) pressure specifications applicable to portable tanks and cargo tanks currently in use are listed in Table D.2.4.4. New construction is not permitted under the older specifications. However, use of these older containers is permitted to continue, provided that they have been maintained in accordance with DOT (ICC) regulations.

D.3 Underground ASME or API-ASME Containers.

D.3.1 Use of Containers Underground.

D.3.1.1 ASME or API-ASME containers are used for underground or partially underground installation in accordance with 6.8.6.1 or 6.8.6.2. The temperature of the soil is normally low so that the average liquid temperature and vapor pressure of product stored in underground containers will be lower than in aboveground containers.

D.3.1.2 Containers listed to be used interchangeably for installation either above ground or under ground must comply as to pressure relief valve rated relieving capacity and filling limit with aboveground provisions when installed above ground *(see 5.9.2.6)*. When installed under ground, the pressure relief valve rated relieving capacity and filling limit can be in accordance with underground provisions *(see 5.9.2.8)*, provided that all other underground installation provisions are met. Containers installed partially under ground are considered as aboveground containers insofar as filling limit and pressure relief valve rated relieving capacity are concerned.

Table D.2.4.4 DOT Pressure Specification for Cargo Tanks

| Specification Number | ASME Construction | | | API-ASME Construction | | |
| | MAWP (psig) | | Safety Factor/ Design Margin | Design Pressure (psig) | | |
	Propane	Butane		Propane	Butane	Safety Factor
ICC-50[a]	200[b]	100[b]	5:1	250	125	4:1
ICC-51[a]	250	125	4:1	250	125	4:1
MC-320[c,d]	200[b]	100[b]	5:1	250	125	4:1
MC-330[c]	250	125	4:1	250	125	4:1
MC-331[c]	250	125	4:1	250	125	4:1

For SI units, 100 psig = 0.69 MPag; 125 psig = 0.86 MPag; 200 psig = 1.40 MPag; 250 psig = 1.72 MPag.
[a]Portable tank container.
[b]Permitted to be re-rated to 125 percent of original ASME MAWP.
[c]Cargo tank.
[d]Requires DOT exemption.

Annex E Pressure Relief Devices

This annex is not a part of the requirements of this NFPA document but is included for informational purposes only.

E.1 Pressure Relief Devices for Department of Transportation (DOT) Cylinders.

E.1.1 Source of Provisions for Relief Devices. The requirements for relief devices on Department of Transportation (DOT) cylinders are established by the DOT. Complete technical information regarding these requirements are found in CGA S-1.1, *Pressure Relief Device Standards, Part 1 — Cylinders for Compressed Gases.*

E.2 Pressure Relief Devices for ASME Containers.

E.2.1 Source of Provisions for Pressure Relief Devices. Capacity requirements for pressure relief devices are in accordance with the applicable provisions of CGA S-1.2, *Pressure Relief Device Standards, Part 2 — Cargo and Portable Tanks for Compressed Gases*; or with CGA S-1.3, *Pressure Relief Device Standards, Part 3 — Compressed Gas Storage Containers.*

△ **E.2.2 Spring-Loaded Pressure Relief Valves for Aboveground and Cargo Containers.** The minimum rate of discharge for spring-loaded pressure relief valves is based on the outside surface of the containers on which the valves are installed. Paragraph 5.2.8.3(C)(6) provides that new containers be marked with the surface area in square feet. The surface area of containers not so marked (or not legibly marked) can be computed by use of one of the following applicable formulas:

(1) The following formula is used for cylindrical containers with hemispherical heads:

$$\text{[E.2.2a]}$$
$$\text{Surface area} = \text{overall length} \times \text{outside diameter} \times 3.1416$$

(2) The following formula is used for cylindrical containers with other than hemispherical heads:

$$\text{[E.2.2b]}$$
$$\text{Surface area} = \left(\text{overall length} + 0.3 \text{ outside diameter}\right) \times \text{outside diameter} \times 3.1416$$

NOTE: This formula is not precise but will give results within the limits of practical accuracy in sizing relief valves.

(3) The following formula is used for spherical containers:

△
$$\text{[E.2.2c]}$$
$$\text{Surface area} = \text{outside diameter squared} \times 3.1416$$

(4) The following formula is used for flow rate for all containers:

$$\text{[E.2.2d]}$$
$$\text{Flow rate CFM Air} = 53.632 \times A^{0.82}$$

where:
A = total outside surface area of container in square feet obtained from E.2.2(1), (2), or (3)

△ **E.2.3 Pressure Relief Valve Testing.**

E.2.3.1 Frequent testing of pressure relief valves on LP-Gas containers is not considered necessary for the following reasons:

(1) The LP-Gases are so-called "sweet gases" having no corrosive or other deleterious effect on the metal of the containers or relief valves.
(2) The relief valves are constructed of corrosion-resistant materials and are installed so as to be protected against the weather.
(3) The variations of temperature and pressure due to atmospheric conditions are not sufficient to cause any permanent set in the valve springs.
(4) The required odorization of the LP-Gases makes escape almost instantly evident.
(5) Experience over the years with the storage of LP-Gases has shown a good safety record on the functioning of pressure relief valves.

△ **E.2.3.2** Because no mechanical device can be expected to remain in operative condition indefinitely, the pressure relief valve manufacturer's recommendations can be consulted for guidance on inspection.

Annex F Liquid Volume Tables, Computations, and Graphs

This annex is not a part of the requirements of this NFPA document but is included for informational purposes only.

F.1 Scope.

F.1.1 Application. This annex explains the basis for Table 7.4.2.2, includes the LP-Gas liquid volume temperature correction table, Table F.3.3, and describes its use. It also explains the methods of making liquid volume computations to determine the maximum permissible LP-Gas content of containers in accordance with Table 7.4.2.3(a), Table 7.4.2.3(b), and Table 7.4.2.3(c).

F.2 Basis for Determination of LP-Gas Container Capacity.
The basis for determination of the maximum permitted filling limits shown in Table 7.4.2.2 is the maximum safe quantity that will ensure that the container will not become liquid full when the liquid is at the highest anticipated temperature.

F.2.1 For portable containers built to Department of Transportation (DOT) specifications and other aboveground containers with water capacities of 1200 gal (4.5 m³) or less, the highest anticipated temperature is assumed to be 130°F (54°C).

F.2.2 For other aboveground uninsulated containers with water capacities in excess of 1200 gal (4.5 m³), including those built to DOT portable or cargo tank specifications, the highest anticipated temperature is assumed to be 115°F (46°C).

F.2.3 For all containers installed under ground, the highest anticipated temperature is assumed to be 105°F (41°C).

F.3 Liquid Volume Correction Table.
Table F.3.3 shows the correction of observed volume to standard temperature condition [60°F (16°C) and equilibrium pressure].

F.3.1 The volume of a given quantity of LP-Gas liquid in a container is directly related to its temperature, expanding as temperature increases and contracting as temperature decreases. Standard conditions, often used for weights and measures purposes and, in some cases, to comply with safety regulations, specify correction of the observed volume to what it would be at 60°F (16°C).

Δ F.3.2 To correct the observed volume to 60°F (16°C), the specific gravity of LP-Gas at 60°F (16°C) in relation to water at 60°F (16°C) (usually referred to as "60°F/60°F") and its average temperature must be known. The specific gravity normally appears on the shipping papers. The average liquid temperature can be obtained as follows:

(1) Insert a thermometer in a thermometer well in the container into which the liquid has been transferred, and read the temperature after the completion of the transfer. *[See F.3.2(3) for proper use of a thermometer.]*

(2) If the container is not equipped with a well but is essentially empty of liquid prior to loading, the temperature of the liquid in the container from which liquid is being withdrawn can be used. Otherwise, a thermometer can be inserted in a thermometer well or other temperature-sensing device installed in the loading line at a point close to the container being loaded. Read temperatures at intervals during transfer and averaging. *[See F.3.2(3).]*

(3) A suitable liquid should be used in thermometer wells to obtain an efficient heat transfer from the LP-Gas liquid in the container to the thermometer bulb. The liquid used should be noncorrosive and should not freeze at the temperatures to which it will be subjected. Water should not be used.

F.3.3 The volume observed or measured is corrected to 60°F (16°C) by use of Table F.3.3. The column headings, across the top of the tabulation, list the range of specific gravities for the LP-Gases. Specific gravities are shown from 0.500 to 0.590 by 0.010 increments, except that special columns are inserted for chemically pure propane, isobutane, and normal butane. To obtain a correction factor, read down the column for the specific gravity of the particular LP-Gas to the factor corresponding with the liquid temperature. Interpolation between the specific gravities and temperatures shown can be used if necessary.

F.4 Use of Liquid Volume Correction Factors in Table F.3.3.

F.4.1 To correct the observed volume in gallons for any LP-Gas (the specific gravity and temperature of which is known) to gallons at 60°F (16°C), Table F.3.3 is used as follows:

(1) Obtain the correction factor for the specific gravity and temperature as described in F.3.3

(2) Multiply the gallons observed by the correction factor to obtain the gallons at 60°F (16°C)

Example: A container has in it 4055 gal (15.3 m³) of LP-Gas with a specific gravity of 0.560 at a liquid temperature of 75°F (23.9°C). The correction factors in the 0.560 column are 0.983 at 74°F (23.3°C) and 0.980 at 76°F (24.4°C), or, interpolating, 0.9815 for 75°F. The volume of liquid at 60°F is 4055 × 0.9815, or 3980 gal (15.1 m³).

F.4.2 To determine the volume in gallons of a particular LP-Gas at temperature, *t*, to correspond with a given number of gallons at 60°F (16°C), Table F.3.3 is used as follows:

(1) Obtain the correction factor for the LP-Gas, using the column for its specific gravity and reading the factor for temperature, *t*

(2) Divide the number of gallons at 60°F (16°C) by the correction factor to obtain the volume at temperature, *t*

Example: It is desired to pump 800 gal (3.03 m³) at 60°F (15.5°C) into a container. The LP-Gas has a specific gravity of 0.510, and the liquid temperature is 44°F (6.7°C). The correction factor in the 0.510 column for 44°F (6.7°C) is 1.025. The volume to be pumped at 44°F (6.7°C) is 800/1.025 = 780 gal (2.95 m³).

F.5 Maximum Liquid Volume Computations.

F.5.1 Maximum Liquid LP-Gas Content of Container at Any Given Temperature.

F.5.1.1 The maximum liquid LP-Gas content of any container depends on the size of the container, whether it is installed above ground or under ground, the maximum permitted filling limit, and the temperature of the liquid. *[See Table 7.4.2.3(a), Table 7.4.2.3(b), and Table 7.4.2.3(c).]*

F.5.1.2 The maximum volume fraction, V_t (in percent of container capacity), of an LP-Gas at temperature, *t*, having a specific gravity, *G*, and a filling limit and weight percent filling limit, *L*, is computed by use of the following formula:

[F.5.1.2a]

$$V_t = \frac{L}{G} \div F$$

or

[F.5.1.2b]

$$V_t = \frac{L}{G \times F}$$

where:
V_t = percent of container capacity that can be filled with liquid
t = liquid temperature [assumed to be 40°F (4.4°C) for above-ground containers or 50°F (10°C) for underground containers]
L = maximum permitted filling limit by weight (*see Table 7.4.2.2*)
G = specific gravity of particular LP-Gas
F = correction factor to correct volume at temperature, *t*, to 60°F (16°C)

Example: The maximum liquid content, in percent of container capacity, for an aboveground 30,000 gal (114 m³) water capacity container of LP-Gas having a specific gravity of 0.508 and at a liquid temperature of 80°F (27°C) is computed as follows:

From Table 7.4.2.2, *L* = 0.45 and, from Table F.3.3, *F* = 0.967. Thus,

[F.5.1.2c]

$$V_{80} = \frac{0.45}{0.508 \times 0.967}$$

$$= 0.915 \ (91\%) \text{ or } 27{,}300 \text{ gal} \ (103 \text{ m}^3)$$

Table F.3.3 Liquid Volume Correction Factors

Observed Temperature (°F)		Specific Gravity at 60°F/60°F											
	0.500	Propane 0.5079	0.510	0.520	0.530	0.540	0.550	0.560	iso-Butane 0.5631	0.570	0.580	n-Butane 0.5844	0.590
						Volume Correction Factor							
−50	1.160	1.155	1.153	1.146	1.140	1.133	1.127	1.122	1.120	1.116	1.111	1.108	1.106
−45	1.153	1.148	1.146	1.140	1.134	1.128	1.122	1.117	1.115	1.111	1.106	1.103	1.101
−40	1.147	1.142	1.140	1.134	1.128	1.122	1.117	1.111	1.110	1.106	1.101	1.099	1.097
−35	1.140	1.135	1.134	1.128	1.122	1.116	1.112	1.106	1.105	1.101	1.096	1.094	1.092
−30	1.134	1.129	1.128	1.122	1.116	1.111	1.106	1.101	1.100	1.096	1.092	1.090	1.088
−25	1.127	1.122	1.121	1.115	1.110	1.105	1.100	1.095	1.094	1.091	1.087	1.085	1.083
−20	1.120	1.115	1.114	1.109	1.104	1.099	1.095	1.090	1.089	1.086	1.082	1.080	1.079
−15	1.112	1.109	1.107	1.102	1.097	1.093	1.089	1.084	1.083	1.080	1.077	1.075	1.074
−10	1.105	1.102	1.100	1.095	1.091	1.087	1.083	1.079	1.078	1.075	1.072	1.071	1.069
−5	1.098	1.094	1.094	1.089	1.085	1.081	1.077	1.074	1.073	1.070	1.067	1.066	1.065
0	1.092	1.088	1.088	1.084	1.080	1.076	1.073	1.069	1.068	1.066	1.063	1.062	1.061
2	1.089	1.086	1.085	1.081	1.077	1.074	1.070	1.067	1.066	1.064	1.061	1.060	1.059
4	1.086	1.083	1.082	1.079	1.075	1.071	1.068	1.065	1.064	1.062	1.059	1.058	1.057
6	1.084	1.080	1.080	1.076	1.072	1.069	1.065	1.062	1.061	1.059	1.057	1.055	1.054
8	1.081	1.078	1.077	1.074	1.070	1.066	1.063	1.060	1.059	1.057	1.055	1.053	1.052
10	1.078	1.075	1.074	1.071	1.067	1.064	1.061	1.058	1.057	1.055	1.053	1.051	1.050
12	1.075	1.072	1.071	1.068	1.064	1.061	1.059	1.056	1.055	1.053	1.051	1.049	1.048
14	1.072	1.070	1.069	1.066	1.062	1.059	1.056	1.053	1.053	1.051	1.049	1.047	1.046
16	1.070	1.067	1.066	1.063	1.060	1.056	1.054	1.051	1.050	1.048	1.046	1.045	1.044
18	1.067	1.065	1.064	1.061	1.057	1.054	1.051	1.049	1.048	1.046	1.044	1.043	1.042
20	1.064	1.062	1.061	1.058	1.054	1.051	1.049	1.046	1.046	1.044	1.042	1.041	1.040
22	1.061	1.059	1.058	1.055	1.052	1.049	1.046	1.044	1.044	1.042	1.040	1.039	1.038
24	1.058	1.056	1.055	1.052	1.049	1.046	1.044	1.042	1.042	1.040	1.038	1.037	1.036
26	1.055	1.053	1.052	1.049	1.047	1.044	1.042	1.039	1.039	1.037	1.036	1.036	1.034
28	1.052	1.050	1.049	1.047	1.044	1.041	1.039	1.037	1.037	1.035	1.034	1.034	1.032
30	1.049	1.047	1.046	1.044	1.041	1.039	1.037	1.035	1.035	1.033	1.032	1.032	1.030
32	1.046	1.044	1.043	1.041	1.038	1.036	1.035	1.033	1.033	1.031	1.030	1.030	1.028
34	1.043	1.041	1.040	1.038	1.036	1.034	1.032	1.031	1.030	1.029	1.028	1.028	1.026
36	1.039	1.038	1.037	1.035	1.033	1.031	1.030	1.028	1.028	1.027	1.025	1.025	1.024
38	1.036	1.035	1.034	1.032	1.031	1.029	1.027	1.026	1.025	1.025	1.023	1.023	1.022
40	1.033	1.032	1.031	1.029	1.028	1.026	1.025	1.024	1.023	1.023	1.021	1.021	1.020
42	1.030	1.029	1.028	1.027	1.025	1.024	1.023	1.022	1.021	1.021	1.019	1.019	1.018
44	1.027	1.026	1.025	1.023	1.022	1.021	1.020	1.019	1.019	1.018	1.017	1.017	1.016
46	1.023	1.022	1.022	1.021	1.020	1.018	1.018	1.017	1.016	1.016	1.015	1.015	1.014
48	1.020	1.019	1.019	1.018	1.017	1.016	1.015	1.014	1.014	1.013	1.013	1.013	1.012
50	1.017	1.016	1.016	1.015	1.014	1.013	1.013	1.012	1.012	1.011	1.011	1.011	1.010
52	1.014	1.013	1.012	1.012	1.011	1.010	1.010	1.009	1.009	1.009	1.009	1.009	1.008
54	1.010	1.010	1.009	1.009	1.008	1.008	1.007	1.007	1.007	1.007	1.006	1.006	1.006
56	1.007	1.007	1.006	1.006	1.005	1.005	1.005	1.005	1.005	1.005	1.004	1.004	1.004
58	1.003	1.003	1.003	1.003	1.003	1.003	1.002	1.002	1.002	1.002	1.002	1.002	1.002
60	1.000	1.000	1.000	1.000	1.000	1.000	1.000	1.000	1.000	1.000	1.000	1.000	1.000
62	0.997	0.997	0.997	0.997	0.997	0.997	0.997	0.998	0.998	0.998	0.998	0.998	0.998
64	0.993	0.993	0.994	0.994	0.994	0.994	0.995	0.995	0.995	0.995	0.996	0.996	0.996
66	0.990	0.990	0.990	0.990	0.991	0.992	0.992	0.993	0.993	0.993	0.993	0.993	0.993
68	0.986	0.986	0.987	0.987	0.988	0.989	0.990	0.990	0.990	0.990	0.991	0.991	0.991
70	0.983	0.983	0.984	0.984	0.985	0.986	0.987	0.988	0.988	0.988	0.989	0.989	0.989
72	0.979	0.980	0.981	0.981	0.982	0.983	0.984	0.985	0.986	0.986	0.987	0.987	0.987
74	0.976	0.976	0.977	0.978	0.980	0.980	0.982	0.983	0.983	0.984	0.985	0.985	0.985
76	0.972	0.973	0.974	0.975	0.977	0.978	0.979	0.980	0.981	0.981	0.982	0.982	0.983
78	0.969	0.970	0.970	0.972	0.974	0.975	0.977	0.978	0.978	0.979	0.980	0.980	0.981
80	0.965	0.967	0.967	0.969	0.971	0.972	0.974	0.975	0.976	0.977	0.978	0.978	0.979
82	0.961	0.963	0.963	0.966	0.968	0.969	0.971	0.972	0.973	0.974	0.976	0.976	0.977
84	0.957	0.959	0.960	0.962	0.965	0.966	0.968	0.970	0.971	0.972	0.974	0.974	0.975
86	0.954	0.956	0.956	0.959	0.961	0.964	0.966	0.967	0.968	0.969	0.971	0.971	0.972

(continues)

Table F.3.3 *Continued*

Observed Temperature (°F)	Specific Gravity at 60°F/60°F												
	0.500	Propane 0.5079	0.510	0.520	0.530	0.540	0.550	0.560	iso-Butane 0.5631	0.570	0.580	n-Butane 0.5844	0.590
	Volume Correction Factor												
88	0.950	0.952	0.953	0.955	0.958	0.961	0.963	0.965	0.966	0.967	0.969	0.969	0.970
90	0.946	0.949	0.949	0.952	0.955	0.958	0.960	0.962	0.963	0.964	0.967	0.967	0.968
92	0.942	0.945	0.946	0.949	0.952	0.955	0.957	0.959	0.960	0.962	0.964	0.965	0.966
94	0.938	0.941	0.942	0.946	0.949	0.952	0.954	0.957	0.958	0.959	0.962	0.962	0.964
96	0.935	0.938	0.939	0.942	0.946	0.949	0.952	0.954	0.955	0.957	0.959	0.960	0.961
98	0.931	0.934	0.935	0.939	0.943	0.946	0.949	0.952	0.953	0.954	0.957	0.957	0.959
100	0.927	0.930	0.932	0.936	0.940	0.943	0.946	0.949	0.950	0.952	0.954	0.955	0.957
105	0.917	0.920	0.923	0.927	0.931	0.935	0.939	0.943	0.943	0.946	0.949	0.949	0.951
110	0.907	0.911	0.913	0.918	0.923	0.927	0.932	0.936	0.937	0.939	0.943	0.944	0.946
115	0.897	0.902	0.904	0.909	0.915	0.920	0.925	0.930	0.930	0.933	0.937	0.938	0.940
120	0.887	0.892	0.894	0.900	0.907	0.912	0.918	0.923	0.924	0.927	0.931	0.932	0.934
125	0.876	0.881	0.884	0.890	0.898	0.903	0.909	0.916	0.916	0.920	0.925	0.927	0.928
130	0.865	0.871	0.873	0.880	0.888	0.895	0.901	0.908	0.909	0.913	0.918	0.921	0.923
135	0.854	0.861	0.863	0.871	0.879	0.887	0.894	0.901	0.902	0.907	0.912	0.914	0.916
140	0.842	0.850	0.852	0.861	0.870	0.879	0.886	0.893	0.895	0.900	0.905	0.907	0.910

For SI units, °C = (⁵⁄₉) (°F − 32).

F.5.2 Alternative Method of Filling Containers.

F.5.2.1 Containers equipped with fixed maximum level gauges or with variable liquid level gauges when temperature determinations are not practical can be filled with either gauge, provided that the fixed maximum liquid level is installed or the variable gauge is set to indicate the volume equal to the maximum permitted filling limit as provided in 7.4.3.2(A). The level is computed on the basis of the liquid temperature being 40°F (4.4°C) for aboveground containers or 50°F (10°C) for underground containers.

F.5.2.2 The percentage of container capacity that can be filled with liquid is computed by use of the formula shown in F.5.1.2, substituting the appropriate values as follows:

$$V_t = \frac{L}{G \times F} \qquad \text{[F.5.2.2a]}$$

where:

V_t = percent of container capacity that can be filled with liquid

t = liquid temperature [assumed to be 40°F (4.4°C) for aboveground containers or 50°F (10°C) for underground containers]

L = loading limit obtained from Table 7.4.2.2 for the following:

(1) Specific gravity of the LP-Gas to be contained
(2) Method of installation, aboveground or underground, and, if aboveground, then:

(a) For containers of 1200 gal (4.5 m³) water capacity or less

(b) For containers of more than 1200 gal (4.5 m³) water capacity

G = specific gravity of the LP-Gas to be contained

F = correction factor [obtained from Table F.3.3, using G and 40°F (4°C) for aboveground containers or 50°F (10°C) for underground containers]

Example: The maximum volume of LP-Gas with a specific gravity of 0.508 that can be in a 1000 gal (3.8 m³) water capacity aboveground container that is filled by use of a fixed maximum liquid level gauge is computed as follows:

t = 40°F (4.4°C) for an aboveground container

L = 0.508 specific gravity and an aboveground container of less than 1200 gal (4.5 m³) water capacity, from Table 7.4.2.2, = 42 percent

G = 0.508

F = 0.508 specific gravity at 40°F (4.4°C) from Table F.3.3 = 1.033

Thus,

$$V_{40} = \frac{0.42}{0.508 \times 1.033} \qquad \text{[F.5.2.2b]}$$

$$= 0.800 \ (80\%) \text{ or } 800 \text{ gal } (3 \text{ m}^3)$$

F.5.2.3 Percentage values, such as those in the example in F.5.2.2, are rounded off to the next lower full percentage point, or to 80 percent in this example.

F.5.3 Location of Fixed Maximum Liquid Level Gauges in Containers.

F.5.3.1 Due to the diversity of fixed maximum liquid level gauges, and the many sizes [from cylinders to 120,000 gal (454 m³) ASME vessels] and types (vertical, horizontal, cylindrical, and spherical) of containers in which gauges are installed, it is not possible to tabulate the liquid levels such gauges should indicate for the maximum permitted filling limits. *[See Table 7.4.2.2 and Table 7.4.2.3(a).]*

F.5.3.2 The percentage of container capacity that fixed maximum liquid level gauges should indicate is computed by use of the formula in F.5.1.2. The liquid level the gauge should indicate is obtained by applying the percentage to the water capacity of the container in gallons [water at 60°F (16°C)] and then using the strapping table for the container (obtained from its manufacturer) to determine the liquid level for this gallonage. If such a table is not available, the liquid level is computed from the internal dimensions of the container, using data from engineering handbooks.

F.5.3.3 Table 5.9.3.2 can be used to determine minimum dip tube length when installing an overfilling prevention device on cylinders for vapor service.

Annex G   Wall Thickness of Copper Tubing

This annex is not a part of the requirements of this NFPA document but is included for informational purposes only.

G.1 Table G.1(a) and Table G.1(b) contain the nominal wall thicknesses of Type K, Type L, and Type ACR copper tubing.

Table G.1(a) Wall Thickness of Copper Tubing (ASTM B88, *Standard Specification for Seamless Copper Water Tube)*

Standard Size (in.)	Nominal Outside Diameter (in.)	Nominal Wall Thickness (in.)	
		Type K	Type L
¼	0.375	0.035	0.030
⅜	0.500	0.049	0.035
½	0.625	0.049	0.040
⅝	0.750	0.049	0.042
¾	0.875	0.065	0.045

For SI units, 1 in. = 25 mm.

Table G.1(b) Wall Thickness of Copper Tubing (ASTM B280, *Standard Specification for Seamless Copper Tube for Air Conditioning and Refrigeration Field Service)*

Standard Size (in.)	Outside Diameter (in.)	Wall Thickness (in.)
¼	0.250	0.030
5⁄16	0.312	0.032
⅜	0.375	0.032
½	0.500	0.032
⅝	0.625	0.035
¾	0.750	0.042
⅞	0.875	0.045

For SI units, 1 in. = 25 mm.

Annex H Procedure for Torch Fire and Hose Stream Testing of Thermal Insulating Systems for LP-Gas Containers

This annex is not a part of the requirements of this NFPA document but is included for informational purposes only.

H.1 Performance Standard. Thermal protection insulating systems, proposed for use on LP-Gas containers as a means of "Special Protection" under 6.29.5.1, are required to undergo thermal performance testing as a precondition for acceptance. The intent of this testing procedure is to identify insulation systems that retard or prevent the release of a container's contents in a fire environment of 50 minutes' duration and that resist a concurrent hose stream of 10 minutes' duration.

△ H.2 Reference Test Standards. The testing procedure described herein was taken with some modification from segments of the following two test standards:

(1) 49 CFR, Transportation, Part 179.105-4, "Thermal Protection"

(2) Section 6.2, Hose Stream Test, of NFPA 252

H.3 Thermal Insulation Test. The thermal insulation shall be tested in accordance with NFPA 290.

H.4 Hose Stream Resistance Test. After 20 minutes' exposure to the torch test, the test sample should be hit with a hose stream concurrently with the torch for a period of 10 minutes. The hose stream test should be conducted in the following manner:

(1) The stream should be directed first at the middle and then at all parts of the exposed surface, making changes in direction slowly.

(2) The hose stream should be delivered through a 2½ in. (64 mm) hose discharging through a National Standard playpipe of corresponding size equipped with a 1⅛ in. (29 mm) discharge tip of the standard-taper smooth-bore pattern without shoulder at the orifice. The water pressure at the base of the nozzle and for the duration of the test should be 30 psig (207 kPag). [Estimated delivery rate is 205 gpm (776 L/min).]

(3) The tip of the nozzle should be located 20 ft (6 m) from, and on a line normal to, the center of the test specimen. If impossible to be so located, the nozzle can be on a line with a deviation not to exceed 30 degrees from the line normal to the center of the test specimen. When so located, the distance from the center should be less than 20 ft (6 m) by an amount equal to 1 ft (0.3 m) for each 10 degrees of deviation from the normal.

(4) Subsequent to the application of the hose stream, the torching should continue until any thermocouple on the uninsulated side of the steel plate indicates a plate temperature in excess of 800°F (427°C).

(5) The thermal insulation system should be judged to be resistant to the action of the hose stream if the time from initiation of torching for any thermocouple on the uninsulated side of the steel plate to reach in excess of 800°F (427°C) is 50 minutes or greater.

(6) One successful combination torch fire and hose stream test should be required for certification.

Annex I Container Spacing

This annex is not a part of the requirements of this NFPA document but is included for informational purposes only.

△ I.1 Spacing of Containers. Figure I.1(a), Figure I.1(b), and Figure I.1(c) illustrate container spacing required in 6.4.1.

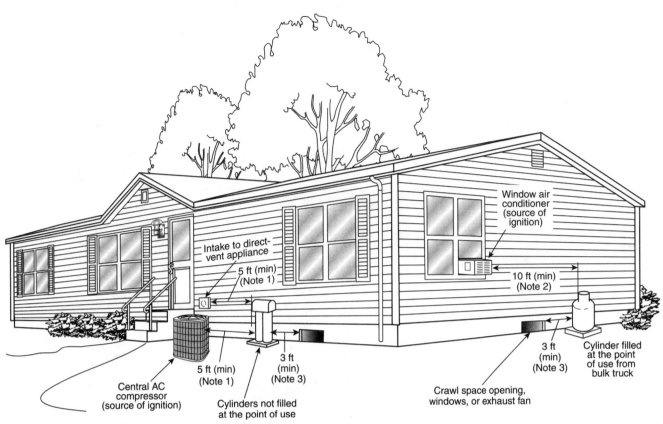

For SI units, 1 ft = 0.3048 m.

Notes:
(1) 5 ft minimum from relief valve in any direction away from any exterior source of ignition, openings into direct-vent appliances, or mechanical ventilation air intakes. Refer to Table 6.4.4.3.
(2) If the cylinder is filled at the point of use from a cargo tank motor vehicle, the filling connection and vent valve must be at least 10 ft from any exterior source of ignition, openings into direct-vent appliances, or mechanical ventilation air intakes. Refer to 6.4.4.3.
(3) Refer to 6.4.4.3.

Δ **FIGURE I.1(a)**   Cylinders. *(Figure for illustrative purposes only; code compliance required.)*

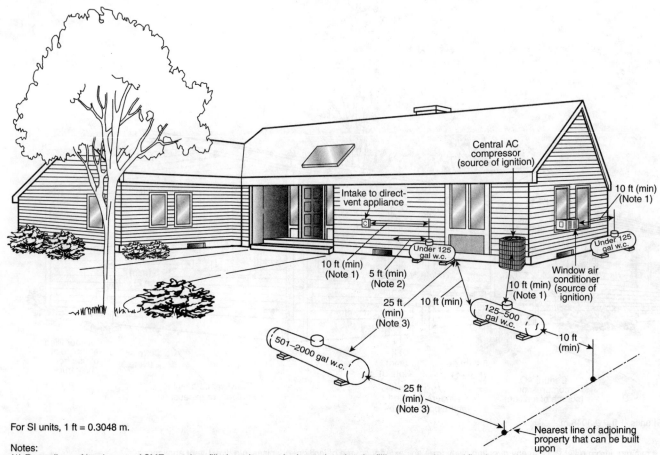

For SI units, 1 ft = 0.3048 m.

Notes:
(1) Regardless of its size, any ASME container filled on site must be located so that the filling connection and fixed
maximum liquid level gauge are at least 10 ft from any external source of ignition (e.g., open flame, window AC, compressor),
intake to direct-vented gas appliance, or intake to a mechanical ventilation system. Refer to 6.4.4.3.
(2) Refer to 6.4.4.3.
(3) This distance can be reduced to no less than 10 ft for a single container of 1200 gal (4.5 m³) water capacity or less, provided such container is
at least 25 ft from any other LP-Gas container of more than 125 gal (0.5 m³) water capacity. Refer to 6.4.1.3.

△ **FIGURE I.1(b)   Aboveground ASME Containers.** *(Figure for illustrative purposes only; code compliance required.)*

Shaded text = Revisions.   △ = Text deletions and figure/table revisions.   • = Section deletions.   *N* = New material.

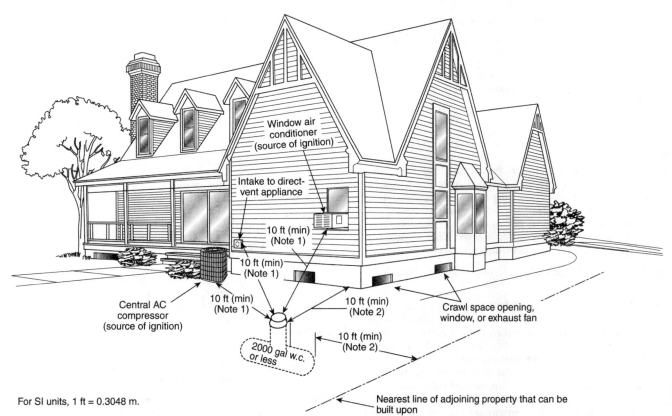

For SI units, 1 ft = 0.3048 m.

Notes:
(1) The relief valve, filling connection, and fixed maximum liquid level gauge vent connection at the container must be at least 10 ft from any exterior source of ignition, openings into direct-vent appliances, or mechanical ventilation air intakes. Refer to 6.4.4.4.
(2) No part of an underground container can be less than 10 ft from an important building or line of adjoining property that can be built upon. Refer to Table 6.4.1.1.

Δ **FIGURE I.1(c)   Underground ASME Containers.** *(Figure for illustrative purposes only; code compliance required.)*

Annex J Sample Ordinance Adopting NFPA 58

This annex is not a part of the requirements of this NFPA document but is included for informational purposes only.

Δ **J.1** The following sample ordinance is provided to assist a jurisdiction in the adoption of this code and is not part of this code.

ORDINANCE NO. _____

An ordinance of the *[jurisdiction]* adopting the *[year]* edition of NFPA 58, *Liquefied Petroleum Gas Code*, documents listed in Chapter 2 of that code; prescribing regulations governing conditions hazardous to life and property from fire or explosion; providing for the issuance of permits and collection of fees; repealing Ordinance No. _____ of the *[jurisdiction]* and all other ordinances and parts of ordinances in conflict therewith; providing a penalty; providing a severability clause; and providing for publication; and providing an effective date.

BE IT ORDAINED BY THE *[governing body]* OF THE *[jurisdiction]*:

SECTION 1 That the *Liquefied Petroleum Gas Code* and documents adopted by Chapter 2, three (3) copies of which are on file and are open to inspection by the public in the office of the *[jurisdiction's keeper of records]* of the *[jurisdiction]*, are hereby adopted and incorporated into this ordinance as fully as if set out at length herein, and from the date on which this ordinance shall take effect, the provisions thereof shall be controlling within the limits of the *[jurisdiction]*. The same are hereby adopted as the code of the *[jurisdiction]* for the purpose of prescribing regulations governing conditions hazardous to life and property from fire or explosion and providing for issuance of permits and collection of fees.

SECTION 2 Any person who shall violate any provision of this code or standard hereby adopted or fail to comply therewith; or who shall violate or fail to comply with any order made thereunder; or who shall build in violation of any detailed statement of specifications or plans submitted and approved thereunder; or failed to operate in accordance with any certificate or permit issued thereunder; and from which no appeal has been taken; or who shall fail to comply with such an order as affirmed or modified by or by a court of competent jurisdiction, within the time fixed herein, shall severally for each and every such violation and noncompliance, respectively, be guilty of a misdemeanor, punishable by a fine of not less than $ _____ nor more than $____ or by imprisonment for not less than _____ days nor more than _____ days or by both such fine and imprisonment. The imposition of one penalty for any violation shall not excuse the violation or permit it to continue; and all such persons shall be required to correct or remedy such violations or defects within a reasonable time; and when not otherwise specified the application of the above penalty shall not be held to prevent the enforced removal of prohibited conditions. Each day that prohibited conditions are maintained shall constitute a separate offense.

SECTION 3 Additions, insertions, and changes — that the *[year]* edition of NFPA 58, *Liquefied Petroleum Gas Code*, is amended and changed in the following respects:

List Amendments

SECTION 4 That ordinance No. _____ of *[jurisdiction]* entitled *[fill in the title of the ordinance or ordinances in effect at the present time]* and all other ordinances or parts of ordinances in conflict herewith are hereby repealed.

SECTION 5 That if any section, subsection, sentence, clause, or phrase of this ordinance is, for any reason, held to be invalid or unconstitutional, such decision shall not affect the validity or constitutionality of the remaining portions of this ordinance. The *[governing body]* hereby declares that it would have passed this ordinance, and each section, subsection, clause, or phrase hereof, irrespective of the fact that any one or more sections, subsections, sentences, clauses, and phrases be declared unconstitutional.

SECTION 6 That the *[jurisdiction's keeper of records]* is hereby ordered and directed to cause this ordinance to be published.

[NOTE: An additional provision may be required to direct the number of times the ordinance is to be published and to specify that it is to be in a newspaper in general circulation. Posting may also be required.]

SECTION 7 That this ordinance and the rules, regulations, provisions, requirements, orders, and matters established and adopted hereby shall take effect and be in full force and effect *[time period]* from and after the date of its final passage and adoption.

Annex K Burial and Corrosion Protection for Underground and Mounded ASME Containers

This annex is not a part of the requirements of this NFPA document but is included for informational purposes only.

K.1 Scope.

K.1.1 This annex provides general information for the burial of underground and mounded ASME containers of 125 gal through 2000 gal (0.5 m³ through 7.6 m³) water capacity.

K.1.2 The location for underground and mounded ASME containers must comply with applicable sections of Chapter 6 of this code and federal and state codes.

K.2 Container Preparation and Burial.

K.2.1 Prior to burial, the container should be inspected for any coating damage that could have been caused during the installation process.

K.2.2 Cathodic protection should be considered as an additional method to minimize corrosion. Anodes are used in this process and should be attached to the container according to the anode manufacturer's instructions. The number and size of anodes installed varies, depending on the container size.

K.2.3 Dielectric couplings should be used to isolate the container from the piping when using metallic piping (e.g., copper, steel) to minimize current flow.

K.2.4 The backfill material used to cover the container should be compacted soil or coarse sand. Backfill material containing crushed rock or other material that could damage the container coating should be avoided.

K.3 Inspection and Testing of Corrosion Protection.

K.3.1 A periodic test program should be established to monitor the effectiveness of the corrosion protection for the container. Inspection records should be made available to the container owner. *[See 6.8.6.1(I).]*

Annex L   Suggested Methods of Checking for Leakage

This annex is not a part of the requirements of this NFPA document but is included for informational purposes only.

L.1 Suggested Methods of Checking for Leakage.

L.1.1 This section describes several methods for conducting a leak check on an LP-Gas system before placing it back into service.

△ **L.1.2** *For Gas Systems Using Undiluted LP-Gas System Preparation for Propane.* A leak check performed on an LP-Gas system being placed back in service can be performed by using one of the following methods:

(1) Insert a pressure gauge between the container gas shutoff valve and the first-stage regulator or integral two-stage regulator in the system, admitting full container pressure to the system and then closing the container shutoff valve. Enough gas should then be released from the system to lower the pressure gauge reading by 10 psi (69 kPa). The system should then be allowed to stand for 3 minutes without showing an increase or a decrease in the pressure gauge reading. [**54:**C.3(2)(a)]

(2) Insert a gauge/regulator test assembly between the container gas shutoff valve and first-stage regulator or integral two-stage regulator in the system. If a gauge/regulator test assembly with an inches water column gauge is inserted, follow the test requirements in L.1.2(3); if a gauge/regulator test assembly with a 30 psi gauge is inserted, follow the test requirements in L.1.2(4). [**54:**C.3(2)(b)]

(3) For systems with an integral two-stage, one or more second-stage, or one or more line pressure regulators serving appliances that receive gas at pressures of ½ psi (3.5 kPa) or less, insert a water manometer or inches water column gauge into the system downstream of the final stage regulator, pressurizing the system with either fuel gas or air to a test pressure of 9 in. w.c. ± ½ in. w.c. (2.2 kPa ± 0.1 kPa), and observing the device for a pressure change. If fuel gas is used as a pressure source, it is necessary to pressurize the system to full operating pressure, close the container service valve, and then release enough gas from the system through a range burner valve or other suitable means to drop the system pressure to 9 in. w.c. ± ½ in. w.c. (2.2 kPa ± 0.1 kPa). This ensures that all regulators in the system upstream of the test point are unlocked and that a leak anywhere in the system is communicated to the gauging device. The gauging device should indicate no loss or gain of pressure for a period of 3 minutes. [**54:**C.3(2)(c)]

(4) When testing a system that has a first-stage regulator, or an integral two-stage regulator, insert a 30 psi (207 kPa) pressure gauge on the downstream side of the first-stage regulator or at the intermediate pressure tap of an integral two-stage regulator, admitting normal operating pressure to the system and then closing the container valve. Enough gas should be released from the system to lower the pressure gauge reading by a minimum of 2 psi (13.8 kPa) so that the first-stage regulator is unlocked. The system should be allowed to stand for 3 minutes without showing an increase or a decrease in pressure gauge reading. [**54:**C.3(2)(d)]

(5) Insert a gauge/regulator test assembly on the downstream side of the first stage regulator or at the intermediate pressure tap of an integral two stage regulator. If a gauge/regulator test assembly with an inches water column gauge is inserted, follow the test requirements in L.1.2(3); if a gauge/regulator test assembly with a 30 psi gauge is inserted, follow the test requirements in L.1.2(4). [**54:**C.3(2)(e)]

△ ## Annex M   Suggested Container Purging Procedure

This annex is not a part of the requirements of this NFPA document but is included for informational purposes only.

△ **M.1 Introduction.** In accordance with 12.3.2.5, all containers that have had their interiors exposed to the atmosphere (that would occur during a service valve change) are to be purged of air and other contaminants. The following methods have been found to be effective.

△ **M.2 Vapor Purge Method.** This procedure should be performed in a well-ventilated and nonenclosed area and at least 35 ft (11 m) away from potential sources of ignition.

The method steps are as follows:

(1) Position the container so that a manually operated (nonelectrically operated/solenoid) valve, installed within the vapor space, is at the topmost portion of the container or in the highest portion of a manifold ASME container.

(2) Using a regulated LP-Gas vapor source, introduce 20 psig (138 kPag) of LP-Gas vapor into the container.

(3) Allow the pressure to stabilize for approximately 5 minutes.

(4) Release the gas until the pressure is between 3 psig and 5 psig (21 kPag to 34 kPag), in accordance with local hydrocarbon emissions regulations and 7.3.1.

(5) Repeat the process a minimum of five times, to ensure that almost all of the air has been removed from the container, and the moisture content has been reduced.

(6) Close the manual valve to prevent re-entry of moisture and air.

CAUTION: This purging method must be followed precisely on containers using internal electronics/electrical circuits to ensure that a combustible mixture of fuel and air cannot be present before energizing electrical circuits.

△ **M.3 Vacuum Purging Method.** The vacuum purging method steps are as follows:

(1) Use a hose suitable for vacuum service to connect a compressor to the ASME container.

(2) Ensure that any protective caps for appurtenances are in place and tightened.

(3) Open the service valve and run the compressor to reduce the pressure in the ASME container to a vacuum of 26 in. Hg (−88 kPa).

Close the service valve and disconnect the compressor.

Annex N Informational References

N.1 Referenced Publications. The documents or portions thereof listed in this annex are referenced within the informational sections of this code and are not part of the requirements of this document unless also listed in Chapter 2 for other reasons.

N.1.1 NFPA Publications. National Fire Protection Association, 1 Batterymarch Park, Quincy, MA 02169-7471.

NFPA 10, *Standard for Portable Fire Extinguishers*, 2018 edition.

NFPA 30, *Flammable and Combustible Liquids Code*, 2018 edition.

NFPA 37, *Standard for the Installation and Use of Stationary Combustion Engines and Gas Turbines*, 2018 edition.

NFPA 51, *Standard for the Design and Installation of Oxygen–Fuel Gas Systems for Welding, Cutting, and Allied Processes*, 2018 edition.

NFPA 54, *National Fuel Gas Code*, 2018 edition.

NFPA 61, *Standard for the Prevention of Fires and Dust Explosions in Agricultural and Food Processing Facilities*, 2017 edition.

NFPA 68, *Standard on Explosion Protection by Deflagration Venting*, 2018 edition.

NFPA 77, *Recommended Practice on Static Electricity*, 2019 edition.

NFPA 80, *Standard for Fire Doors and Other Opening Protectives*, 2019 edition.

NFPA 101®, *Life Safety Code*®, 2018 edition.

NFPA 160, *Standard for the Use of Flame Effects Before an Audience*, 2016 edition.

NFPA 252, *Standard Methods of Fire Tests of Door Assemblies*, 2017 edition.

NFPA 290, *Standard for Fire Testing of Passive Protection Materials for Use on LP-Gas Containers*, 2018 edition.

NFPA 302, *Fire Protection Standard for Pleasure and Commercial Motor Craft*, 2020 edition.

NFPA 780, *Standard for the Installation of Lightning Protection Systems*, 2020 edition.

NFPA 1192, *Standard on Recreational Vehicles*, 2018 edition.

Fire Safety Analysis Manual for LP-Gas Storage Facilities, 2011 edition.

National Fuel Gas Code Handbook, 2015 edition.

N.1.2 Other Publications.

N.1.2.1 API Publications. American Petroleum Institute, 1220 L Street, NW, Washington, DC 20005-4070.

ANSI/API 521, *Guide for Pressure-Relieving and Depressuring Systems*, 2014.

API 620, *Design and Construction of Large, Welded, Low-Pressure Storage Tanks*, 2013.

API RP 1632, *Cathodic Protection of Underground Petroleum Storage Tanks and Piping Systems*, 2010.

API 2510, *Design and Construction of LP-Gas Installations*, 2001, reaffirmed 2011.

API-ASME *Code for Unfired Pressure Vessels for Petroleum Liquids and Gases*, Pre-July 1, 1961.

Battelle Memorial Institute report, "The Effect of Velocity, Temperature, and Gas Molecular Weight on Flammability Limits in Wind-Blown Jets of Hydrocarbon Gases," 1970.

N.1.2.2 ASCE Publications. American Society of Civil Engineers, 1801 Alexander Bell Drive, Reston, VA 20191-4400.

ASCE/SEI 7, *Minimum Design Loads for Buildings and Other Structures*, 2016.

N.1.2.3 ASME Publications. American Society of Mechanical Engineers, Two Park Avenue, New York, NY 10016-5990.

ASME *Boiler and Pressure Vessel Code*, 2015.

ASME B31.3, *Process Piping*, 2014.

N.1.2.4 ASTM Publications. ASTM International, 100 Barr Harbor Drive, P.O. Box C700, Conshohocken, PA 19428-2959.

ASTM A47/A47M, *Standard Specification for Ferritic Malleable Iron Castings*, 1999, reapproved 2014.

ASTM A395/A395M, *Standard Specification for Ferritic Ductile Iron Pressure-Retaining Castings for Use at Elevated Temperatures*, 1999, reapproved 2014.

ASTM B88, *Standard Specification for Seamless Copper Water Tube*, 2016.

ASTM B280, *Standard Specification for Seamless Copper Tube for Air Conditioning and Refrigeration Field Service*, 2018.

ASTM D638, *Standard Test Method for Tensile Properties of Plastics*, 2014.

ASTM D1835, *Standard Specification for Liquefied Petroleum (LP) Gases*, 2016.

ASTM D5305, *Standard Test Method for Determination of Ethyl Mercaptan in LP-Gas Vapor*, 2012.

ASTM E84, *Standard Test Method for Surface Burning Characteristics of Building Materials*, 2018.

N.1.2.5 AWS Publications. American Welding Society, 8669 NW 36 Street, #130, Miami, FL 33166-6672.

AWS Z49.1, *Safety in Welding, Cutting, and Allied Processes*, 2012.

N.1.2.6 BOE Publications. Bureau of Explosives, American Railroads Building, 1920 L Street, NW, Washington, DC 20036.

Tariff No. BOE-6000.

N.1.2.7 CAN/CGSB Publications. Canadian General Standards Board, Public Works and Government Services Canada, 11 Laurier Street, Phase III, Place du Portage, Gatineau, QC, K1A 0S5, Canada.

CAN/CGSB-3.0 No. 18.5, *Test for Ethyl Mercaptan Odorant in Propane, Field Method*, August 2015.

△ **N.1.2.8 CGA Publications.** Compressed Gas Association, 14501 George Carter Way, Suite 103, Chantilly, VA 20151-2923.

CGA C-6, *Standard for Visual Inspection of Steel Compressed Gas Cylinders*, 2013.

CGA C-6.3, *Standard for Visual Inspection of Low Pressure Aluminum Alloy Compressed Gas Cylinders*, 2013.

CGA S-1.1, *Pressure Relief Device Standards, Part 1 — Cylinders for Compressed Gases*, 2011.

CGA S-1.2, *Pressure Relief Device Standards, Part 2 — Cargo and Portable Tanks for Compressed Gases*, 2009.

CGA S-1.3, *Pressure Relief Device Standards, Part 3 — Compressed Gas Storage Containers*, 2008.

N.1.2.9 GPA Publications. Gas Processors Association, 6526 East 60th Street, Tulsa, OK 74145.

GPA 2140, *Liquefied Petroleum Gas Specifications and Test Methods*, 1997.

N.1.2.10 NACE Publications. NACE International, 15835 Park Ten Place, Houston, TX 77084-4906.

SP0169, *Control of External Corrosion on Underground or Submerged Metallic Piping Systems*, 2013.

SP0285, *External Corrosion Control of Underground Storage Tank Systems by Cathodic Protection*, 2011.

N.1.2.11 NBBI Publications. National Board of Boiler and Pressure Vessel Inspectors, 1055 Crupper Avenue, Columbus, OH 43229.

NBBI NB23, *National Board Inspection Code*, 2017.

N.1.2.12 NPGA Publications. National Propane Gas Association, 1899 L St., NW, Suite 350, Washington, DC 20036.

SwRI 18.19083.01.107, "Evaluation of Collision Protection Provided by Vehicle Impact Bollards and Propane Cylinder Exchange Cabinets," 2013.

N.1.2.13 PERC Publications. Propane Education and Research Council, Suite 1075, 1140 Connecticut Avenue, NW, Washington, DC 20036.

Cathodic Protection Manual and Quiz #20689590.

"Cathodic Protection Systems" (video).

Certified Employee Training Program (CETP).

N **N.1.2.14 SAE Publications.** SAE International, Society of Automotive Engineers, 400 Commonwealth Drive, Warrendale, PA 15096.

SAE J2618, *Recommended Testing Methods for Physical Protection of Wiring Harnesses*, 2016.

△ **N.1.2.15 UL Publications.** Underwriters Laboratories, Inc., 333 Pfingsten Rd., Northbrook, IL 60062-2096.

ANSI/UL 651, *Standard for Schedule 40, 80, Type EB and A Rigid PVC Conduit and Fittings*, 2011, revised 2014.

ANSI/UL 723, *Standard for Test for Surface Burning Characteristics of Building Materials*, 2008, revised 2013.

ANSI/UL 1746, *External Corrosion Protection Systems for Steel Underground Storage Tanks*, 2007, revised 2012.

△ **N.1.2.16 ULC Publications.** Underwriters' Laboratories of Canada, 7 Underwriters Road, Toronto, ON M1R 3A9, Canada.

CAN/ULC S603.1, *Standard for External Corrosion Protection Systems for Steel Underground Tanks for Flammable and Combustible Liquids*, 2017.

N **N.1.2.17 United Nations Economic Commission for Europe Publications.** UN Economic Commission for Europe Information Services, Palais des Nations, CH-1211 Geneva 10, Switzerland.

ECE R67.01, *Agreement Concerning the Adoption of Uniform Technical Prescriptions for Wheeled Vehicles, Equipment and Parts Which Can Be Fitted and/or Be Used on Wheeled Vehicles and the Conditions for Reciprocal Recognition of Approvals Granted on the Basis of these Prescriptions*, Revision 4, 1998.

N.1.2.18 U.S. Government Publications. U.S. Government Publishing Office, 732 North Capitol Street, NW, Washington, DC 20401-0001.

A New Look at Odorization Levels for Propane Gas, BERC/RI-77/1, United States Energy Research and Development Administration, Technical Information Center, September 1977.

15 U.S.C. 1261, Federal Hazardous Substances Act.

Title 16, Code of Federal Regulations, Part 1500, "Hazardous Substances and Articles."

Title 33, Code of Federal Regulations, "Navigation and Navigable Waters."

Title 49, Code of Federal Regulations, Part 178, "Specifications for Packaging."

Title 49, Code of Federal Regulations, Part 179.105-4, "Thermal Protection."

Title 49, Code of Federal Regulations, Part 180.209.

Title 49, Code of Federal Regulations, Parts 192.281(e) and 192.283(b).

Title 49, Code of Federal Regulations, Parts 192 and 195, "Transportation of Hazardous Liquids by Pipeline."

N.2 Informational References. (Reserved)

N.3 References for Extracts in Informational Sections.

NFPA 54, *National Fuel Gas Code*, 2018 edition.

NFPA *101®*, *Life Safety Code®*, 2018 edition.

Index

Sequence of Events for the Standards Development Process

Once the current edition is published, a Standard is opened for Public Input.

Step 1 – Input Stage

- Input accepted from the public or other committees for consideration to develop the First Draft
- Technical Committee holds First Draft Meeting to revise Standard (23 weeks); Technical Committee(s) with Correlating Committee (10 weeks)
- Technical Committee ballots on First Draft (12 weeks); Technical Committee(s) with Correlating Committee (11 weeks)
- Correlating Committee First Draft Meeting (9 weeks)
- Correlating Committee ballots on First Draft (5 weeks)
- First Draft Report posted on the document information page

Step 2 – Comment Stage

- Public Comments accepted on First Draft (10 weeks) following posting of First Draft Report
- If Standard does not receive Public Comments and the Technical Committee chooses not to hold a Second Draft meeting, the Standard becomes a Consent Standard and is sent directly to the Standards Council for issuance (see Step 4) or
- Technical Committee holds Second Draft Meeting (21 weeks); Technical Committee(s) with Correlating Committee (7 weeks)
- Technical Committee ballots on Second Draft (11 weeks); Technical Committee(s) with Correlating Committee (10 weeks)
- Correlating Committee Second Draft Meeting (9 weeks)
- Correlating Committee ballots on Second Draft (8 weeks)
- Second Draft Report posted on the document information page

Step 3 – NFPA Technical Meeting

- Notice of Intent to Make a Motion (NITMAM) accepted (5 weeks) following the posting of Second Draft Report
- NITMAMs are reviewed and valid motions are certified by the Motions Committee for presentation at the NFPA Technical Meeting
- NFPA membership meets each June at the NFPA Technical Meeting to act on Standards with "Certified Amending Motions" (certified NITMAMs)
- Committee(s) vote on any successful amendments to the Technical Committee Reports made by the NFPA membership at the NFPA Technical Meeting

Step 4 – Council Appeals and Issuance of Standard

- Notification of intent to file an appeal to the Standards Council on Technical Meeting action must be filed within 20 days of the NFPA Technical Meeting
- Standards Council decides, based on all evidence, whether to issue the standard or to take other action

Notes:

1. Time periods are approximate; refer to published schedules for actual dates.
2. Annual revision cycle documents with certified amending motions take approximately 101 weeks to complete.
3. Fall revision cycle documents receiving certified amending motions take approximately 141 weeks to complete.

Committee Membership Classifications[1,2,3,4]

The following classifications apply to Committee members and represent their principal interest in the activity of the Committee.

1. M *Manufacturer:* A representative of a maker or marketer of a product, assembly, or system, or portion thereof, that is affected by the standard.
2. U *User:* A representative of an entity that is subject to the provisions of the standard or that voluntarily uses the standard.
3. IM *Installer/Maintainer:* A representative of an entity that is in the business of installing or maintaining a product, assembly, or system affected by the standard.
4. L *Labor:* A labor representative or employee concerned with safety in the workplace.
5. RT *Applied Research/Testing Laboratory:* A representative of an independent testing laboratory or independent applied research organization that promulgates and/or enforces standards.
6. E *Enforcing Authority:* A representative of an agency or an organization that promulgates and/or enforces standards.
7. I *Insurance:* A representative of an insurance company, broker, agent, bureau, or inspection agency.
8. C *Consumer:* A person who is or represents the ultimate purchaser of a product, system, or service affected by the standard, but who is not included in (2).
9. SE *Special Expert:* A person not representing (1) through (8) and who has special expertise in the scope of the standard or portion thereof.

NOTE 1: "Standard" connotes code, standard, recommended practice, or guide.

NOTE 2: A representative includes an employee.

NOTE 3: While these classifications will be used by the Standards Council to achieve a balance for Technical Committees, the Standards Council may determine that new classifications of member or unique interests need representation in order to foster the best possible Committee deliberations on any project. In this connection, the Standards Council may make such appointments as it deems appropriate in the public interest, such as the classification of "Utilities" in the National Electrical Code Committee.

NOTE 4: Representatives of subsidiaries of any group are generally considered to have the same classification as the parent organization.

Submitting Public Input / Public Comment Through the Online Submission System

Following publication of the current edition of an NFPA standard, the development of the next edition begins and the standard is open for Public Input.

Submit a Public Input

NFPA accepts Public Input on documents through our online submission system at www.nfpa.org. To use the online submission system:

- Choose a document from the List of NFPA codes & standards or filter by Development Stage for "codes accepting public input."
- Once you are on the document page, select the "Next Edition" tab.
- Choose the link "The next edition of this standard is now open for Public Input." You will be asked to sign in or create a free online account with NFPA before using this system.
- Follow the online instructions to submit your Public Input (see www.nfpa.org/publicinput for detailed instructions).
- Once a Public Input is saved or submitted in the system, it can be located on the "My Profile" page by selecting the "My Public Inputs/Comments/NITMAMs" section.

Submit a Public Comment

Once the First Draft Report becomes available there is a Public Comment period. Any objections or further related changes to the content of the First Draft must be submitted at the Comment Stage. To submit a Public Comment follow the same steps as previously explained for the submission of Public Input.

Other Resources Available on the Document Information Pages

Header: View document title and scope, access to our codes and standards or NFCSS subscription, and sign up to receive email alerts.

Current & Prior Editions	Research current and previous edition information.
Next Edition	Follow the committee's progress in the processing of a standard in its next revision cycle.
Technical Committee	View current committee rosters or apply to a committee.
Ask a Technical Question	For members, officials, and AHJs to submit standards questions to NFPA staff. Our Technical Questions Service provides a convenient way to receive timely and consistent technical assistance when you need to know more about NFPA standards relevant to your work.
News	Provides links to available articles and research and statistical reports related to our standards.
Purchase Products & Training	Discover and purchase the latest products and training.
Related Products	View related publications, training, and other resources available for purchase.

I. Applicable Regulations. The primary rules governing the processing of NFPA standards (codes, standards, recommended practices, and guides) are the NFPA *Regulations Governing the Development of NFPA Standards (Regs)*. Other applicable rules include NFPA *Bylaws*, NFPA *Technical Meeting Convention Rules*, NFPA *Guide for the Conduct of Participants in the NFPA Standards Development Process*, and the NFPA *Regulations Governing Petitions to the Board of Directors from Decisions of the Standards Council*. Most of these rules and regulations are contained in the *NFPA Standards Directory*. For copies of the *Directory*, contact Codes and Standards Administration at NFPA headquarters; all these documents are also available on the NFPA website at "www.nfpa.org/regs."

The following is general information on the NFPA process. All participants, however, should refer to the actual rules and regulations for a full understanding of this process and for the criteria that govern participation.

II. Technical Committee Report. The Technical Committee Report is defined as "the Report of the responsible Committee(s), in accordance with the Regulations, in preparation of a new or revised NFPA Standard." The Technical Committee Report is in two parts and consists of the First Draft Report and the Second Draft Report. (See *Regs* at Section 1.4.)

III. Step 1: First Draft Report. The First Draft Report is defined as "Part one of the Technical Committee Report, which documents the Input Stage." The First Draft Report consists of the First Draft, Public Input, Committee Input, Committee and Correlating Committee Statements, Correlating Notes, and Ballot Statements. (See *Regs* at 4.2.5.2 and Section 4.3.) Any objection to an action in the First Draft Report must be raised through the filing of an appropriate Comment for consideration in the Second Draft Report or the objection will be considered resolved. [See *Regs* at 4.3.1(b).]

IV. Step 2: Second Draft Report. The Second Draft Report is defined as "Part two of the Technical Committee Report, which documents the Comment Stage." The Second Draft Report consists of the Second Draft, Public Comments with corresponding Committee Actions and Committee Statements, Correlating Notes and their respective Committee Statements, Committee Comments, Correlating Revisions, and Ballot Statements. (See *Regs* at 4.2.5.2 and Section 4.4.) The First Draft Report and the Second Draft Report together constitute the Technical Committee Report. Any outstanding objection following the Second Draft Report must be raised through an appropriate Amending Motion at the NFPA Technical Meeting or the objection will be considered resolved. [See *Regs* at 4.4.1(b).]

V. Step 3a: Action at NFPA Technical Meeting. Following the publication of the Second Draft Report, there is a period during which those wishing to make proper Amending Motions on the Technical Committee Reports must signal their intention by submitting a Notice of Intent to Make a Motion (NITMAM). (See *Regs* at 4.5.2.) Standards that receive notice of proper Amending Motions (Certified Amending Motions) will be presented for action at the annual June NFPA Technical Meeting. At the meeting, the NFPA membership can consider and act on these Certified Amending Motions as well as Follow-up Amending Motions, that is, motions that become necessary as a result of a previous successful Amending Motion. (See 4.5.3.2 through 4.5.3.6 and Table 1, Columns 1-3 of *Regs* for a summary of the available Amending Motions and who may make them.) Any outstanding objection following action at an NFPA Technical Meeting (and any further Technical Committee consideration following successful Amending Motions, see *Regs* at 4.5.3.7 through 4.6.5) must be raised through an appeal to the Standards Council or it will be considered to be resolved.

VI. Step 3b: Documents Forwarded Directly to the Council. Where no NITMAM is received and certified in accordance with the *Technical Meeting Convention Rules*, the standard is forwarded directly to the Standards Council for action on issuance. Objections are deemed to be resolved for these documents. (See *Regs* at 4.5.2.5.)

VII. Step 4a: Council Appeals. Anyone can appeal to the Standards Council concerning procedural or substantive matters related to the development, content, or issuance of any document of the NFPA or on matters within the purview of the authority of the Council, as established by the *Bylaws* and as determined by the Board of Directors. Such appeals must be in written form and filed with the Secretary of the Standards Council (see *Regs* at Section 1.6). Time constraints for filing an appeal must be in accordance with 1.6.2 of the *Regs*. Objections are deemed to be resolved if not pursued at this level.

VIII. Step 4b: Document Issuance. The Standards Council is the issuer of all documents (see Article 8 of *Bylaws*). The Council acts on the issuance of a document presented for action at an NFPA Technical Meeting within 75 days from the date of the recommendation from the NFPA Technical Meeting, unless this period is extended by the Council (see *Regs* at 4.7.2). For documents forwarded directly to the Standards Council, the Council acts on the issuance of the document at its next scheduled meeting, or at such other meeting as the Council may determine (see *Regs* at 4.5.2.5 and 4.7.4).

IX. Petitions to the Board of Directors. The Standards Council has been delegated the responsibility for the administration of the codes and standards development process and the issuance of documents. However, where extraordinary circumstances requiring the intervention of the Board of Directors exist, the Board of Directors may take any action necessary to fulfill its obligations to preserve the integrity of the codes and standards development process and to protect the interests of the NFPA. The rules for petitioning the Board of Directors can be found in the *Regulations Governing Petitions to the Board of Directors from Decisions of the Standards Council* and in Section 1.7 of the *Regs*.

X. For More Information. The program for the NFPA Technical Meeting (as well as the NFPA website as information becomes available) should be consulted for the date on which each report scheduled for consideration at the meeting will be presented. To view the First Draft Report and Second Draft Report as well as information on NFPA rules and for up-to-date information on schedules and deadlines for processing NFPA documents, check the NFPA website (www.nfpa.org/docinfo) or contact NFPA Codes & Standards Administration at (617) 984-7246.

Xchange

**The Online Community of the
National Fire Protection Association®**

CONNECT WITH YOUR PEERS FROM
AROUND THE WORLD

NFPA® Xchange™ is an online forum for finding and sharing knowledge among an open community of professionals worldwide. This educational tool and job aid allows you to explore content relevant to you, participate in discussions with peers and industry leaders, ask and answer questions, and receive expert advice.

Membership to NFPA Xchange is free and provides access to:

- An active community of more than **50,000 professionals collaborating** in a single place

- Insights and information on **trending topics, emerging issues, and new technologies**

- **Blogs and webinars for learning on-the-job skills, and forums** for submitting queries to be answered by peers and NFPA® technical staff

- **Job board for posting open positions and discovering employment opportunities** from NFPA and partner organizations

- **A robust collection of previously asked questions and subject matter** in a searchable database accessible anywhere, anytime, from any device

Have the resources you need by your side at all times. NFPA Xchange provides the knowledge and support to help you do your job better and help protect lives and property. **Join the conversation today!**

Join now for free at **nfpa.org/xchange-community**